Newnes
Electronics Assembly Handbook

Preface

Electronics assembly, if nothing else, is about the many ways in which components are joined together to form a circuit. There are large numbers of types of components so, understandably, there are large numbers of ways to join them together. In the past, types of components have been thrust upon the manufacturer of electronics assemblies, simply as the component manufacturer finds a new component type. However, we are witnessing a change in this position: as electronics assemblers themselves begin to define the requirements for new component types from the manufacturer. This, of course, means that not only can the components be designed to fit an existing assembly method, but that new assembly methods can be developed for which components can be specified.

Consequently, electronics assembly is dynamic. I have tried to show in this book how dynamic it is; and indicated the ways in which it will change in the future.

1 Introduction

Electronics assembly, in the broad sense, is about how to bring together a multitude of electronic components and component types to form a working, reliable, appliance.

Of course, many of the basic decisions and problems have been overcome by the integrated circuit manufacturers, who have combined hundreds, thousands, even hundreds of thousands of components on to single devices – to effectively ease the job of the electronics assembler, or at least allow the electronics assembler to construct more complicated appliances for the same work. Who could envisage, for example, the sale of microprocessor-based computers in their millions if no integrated circuits existed?

Nevertheless, many problems remain for the electronics assembler. Indeed, the use of very large scale integrated circuits has generated, arguably, even greater numbers of problems to contend with.

This book is about printed circuit boards: their design; their manufacture; their assembly; their production; their component parts; their packaging; their testing; their standardization; their quality. For printed circuit boards of one form or another are used in all but the simplest of electronics assemblies. In many respects, the whole topic of electronics assembly may be viewed as just a collection of the multitude of considerations regarding printed circuit boards.

Bringing together varied disciplines

The art of electronics assembling requires that a number of methods of printed circuit board manufacture be available for the purpose of combining components and, through time, many have evolved and nearly as many fallen by the wayside. The methods of note, however, are:

- Through-hole circuits.
- Hybrid circuits.
- Surface mounted circuits.

Often, combinations of two or more of these methods are used to create single assemblies.

Through-hole circuits

Through-hole circuits use printed circuit boards with holes, to hold components with wire leads. On one or both board surfaces, or even within the board, is a conductive track which interconnects the components into the complete circuit. Wire leads of the components are inserted through holes in the board and track and then bonded to this track, by soldering. The fact that component leads are inserted through holes in the board accounts for the term *through-hole circuits*.

Hybrid circuits

These are a combination of film technologies to create some passive components on to a base, and discrete component technologies to add on the remaining passive components and the required active components, thus forming the complete circuit.

Remaining discrete components, added after the film has been made, may be leaded (that is, with wire leads allowing connection into circuit, in a similar manner to through-hole printed circuits) or, more important, may be leadless (that is, they have no wire terminations, merely metal feet which sit on the connecting pad of the film, prior to soldering).

Two forms of film technologies exist: thin film and thick film. In thin film assemblies passive components are manufactured by vapour deposition and selective etching. In thick film assemblies they are manufactured by printing, drying and firing pastes. Needless to say, each film technology has pros and cons.

Surface mounted circuits

Surface mounted assemblies are essentially a marriage of printed and hybrid circuit methods. The same principle on which through-hole circuits are based is used: that of mounting discrete components on to a printed circuit board then soldering. However, where through-hole printed circuit components are mounted with their wire leads inserted through holes in the board, the hybrid principle of simply positioning leadless components in place prior to soldering is used to complete the surface mounted circuit.

Applications

Through-hole printed circuit boards are, without doubt, the electronics assembly medium of the late twentieth century. They have allowed vast reductions in size and increases of circuit complexity, since their widespread acceptance about twenty years ago. However, printed circuit boards in this through-hole form, using wire leaded components, are beginning to reach a natural limit to miniaturization and complexity. Certain techniques can extend the limit somewhat, but only at significant cost.

There is an axiom which says that through-hole printed circuit boards – originally designed to hold components together – now just hold them apart.

Surface mounted assemblies, on the other hand, look set to greatly exceed this limit without too much extra cost – in certain cases surface mounted assemblies will be even cheaper than their through-hole counterpart. For example, surface mounted assemblies allow significant individual component complexity – the latest high-density surface mounted integrated circuits feature around 400 connection pins. Size reductions also result from the surface mounting of components on both sides of the base. With these in mind, one can easily forecast that surface mounted assemblies will be the electronics assembly medium of the early twenty-first century.

Previously, though, although the potential of surface mounted assemblies has long been appreciated, actual assembly has been a tricky job which has held back the widespread use of surface mounting as a production tool. The key factor is the soldering process used. Advances in soldering technique have, however, finally released surface mounting.

On the subject of soldering in electronics assembly, there is a firm division into two entirely different categories of mass soldering processes, called:

- CS processes, where components are applied to the printed circuit board first, followed by application of molten solder.
- SC processes, where solder is applied first, in the form of solder paste (or sometimes solder preforms). Following this, the components are added, and heat is applied to melt the solder.

Although these names are new, they are justifiable in that they describe the two soldering processes far better than existing terms. Often, for example, CS processes are given the title *wave soldering processes*, but this is incorrect – wave soldering is a distinct process *not a generic name*. Similarly incorrect is the commonly used misnomer for SC soldering processes – *reflow*. The term reflow describes, once again, a single process which happens to be an SC soldering process; like wave soldering it is not a generic name. The two processes, and all their derivatives, are described fully.

Already, the use of surface mounted assemblies shows significant growth, and has been well documented. Figure 1.1 shows the worldwide trend upwards of surface mounted technology as a percentage of all

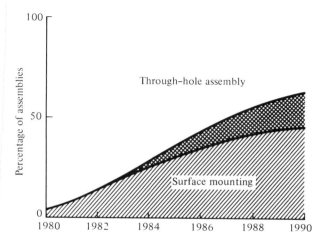

Figure 1.1 *Worldwide trend of usage of surface mount and through-hole technologies as percentages of total*

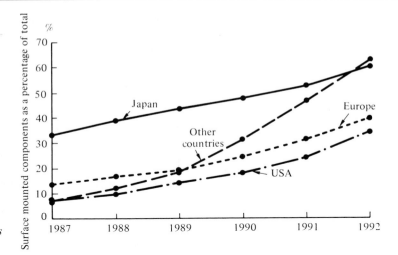

Figure 1.2 *Use of surface mounted components as percentages of totals, for various countries around the world*

electronics assemblies, over the ten years since its first use. Figure 1.2 shows the current period, forecasting the use of surface mounted technologies in various parts of the world, in terms of percentages of discrete surface mounted components. Given these illustrations, it is fairly obvious that surface mounted assemblies will, very soon, form the larger part of all electronics assemblies.

Standardization

There are three main levels of standards: national; regional; international. National standards are those promoted by a designated organization within a country, for instance BSI within the UK. Regional standards usually apply, say, transcontinentally. International standards apply intercontinentally.

We should be, and are, working towards worldwide international standards. International standards are the *Esperanto* of standardization: where at national levels (and even regional levels) standards of different bodies may be significantly different; at international standard level we all speak the same language.

What is the purpose of standardization? Is it to ensure all manufacturers make functionally identical equipment? Surely that would imply that little, if any, difference occurs between the equipment made by different manufacturers. No, the real meaning of standardization is to ensure quality.

Standardization of processes and capabilities mean that component parts are of high quality, and that assemblers are of high manufacturing competence. The result is a product of assured high quality. Everyone benefits: component manufacturer; electronics assembly producer; user.

Standardization is essential to the just-in-time (JIT) philosophy of manufacture. Implicit in the use of JIT is the requirement that component parts do not need to be tested as they arrive at the production line. Instead, the supplier ensures that the parts all function correctly by testing either each component as it is made, or the supply manufacturing processes.

Book layout and description

My intention in writing this book has been to clarify the numerous aspects of electronics assembling. Book layout, therefore, broadly follows the main aspects of electronics assembly: through-hole printed circuit boards and assembly; surface mounted printed circuit boards and assembly; assembly packaging; soldering; testing; standardization, and a chapter is devoted to each. In addition, a chapter describes the Ministry of Defence and how to set about selling to it.

The large topic of standards has also been tackled, in depth, as an appendix. Worldwide standards and publications are first listed in an alphabetical index, which may be then cross-referred with following tables giving fuller descriptions of their contents.

A further appendix lists names and addresses of worldwide organizations of importance to electronics assembly.

A full glossary of all the terms used completes the book.

2 Electronics assembly: the PCB

The printed circuit board

In principle, a printed circuit board (PCB), sometimes called a **printed wiring board** (PWB), or simply printed board, comprises: a **base**, which is a thin board of insulating material supporting all the components which make up a circuit; conducting **tracks**, usually copper, on one or both sides of the base making up the interconnections between components. Component connecting leads are electrically connected in some form of permanent or semipermanent way, usually by soldering to the **lands**, sometimes called **pads** – the areas of track specially designated for component connection purposes. Lands may have holes drilled or punched through the board to facilitate component mounting. If lands *do* have holes for component mounting, the board is known as a **through-hole printed circuit board**.

To clarify, the term *printed* is somewhat misleading, as tracks are *not* printed directly on to the board. It refers instead to just one stage within the whole printed circuit board manufacturing process, where the conducting track **layout**, sometimes called **pattern** or **image**, may be produced using some form of printing technique.

Printed circuit boards can be made in one of two main ways. First, in an **additive** process, the conductive track may be added to the surface of the base material. There are a number of ways in which this can be done, all of which are covered later in this chapter. Second, in a **subtractive** process, the base material is supplied with its whole surface covered with a conductive layer, the track pattern is defined, and the excess conductive material is removed, leaving the required track. Sometimes, both processes may be combined to produce printed circuit boards with more than one layer of conductive track.

Printed circuit boards have been around as an electronics assembly technique in one form or another for fifty years. Nevertheless, considering the early nature of valve-based electronic assembly it is easy to see why printed circuit boards did not start to be refined and gain significant use until the 1960s when transistor circuits became more and more popular.

Valve circuits have always been built by the direct positioning and manual soldering of individual connecting leads between the required circuit parts. Initially, transistor circuits were constructed in a similar way, but the advantages of the printed circuit board in this respect became quickly apparent.

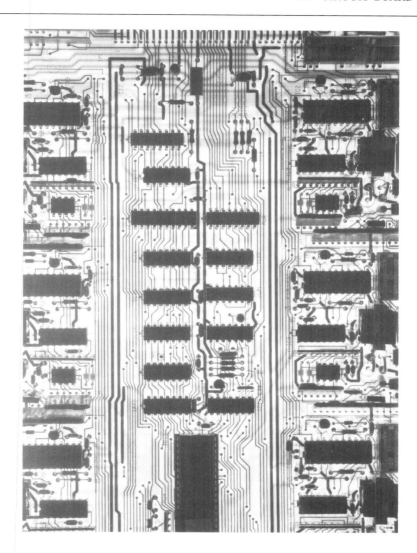

Plate 2.1 *Typical through-hole printed circuit board, loaded with leaded components (Ultraviolet Products)*

Among other things, electronics assembly using a printed circuit board means that:

- Circuits are repeatable. After a prototype has been finalized, all following circuits will be exact copies, unlike the situation in the previous interconnection assembly method.
- Insertion of components may be automated.
- Soldering of components may be automated.
- Testing of final product may be automated.
- Products may be manufactured in large quantities, more cheaply.
- Reliability increases.

Of course, transistors have now, in most circuits, been superseded by integrated circuits (ICs). Even more than transistors, integrated circuits require a method of circuit assembly with the previous features. Integrated circuits, after all, have more connection leads, closer together and, by definition, contain complicated circuits.

Even the simplest 8-pin dual-in-line (DIL – sometimes referred to as dual in-line package (DIP)) integrated circuit, requires a printed circuit board for assembly into its complete circuit. Modern integrated circuits with many more external connections are now available, for example the latest high-density interconnect integrated circuits can have as many as 400 connections.

This quite rapid pace of change in circuit types, from transistor-based circuits to high-density IC-based circuits, through all the intermediary integrated circuit stages, has meant that printed circuit boards have had to evolve at an equally rapid pace. First transistor-based printed circuit boards were quite simple: transistors are discrete components and so only a limited number will fit on to a printed circuit board. As a consequence manufacturing methods were not particularly exact. Positions of component lands were not critical, as a transistor's connecting leads could themselves be adjusted to suit. Further, the number of individual copper tracks on a board was always small.

On the other hand, even the simplest integrated circuit requires an exact track layout. IC connections are always to an exact pattern, and the lands must correspond. The greater number of connections per component (three for a transistor, typically forty or so for an integrated circuit) means that a greater number of tracks per unit area results. These reasons, coupled with the constant requirement for greater and greater packaging density which results in integrated circuits with more and more connections and smaller printed circuit boards, mean that electronics assembly techniques using PCBs are always undergoing improvements. To be fair, the majority of development work in electronics assembly techniques *is* now directed towards printed circuit boards in one form or another. It is the PCB which is of most interest to the electronics manufacturing engineer.

Plate 2.2 *An 8-pin dual-in-line integrated circuit (RJ)*

Plate 2.3 *A 28-pin dual-in-line integrated circuit (RJ)*

PCB classification

There are a number of types of printed circuit board. This is hardly surprising when the large number of component types is considered – every time a more complex component is developed, at least one new form of board usually has to accompany it. Consequently, the number of types is regularly increasing. Often the types of PCB overlap somewhat, and they are pretty arbitrary anyway, so that any particularly board may fall into more than one type. This makes the task of defining types quite difficult. However, the following list attempts to clarify the situation. Whatever the type of printed circuit board, it falls into one of the three main categories.

Single-sided

A single-sided printed circuit board has conductive tracks on only one side of the base material. Usually, but not always, the components are mounted only on the other side. Typically, holes are drilled or punched through the board at lands, so that component leads can be positioned before soldering. Figure 2.1 shows a cross-sectional view of a single-sided PCB.

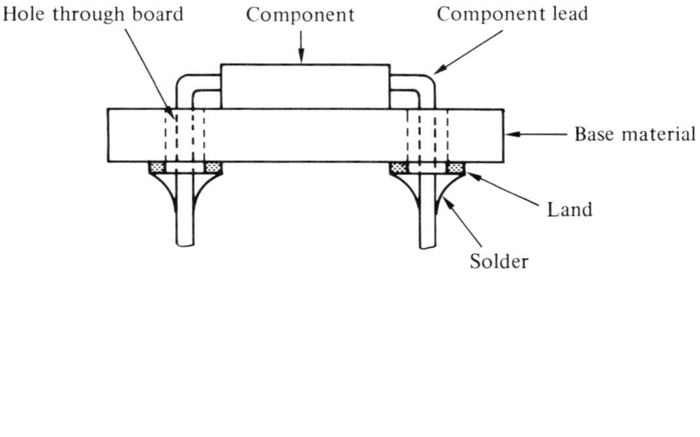

Figure 2.1 *Showing a single-sided printed circuit board. Track is present on only one side of the base material and components are usually mounted on the other side. Component leads connect, through holes in the PCB, to lands on the track*

Hole through board   Component   Component lead

Base material

Land

Solder

Double-sided

Double-sided printed circuit boards have tracks on both sides of the base material. This simple fact allows component density to increase greatly, without having to reduce track size. It is usually necessary to make electrical connections between the tracks on opposing sides, and the norm is to metallize the walls of holes through the board, in some plating process. Such **plated-through holes** (PTHs) which are for the specific purpose of track connection are known as **vias**. Note that the term *plated-through hole* has no connection with the descriptive term *through-hole* in reference to printed circuit boards – the first refers to the fact that a hole through the board is metallized, the other refers to the fact that holes are used to mount components. Other methods are occasionally used to make connections between tracks, such as eyelets, wire, component leads, all of which require the two sides of the connection to be soldered. Figure 2.2 shows a cross-sectional view of a double-sided PCB.

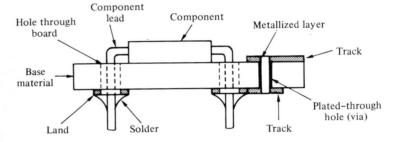

Figure 2.2 *Showing a double-sided printed circuit board. Track is present on both sides of the base material. PTH vias connections between the two tracks*

Multi-layer

Multi-layer boards have several layers of tracks, two of which are on the outside surfaces of the board (as double-sided boards). The remainder, however, are internal to the base material, being laminated together along with insulating layers to provide electrical insulation, with PTH vias to give required electrical connections. Holes used purely for connection purposes are known as **through vias**, while vias which do not pass completely through the board are called **buried vias** or **blind vias**. Figure 2.3 shows a cross-sectional view of a multi-layer PCB.

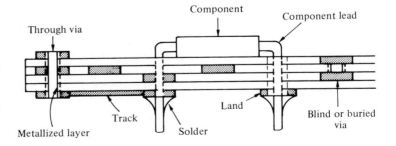

Figure 2.3 *Showing a multi-layer PCB. Tracks are layered and laminated together to form a single board. Vias passing through the board are called through vias, and vias connecting internal tracks are called blind vias or buried vias*

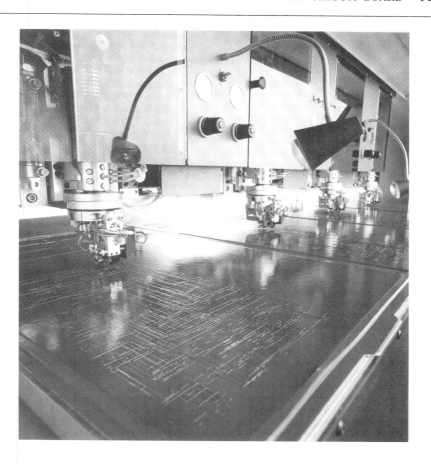

Plate 2.4 *Multi-wired printed circuit board manufacture (BEPI Matrix Systems)*

After these three categories of printed circuit board, all following types can be seen to be derivatives.

Multi-wire

Multi-wired printed circuit boards are, effectively, multi-layer boards, with one essential difference: layers are added *externally* and are not internal laminations. Circuit connections on a multi-wired printed circuit board are made with discrete, small gauge insulated wires. Each wire is terminated with a drilled hole, which is metallized in the usual way to provide PTH vias. Generally, a single- or double-sided board is used as a substrate – these tracks usually giving power distribution tracks – and an adhesive is applied. Wire is then laid on to the substrate using a computer-controlled stylus, building up the remainder of the circuit one connection at a time. The insulation on each wire allows multiple crossovers, which means that extremely complex circuits can be laid in this single extra layer. Figure 2.4 shows a cross-sectional view of such a multi-wired PCB.

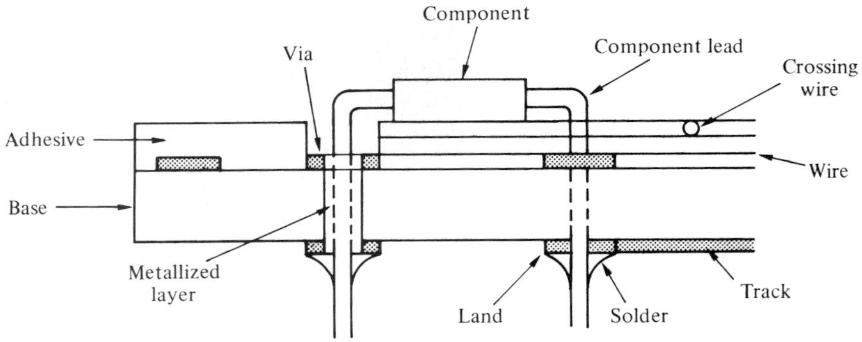

Figure 2.4 *Showing a multi-wired PCB. A single- or double-sided PCB is used as a base, on to which insulated wires are laid to make up the circuit connections*

Polymer-written

Polymer-written printed circuit boards are constructed in a similar way to multi-wired boards, except that conductive extrusions of thick-film polymer form the conductive tracks between components, and insulative thick-film polymer extrusions cover them.

Moulded printed circuit boards

Also known as **three-dimensional moulded circuit boards** (3-D MCBs), **moulded electronic assemblies**, or simply **moulded circuit boards** (MCBs), moulded PCBs feature an injection-moulded thermoplastic as the board base material, on to which track is plated to form the circuit. By injection-moulding the base, integral connectors, stand-offs, recesses and so on can be incorporated. The moulded printed circuit board can even be moulded to form an enclosure. It is one of the most recent developments in PCB technology.

Flexible and flexi-rigid

Flexible printed circuit boards are produced using the methods already listed (with the current exception of multi-wire), using a flexible, rather than a rigid, base material. All features, such as PTH vias and multi-layer constuction are available.

   Flexi-rigid printed circuit boards combine flexible circuits with rigid boards, so that the rigid board is said to have a flexible **tail**. If two such rigid boards are joined using a flexible circuit, the boards may be folded to give a multiple-tiered arrangement.

Hybrid and surface mounted assemblies

Although included here, **hybrid** and **surface mounted** assemblies (surface mounted assemblies are covered in detail in Chapter 3) are not really different categories of printed circuit boards. They are, rather, variations of the categories already listed. The difference, however, between component

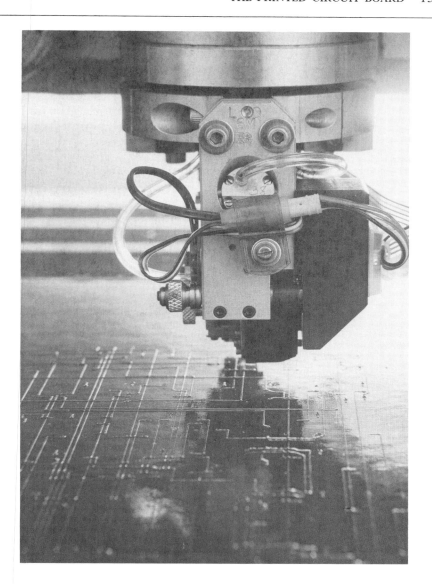

Plate 2.5 *Close-up of a T2000 printed circuit board multi-wiring head (BEPI Matrix System)*

mounting systems in hybrid and surface mounted assemblies compared with those of ordinary printed circuit boards should be stressed. As explained in Chapter 1, hybrid assemblies are combinations of thick- or thin-film passive components, on to which discrete leaded or leadless passive and semiconductive components are mounted. Original development on hybrid assemblies began around thirty years ago, and techniques of manufacture are fairly well established, albeit quite specialized.

Surface mounted assemblies, on the other hand, are simply a development of printed circuit and hybrid processes, where leadless components are used. In practice, increasingly, standard printed circuit board assemblies with leaded components may have a number of leadless components surface mounted, too.

Where standard printed circuit boards rely on *insertion* of components, that is, the leads of components go through holes in the board before soldering, some hybrid and all surface mounted assemblies rely on components being merely *placed* on the board before soldering. Holes are not used to attach surface mounted components – if holes do exist they are plated-through holes and used as vias, that is interconnections between track layers only.

This elimination of through-holes effectively means two things:

• Components are held by small butt or lap soldered joints instead of large through-hole connections. This means that manufacturers have to be aware of potential stresses which can break these small joints (see Chapter 5).
• Components with larger numbers of leads, more closely spaced, can result. This, in turn, means that packing densities are automatically increased. However, as a direct result of increased packing densities, problems can arise owing to the heat generated within such small spaces, and so boards which eliminate or at least reduce the effects of heat may have to be used – see later.

Table 2.1   Common printed circuit board laminate materials, listed alphabetically by BS/IEC laminate code classification. Where applicable, the non-existent NEMA LI1 classification is also listed

Base-materials BS 4584/IEC249	Classification	NEMA LI1
Epoxide resin, woven glass fabric, bonding sheet for multi-layer printed circuit boards	EP–GC	
Epoxide resin, non-woven glass filaments in addition to woven glass fabric, copper conductor	EP–GCA–Cu	
Epoxide resin, woven glass fabric, copper conductor	EP–GC–Cu	G–10, G–11, FR–4, FR–5, CEM–1, CEM–3
Phenolic resin, cellulose paper, copper conductor	PF–CP–Cu	X, XP, XPC, XX, XXP, XXPC, XXX, XXXP, XXXPC, FR–2
Polyethylene terephthalate (polyester) films, adhesive coated cover sheet for flexible printed circuit boards	PETP–F	
Polyethylene terephthalate (polyester), flexible, copper conductor	PETP–F–Cu	
Polyimide film, adhesive coated cover sheet for flexible printed circuit boards		
Polyimide, flexible, copper	PI–F–Cu	
Silicone resin, woven glass fabric, copper	Si–GC–Cu	

Base materials

There are a number of materials used for construction of printed circuit board bases. Generally, for standard boards, these are reinforced plastic, either thermoplastic or thermosetting. Reinforcing materials include sheet paper, glass fibre cloth, cotton fabric and nylon. Choice should be made regarding such factors as chemical, electrical, mechanical, thermal characteristics. Fillers can be added to influence characteristics accordingly. Table 2.1 lists common printed circuit board laminates, according to British Standard BS 4584 and IEC 249 classifications. These standards are to be used wherever possible. Where applicable, classifications according to the commonly known ANSI NEMA LI1 standard – which does not, incidentally, exist – are also listed, but are present merely for informational purposes.

As an aid to clarification of letter codes used in the standard classifications, Table 2.2 lists letter codes for the various printed circuit board types, along with descriptions.

Where extremely high component densities are achieved on printed circuit boards, particularly in the cases of hybrid and surface mounted assemblies, there is often the problem of heat – see later. Sometimes, therefore, it is necessary to use a base material with closely specified thermal characteristics. Many modern bases have been developed with this

Table 2.2 Letter codes for printed circuit board types

Letter code BS 4584/IEC249	NEMA LI1	Description
CP		Cellulose paper
Cu		Copper conductor
EP		Epoxide resin
F		Flexible
GC		Woven glass fabric
GCA		Woven glass fabric with reinforcement of non-woven glass filaments
PETP		Polyethylene terephthalate (polyester)
PF		Phenolic resin
PI		Polyimide
Si		Silicone resin
	FR	Flame retardant
	G	Glass fabric reinforced
	P	Punchable, if heated to between 50 and 80°C
	PC	Cold punchable, above 25°C
	X	Paper reinforced, poor electrical characteristics
	XX	Paper reinforced, fair electrical characteristics
	XXX	Paper reinforced, good electrical characteristics

objective, simply because high packing densities are becoming the norm, rather than the exception.

Resins

The resins most commonly used for rigid base materials are epoxy, phenolic, and silicone. Epoxy-resins take the lion's share of the market, with the norm being epoxy-resin reinforced with glass fibre cloth (IEC classification: EP-GC-Cu).

Hybrid and surface mounted assembly bases

A special case in point is the range of bases, normally called **substrates**, used for hybrid and, sometimes, surface mounted assemblies. It is usually the problems associated with the generation of heat and its dissipation which define the substrates used. Typical substrates are of alumina, beryllia, metal-cored sheet, porcelain-enamelled steel and glass-ceramic coated metal-cores. By no means are these substrates limited to purely hybrid or surface mounted assemblies, however, although their cost may be a significant factor in preventing their use in through-hole printed circuit board assemblies.

   Hybrid and surface mounted assemblies can have peculiar problems with regard to heat. Internally generated heat from the components themselves, and external heat from the ambient environment can affect assemblies in two main ways:

- Excessive heat can internally damage a circuit.
- Different thermal coefficients of expansion of components and substrates can cause stresses which may fracture the soldered joints or the components themselves.

For these reasons, substrates used for such assemblies must dissipate

Table 2.3 Common overall thicknesses of printed circuit board laminates, imperial and metric quantities

	Thickness		
(in)		*(mm)*	
Fraction	Decimal	Exact	Rounded
$\frac{1}{32}$	0.031	0.79	0.8
$\frac{3}{64}$	0.047	1.19	1.2
$\frac{1}{16}$	0.062	1.59	1.6
$\frac{5}{64}$	0.078	1.96	2.0
$\frac{3}{32}$	0.093	2.38	2.4
$\frac{1}{8}$	0.125	3.17	3.0
$\frac{5}{32}$	0.156	3.96	4.0
$\frac{3}{16}$	0.187	4.76	5.0
$\frac{1}{4}$	0.250	6.35	6.4

heat well and must have a thermal coefficient of expansion which closely
matches that of the components used.

Chapter 3 covers the subject of surface mounted assemblies in detail.

Standards

The manufacturer of electronics assemblies need not be familiar with the
details of laminates, resins and fillers, substrates and cores; merely the
required characteristics, because standards exist to ensure that laminate
and substrate manufacturers prepare precisely controlled materials.

UK	IEC	USA	European
BS 3953	IEC249	IPC L108	DIN 40802
BS 4584		IPC L109	DIN LN9407
BS 5102		IPC L112	
BS 6673		IPC L115	
Def Stan 59–50		IPC L125	
		IPC AM361	
		Mil P13949	

Basic mechanical properties

Laminate thickness

Laminate thicknesses are measured in terms of the overall thickness, and
the thickness of the copper conductive foil. Owing to the fairly standard
and long-term nature of laminates, thicknesses are still often incorrectly
stated in old imperial quantities. Table 2.3, therefore, lists common overall
thicknesses of laminates in both imperial and metric quantities. However,
as IEC249 and BS4584 specify overall thicknesses (and foil thicknesses, for
that matter) in metric quantities, imperial quantities should no longer be
used – they are mentioned here purely for informational purposes.

Copper foil thicknesses, too, are often incorrectly stated in terms of
imperial mass per unit area. Table 2.4 lists common imperial masses per
unit area, with corresponding metric equivilants. Again, as IEC249 and

Table 2.4 Printed circuit board copper foil masses per unit area/thicknesses,
comparing metric quantities with imperial equivalents

Mass per unit area		Nominal thickness	
gm^{-2}	oz/ft^2	$in \times 10^{-3}$	μm
152	0.5	0.7	18
305	1.0	1.4	35
610	2.0	2.8	70
915	3.0	4.2	115
1220	4.0	5.6	140

Table 2.5   Printed circuit board copper foil masses per unit area and thicknesses, metric quantities

Mass per unit area (gm^{-2})			Thickness (μm)		
Minimum	Nominal	Maximum	Minimum	Nominal	Maximum
137	152	167	13	18	25
275	305	335	30	35	45
545	610	675	62	70	88

Table 2.6   Preferred combinations of copper foil and polyester film

	Foil Nominal thickness (μm)	Polyester film Film thickness					
		$23\,\mu m$	$36\,\mu m$	$50\,\mu m$	$75\,\mu m$	$100\,\mu m$	$125\,\mu m$
		Overall thickness (μm)					
Single-sided	20	56					
	35		86	100	125	150	175
	70			135	160		210
Double-sided	20	89					
	35			150	175		225
	70			220	245		295

This assumes the use of a 15 µm thick adhesive layer between foil and film.

Table 2.7   Preferred combinations of copper foil and polyimide film

	Foil Nominal thickness (μm)	Polyimide film Film thickness		
		$25\,\mu m$	$50\,\mu m$	$75\,\mu m$
		Overall thickness (μm)		
Single-sided	20		83	
	35	75	100	125
	70			160
Double-sided	20			
	35			175
	70			

This assumes the use of a 15 µm thick adhesive layer between foil and film.

BS 4584 specify copper foil in metric terms, the imperial quantities are mentioned purely for informational purposes. Often, very loosely, imperial weights alone are stated to imply copper foil thickness (for example, $\frac{1}{2}$ oz, meaning 18 µm; 2 oz, meaning 70 µm).

Table 2.5 lists common masses per unit area and thicknesses of copper foil, as nominal quantities, along with minimum and maximum variations, according to BS 4584.

Where the printed circuit board base material is a flexible film (PETP-F-Cu, or PI-F-Cu according to IEC249) there are preferred thicknesses of film for given copper foil thicknesses. Table 2.6 lists preferred combinations of copper foil and polyester film printed circuit boards (PETP-F-Cu), in terms of foil thickness, film thickness, and overall thickness. Table 2.7 lists preferred combinations of copper foil and polyimide film (PI-F-Cu) in the same terms. Note that the overall thicknesses given assume a 15 µm thick adhesive layer has been used to bond foil and film. If other thicknesses of adhesive are used, the overall thicknesses should be adjusted correspondingly.

Other properties

Other properties relevant to printed circuit boards, specified in IEC249 and BS 4584, are summarized and listed in Table 2.8. By standardizing such physical and electrical properties in international standards, users of printed circuit board laminates, that is, electronics assemblers, are assured of consistent input product quality.

Standards

UK	IEC	USA	European
BS 4584	IEC249	EIA216	DIN 40801
BS 6221	IEC326	IPC L108	DIN 40802
BS 9760		IPC L109	DIN LN9407
BS 9761		IPC L112	DIN VDE3710
BS 9762		IPC L115	
BS 9763		IPC L125	
BS 9764		IPC CF150	
BS 9765		IPC FC231	
BS 9766		IPC FC232	
Def Stan 59–50		IPC FC233	
		IPC FC240	
		IPC AM361	
		UL746	
		UL796	
		Mil Std275	
		Mil P13949	
		Mil P28809	
		Mil P50884	
		Mil P55110	

Table 2.8 Summarized properties of common clad printed circuit board laminates

Laminate	Resistance of foil at 305 gm^{-2} (mΩ)	Surface resistance at 125°C or 100°C*, minimum value (MΩ)	Surface resistance after damp heat and recovery, minimum value (MΩ)	Volume resistivity at 125°C or 100°C*, minimum value (MΩm)	Volume resistivity after damp heat and recovery, minimum value (MΩm)	Permittivity, maximum value	Loss tangent, maximum value	d value for bow, 305 gm^{-2}, 1.6 mm laminate, single-sided	d value for bow, 305 gm^{-2}, 1.6 mm laminate, double-sided	e value for twist, 305 gm^{-2}, 1.6 mm laminate, single-sided	e value for twist, 305 gm^{-2}, 1.6 mm laminate, double-sided	Pull-off strength, 152 gm^{-2} (N)	Pull-off strength, 305 gm^{-2} (N)	Peel strength after heat shock, 152 gm^{-2} (kNm^{-1})	Peel strength after dry heat, 152 gm^{-2} (kNm^{-1})	Peel strength after solvent exposure, 152 gm^{-2} (kNm^{-1})	Peel strength after plating, 152 gm^{-2} (kNm^{-1})	Flex strength (MNm^{-2})	Flammability: average burning time (s)
EP–GC–Cu–2	3.5	1000	50000	100	20000	5.5	0.04	23	15	18	14	60	90	1.1	1.1	1.1	0.9	300	
EP–GC–Cu–3	3.5	500	50000	100	20000	5.5	0.04	23	15	18	14	60	90	1.1	1.1	1.1	0.9	300	10
EP–GCA–Cu–16	3.5	500	50000	100	20000	5.5	0.04	23	15	18	14	60	90	1.1	1.1	1.1	0.9	250	10
PETP–F–Cu–9	3.6		10^5		10^6	4									0.5	0.375	0.375		
PF–CP–Cu–4																			
PF–CP–Cu–5	3.5	100*	1000	10*	500	7	0.07	61	30	13	10	45	45	1.05	1.05	1.05	0.6	82	
PF–CP–Cu–6	3.5	15*	1000	10*	500	7	0.08	61	30	13	10	45	45	1.05	1.05	1.05	0.6	82	15
PF–CP–Cu–7																			
PF–CP–Cu–8	3.5	100*	1000	15*	1600	5.5	0.06	61	30	13	10	45	45	1.05	1.05	1.05	0.6	70	15
PF–CP–Cu–14	3.5	15*	1000	15*	500	6	0.07	61	30	13	10	45	45	1	1	1	0.6	80	10
PI–F–Cu–10	3.5		10^5		10^6	4								0.5	0.5	0.375	0.375		
Si–GC–Cu–13	3.5		50000		10000	4	0.008	23	15	18	14	63	63	0.7			0.7	100	

Notes:
Numbers at end of laminate code are serial numbers, indicating the part of **BS 4584** which applies.
Tests as defined by **BS 4584** Part 1.
Letter codes as defined in Table 2.2.

PCB manufacture

An understanding of the processes involved in manufacture of a printed circuit board is useful, even if assembly personnel have no intimate contact with its manufacture. After discussing a method of analysing the techniques of manufacture, this section looks at the techniques in detail. The following section defines the main processes which make up the techniques. Many of these processes are used in more than one of the techniques, however, and this creates a problem in describing the techniques in anything like a clear manner. For this reason it is assumed the reader is familiar with any preceding process – if a process is found which is not described anywhere in the text describing a technique that is, hopefully, because it has been described previously. If a reader finds such a process: look back to earlier techniques; then look to the next section to see the process described in detail.

Although printed circuit boards were categorized previously in the chapter as being of only three main types – single-sided, double-sided, multi-layered – when considering the manufacture of printed circuit boards another method of categorizing them becomes apparent. This method takes into account the manufacturing processes involved in producing the conductive track or tracks on the board.

At the extremes, there are two main manufacturing techniques. The first starts with copper-clad base material and uses an etchant to dissolve away the copper which is not needed; leaving behind the track on the surface of the base. This is called **subtractive manufacture**. Techniques which are purely subtractive are often classed as **conventional** techniques. Sometimes, they are also called **print and etch** techniques, a name which refers to the two main steps in subtractive printed circuit board production:

- Printing a pattern on the copper surface which corresponds to the required track. Some form of **etch resist** chemical is used here, to protect the track during the following step.
- Etching away the unwanted areas of copper from the board surface, leaving behind the wanted track.

The second starts with base laminate without copper, adding the track where required. Naturally enough, this is called **additive manufacture**. At first sight, this may seem the best and cheapest option – only the copper required must be bought, unlike subtractive manufacture which must waste a significant amount of copper. But, adding copper to a base material is a technically difficult job with many drawbacks – the processes involved are time-consuming and, often, complicated.

So, in reality, there are few purely additive manufacturing techniques; most printed circuit boards are made using mixtures of additive *and* subtractive processes, and here the name **semi-additive manufacture** is more correct, although there are many different processes included in this title. Usually, copper-clad base material is the starting point, although thickness of the copper laminated layer is much less than in subtractive manufacture.

Subtractive manufacture

A flow diagram of simple single-sided printed circuit board subtractive manufacture is shown in Figure 2.5. At its heart is the application of etch resist to cover the track, prior to etching. It is this application which is usually referred to as printing, and is the reason why PCBs are actually called *printed* circuit boards. Such a manufacturing technique generally produces boards of only limited accuracy and quality, although perfectly acceptable for many applications. That is not to say the technique is not capable of higher accuracy – it is just that if higher accuracy is wanted, the reason is because higher packing density is required, and so semi-additive manufacture is the preferred option, anyway.

Semi-additive manufacture

Figure 2.6. illustrates the change from the purely subtractive manufacturing technique to a semi-additive one, and shows how manufacture may be

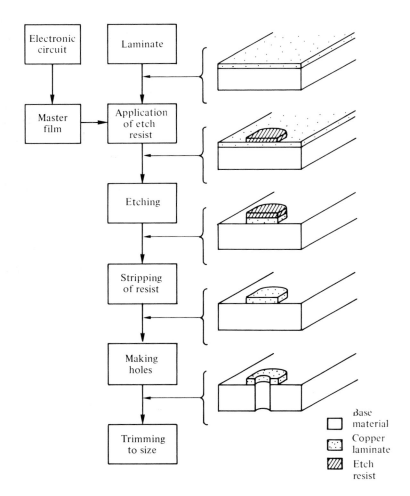

Figure 2.5 *Flow diagram of subtractive single-sided printed circuit board manufacture*

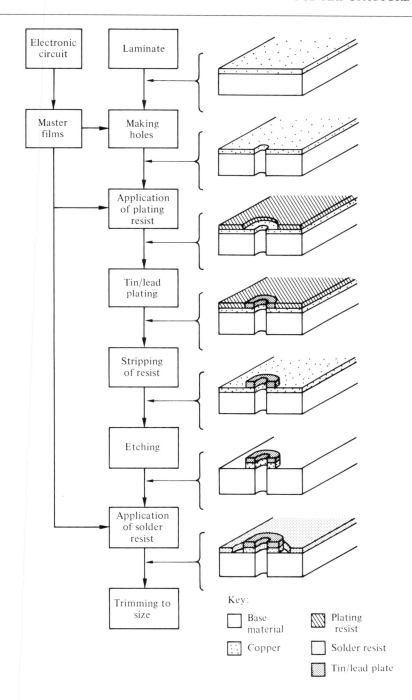

Figure 2.6 *Flow diagram of semi-additive printed circuit board manufacture*

improved and adapted with the inclusion of extra processes. Primary differences are the facts that holes are made as a first stage in the technique (before etching), and the two resists used are to protect the copper from plating and soldering, not from etching – the tin/lead plating instead acts as an etch resist to protect the copper track while the unwanted copper is etched. Although large areas of copper are still being wasted by the etching process, benefits of greater accuracy arise if the original base laminate has thinner copper-cladding – in general, the thinner the copper cladding the finer and closer the tracks can be.

Such semi-additive techniques can produce much higher quality printed circuit boards than basic print and etch ones, but their real potential is not realized unless double-sided boards are the object, where PTH vias and component holes are required. Figure 2.7 illustrates a technique for manufacture of double-sided PCBs with plated-through holes. Key process in the technique is the electroless deposition of copper through the barrel of the hole. The barrel cannot be directly electroplated, of course, because the two tracks are separated by the base material layer. Electroless deposition creates a thin layer of copper, upon which more may be plated later in the technique. The processes of electroless deposition followed by electroplating are given the collective term **metallization**. At the finish, a good quality board with fully plated and tinned holes results.

Multi-layer printed circuit boards are manufactured using these semi-additive processes, and the technique used to manufacture a single layer is illustrated in Figure 2.8, while the overall technique for a four-layer board is illustrated in Figure 2.9. Note that outer layers are of single-sided laminate, and remain unetched until bonded. Inner layer holes (like that shown in the illustration), although previously plated, must be plated again as part of the metallization process if new holes through the whole board pass through them.

Boards of up to around thirty layers can be manufactured with the technique, which supposes a basic difference between voltage layers (that is, those track layers which carry supply and earth connections and logic layers (that is, track layers carrying signals), as voltage layers usually have no plated-through holes. Extremely fine tracks (known as **fine lines**) and spaces between tracks (known as **gaps**) of as little as 100 μm each are possible, consequently extremely complex circuit layouts are easily obtained. Needless to say, though, costs of multi-layer printed circuit boards are appreciably more than more conventional double-sided and single-sided boards. The fine lines and gaps are a direct consequence of the use of thinner copper laminates, often only 10 μm thick on each 200 μm material layer.

Individual layers of the printed circuit board are bonded together with insulating bonding sheets, which are usually of thin fibre glass cloth impregnated with epoxy resin, and given the name **prepreg**. Various additives are used in prepreg, to determine its viscosity, giving rise to three basic types:

- High-flow prepreg, which has a low viscosity. As a result, lower pressures can be used when bonding boards. A disadvantage, however, is the difficulty in controlling resin flow, resin often seeping into holes.

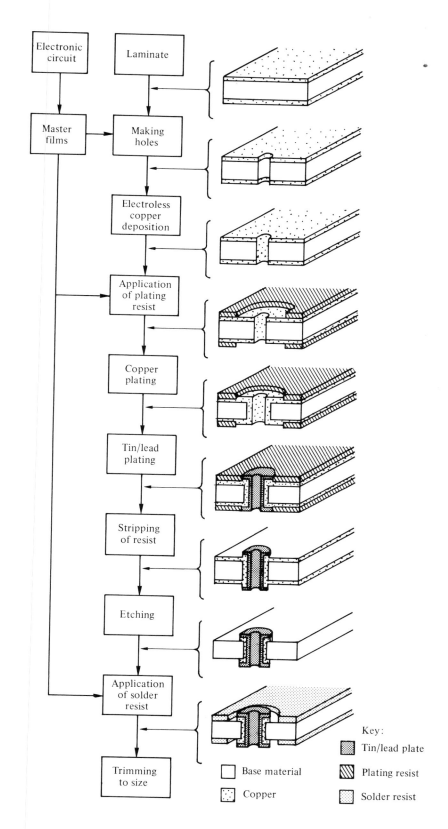

Figure 2.7 *Flow diagram of double-sided printed circuit board with plated-through holes manufacture*

Electronic circuit

Laminate

Master films

Making holes

Electroless copper deposition

Application of plating resist

Copper plating

Tin/lead plating

Stripping of resist

Etching

Application of solder resist

Trimming to size

Key:

☐ Base material

⋯ Copper

▨ Tin/lead plate

▧ Plating resist

▦ Solder resist

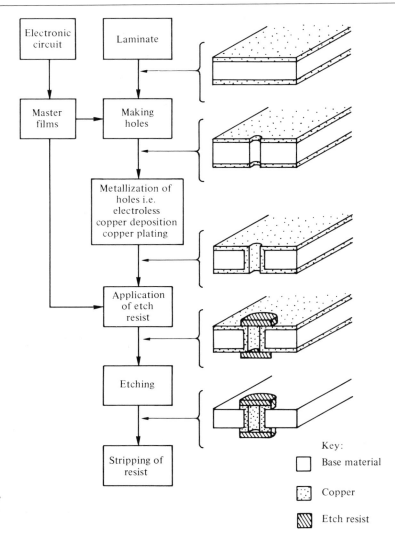

Figure 2.8 *Flow diagram illustrating manufacturing stages of a single layer of a multi-layer printed circuit board*

- Low-flow prepreg, with a high viscosity, hence low seepage. The disadvantage, of course, being the high bonding pressure required.
- No-flow prepreg. These prepregs have been specially developed for production of connections where one face is resin-free, such as the bonding of rigid and flexible circuits or for attachments of heat sinks to the board surface.

Prepreg seepage into holes means that the inner track layers may be insulated from the plated-through hole deposits, so the process of **etchback** is used prior to metallization.

Multi-wired printed circuit boards can, in theory, be made by a purely additive process. However, a double-sided base laminate is usually used; conventionally made with PTH vias, on to which the wires making up the

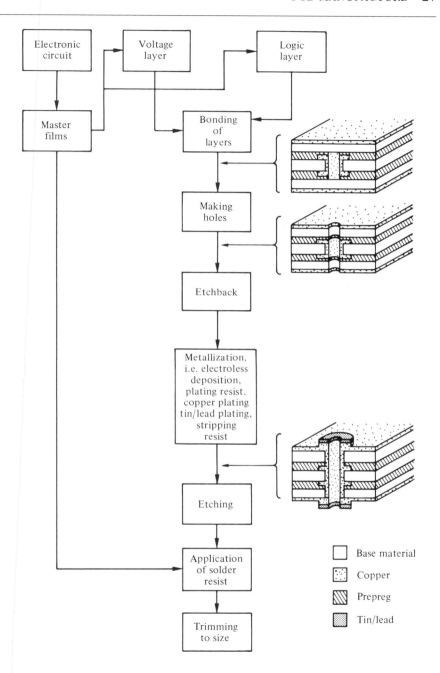

Figure 2.9 *Flow diagram illustrating manufacture of a four layer multi-layer printed circuit board*

remainder of the circuit are added, so they are normally classed as printed circuit boards made by a semi-additive manufacturing technique. The originating technique, *Multiwire* – patented by the Photocircuit Corporation – uses the base laminate for power, earth and any ground planes, while all signal tracks are built up using wire. This technique is illustrated in

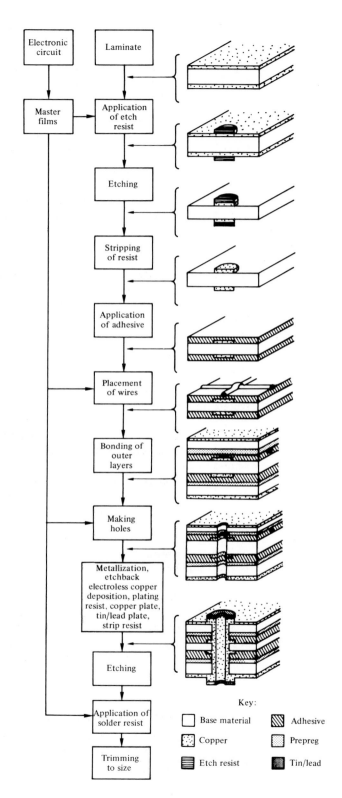

Figure 2.10 *Basic manufacture of a multi-wired printed circuit board*

Figure 2.10. It is usual to produce the board with outer layers of copper foil which are then printed and etched using more conventional techniques.

Wire used varies with multi-wired process, but there are three basic sizes:

- 0.16 mm (0.0063 in; 6.3 mils; 34 AWG).
- 0.1 mm (0.0039 in; 3.9 mils; 38 AWG).
- 0.063 mm (0.0025 in; 2.5 mils; 42 AWG).

The second wire size is used by Hitachi on its *Multiwire* interconnection board system, while the third is used on the *Microwire* board system. The smaller the wire, of course, the higher will be the track resistivity, so there is a practical limit to how fine wire can be. For reference, a 0.16 mm wire has a resistivity of $0.855 \Omega \, \text{m}^{-1}$, which is equivalent to a 0.7 mm wide track conductor etched out of 35 μm thick copper foil.

It is said that as few as two wiring levels of 0.16 mm wire (one on either side of a double-sided base laminate) are capable of producing a board with the same potential complexity as eight layers of a multilayer board. Smaller wire techniques are capable of even greater improvements. The consequent lower price of a multi-wired PCB, compared with a multi-layered counterpart, is an obvious advantage.

Additive manufacture

A fully additive printed circuit board manufacturing technique is illustrated in Figure 2.11, where the unclad base laminate undergoes electroless copper deposition onto its surface to make up the circuit tracks. Such techniques are, however, few and far between and, with the possible exception of moulded techniques, do not yet pose serious competition to semi-additive techniques.

Moulded printed circuit boards are a relatively new type of board which are made using a completely additive manufacturing technique. First, the base laminate is moulded from thermosetting plastic. This moulding process means that features previously only achieved with hardware additions can be built-in. Such features include large component mounting clips, battery mounting clips, connectors, structural ribs, snap-fits and so on. Moulded boards effectively change the principle of PCBs being a single plane method of holding components, into a three-dimensional method. It is not difficult to envisage complete appliances, with circuit components mounted on the inside of the moulded case.

Second, the track is added, using additive processes. ICI Electronics' manufacturing technique, for example, uses an ultraviolet imaging process followed by plating processes, to produce plated through holes and three-dimensional circuit tracks.

PCB manufacturing processes

In this section the main processes of printed circuit board manufacturing techniques are considered. These are in alphabetical order: no other priority is assumed.

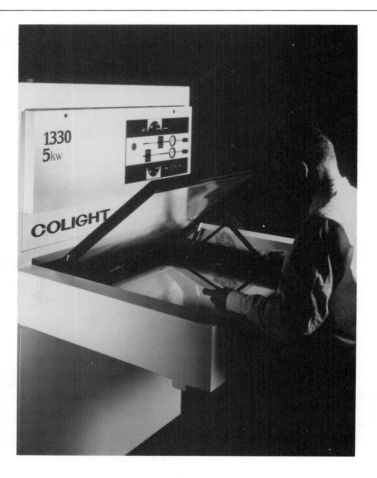

Plate 2.6 *Colight 1330 ultra-violet exposure unit for printed circuit board manufacture (Astro Technology)*

Application of resist

There are a number of types of resist:

- Etch resist.
- Plating resist.
- Solder resist.

All provide a means whereby the copper laminate or track is protected from any following processes.

Two main methods are used to get the required resist image onto the printed circuit board surface:

- **Screen printing**. This process, simple and fairly cheap, is shown in Figure 2.12. It is an adaptation of the standard screen printing process, used to print panels, cloths and the like. A wood or metal frame supports a stretch mesh of material – before the advent of man-made fibres this would be silk (often the process is still referred to as **silk-**

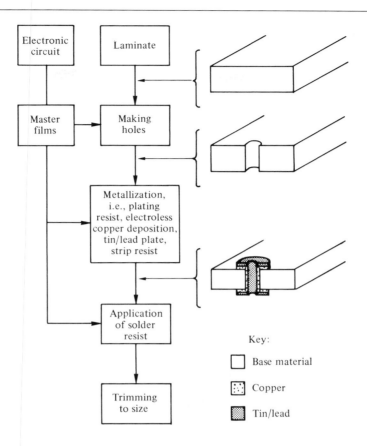

Figure 2.11 *Illustrating a purely additive printed circuit board manufacturing technique*

screen printing) but is now usually nylon or similar material – a small distance above the board to be printed (Figure 2.12(a)). Holes between the fibres of the screen must be selectively filled with lacquer or similar substance prior to printing with a negative image of the image required on the board: that is, areas which are required to be clear of resist have a corresponding area on the screen which has been filled with lacquer. Ink, which has the required resist qualities, is applied to the top of the screen, and a squeegee is used to push the screen down (Figure 2.12(b)) and force the ink through the screen on to the board, so that only those areas of screen which are unfilled will pass the ink.

Definition of the printed image depends on the screen's hole size, which depends on what is called its **mesh size**; the number of openings per linear measure. Accuracy is fairly limited, and depends largely on the operator, although it may be suitable for many applications.

- **Photoprinting**. Photoprinting of printed circuit boards is a three-stage process, shown in Figure 2.13. First, the board is laminated with a **photoresist**, by heating and applying pressure, usually with rollers as shown in Figure 2.13(a). Photoresist itself comprises three layers: a thin (2.5 μm) layer of polyester, a photosensitive polymer layer (25 to

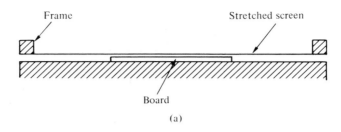

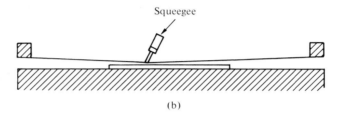

Figure 2.12 *Applying resist to a circuit board by screen printing. (a) A mesh screen is held a small distance above the board. (b) A squeegee forces resist through the screen on to the board*

50 μm), and a protective polyethylene film. The protective film is discarded during the lamination process. It is the layer of polyester which acts as a dry barrier between the photosensitive polymer and the outside world which gives such photoresists the name of **dry-film photoresists**. Without the polyester the polymer-coated board surface is tacky, and obvious difficulties in handling arise – although high-accuracy fine-line imaging may require it.

Second, the photoresist-coated board is exposed, normally with an ultraviolet light source (the spectral response of photoresist is usually around 360 nm) using a film of the required image (Figure 2.13(b)). In most production, negative-acting photoresist is used, that is, the photosensitive layer polymerizes on exposure to ultraviolet light and so can be dissolved using a developing solution. This means that a positive image film can be used with the light source.

Finally, the board is developed. The developing solution depends upon the type of photosensitive polymer used, being either aqueous, semi-aqueous, or solvent. The laminated, exposed and developed board is shown in Figure 2.13(c).

Bonding of PCB layers

Multi-layer boards are bonded together using heated presses; for a time, temperature and pressure dependent upon the prepreg and equipment. On initial application of heat and light pressure – known as **kiss pressure** – the resin in the prepreg softens and flows to fill all voids between the lamination surfaces. Full bonding pressure is then applied, polymerization results and the prepreg then hardens.

Copper plating

Copper plating of printed circuit boards is carried out using fairly conventional plating baths, normally based on copper sulphate. Plating normally follows electroless copper deposition, as a conductive surface is required by the plating process.

Electroless copper deposition

Although the process of electroless copper deposition itself is fairly straightforward, to create a thin layer of copper over an insulating base, other processes are required to prepare the surface of the insulating board beforehand. The whole technique, therefore, comprises a number of stages:

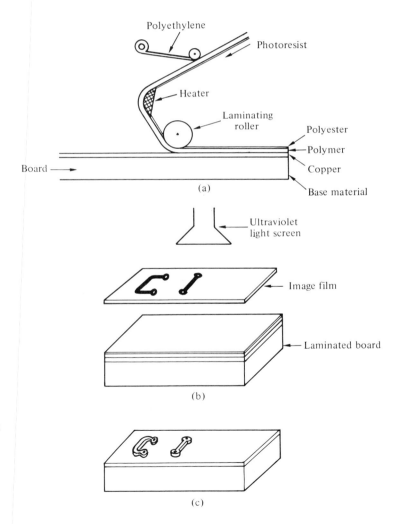

Figure 2.13 *Applying resist to a circuit board by photo-printing. (a) Board is initially laminated with a photoresist. (b) The photo-resist coated board is exposed. (c) After developing the board is complete*

- Conditioning. This stage ensures all holes and surfaces of the board are clean and free from grease or metal contaminants. Deburring of holes and surfaces is undertaken, normally, by rotating brushes. Degreasing is undertaken by dipping in a suitable chemical agent.
- Etching. This stage is often known as **pickling**, to differentiate it from the more usual copper etching process. Its main purpose is to prepare the board surface for subsequent copper deposition, but it also serves to remove any minor deformities left after the preceding stage. Heated sulphuric acid and hydrogen peroxide mixtures are commonly used here as they are regenerative – copper etched from the board can be precipitated by cooling the mixture – and therefore allow indefinite usage.
- Activating. The purpose of this stage is to create a chemically reducing surface, ready for copper deposition. Traditionally, two processes are normally involved in this stage. First, the board is **sensitized** by dipping into an acidic stannous solution. Stannous ions are adsorbed on to the surface of the board. Second, the board is **seeded** by dipping into an acidic solution of palladium chloride. Palladium ions are reduced to the colloidal state where stannous ions are present on the board surface. Copper-based activators are currently being developed.
- Depositing. In this stage, the board is dipped in a solution based on copper ions. The chemically reducing board surface causes a reaction which deposits and builds up copper on the prepared surfaces. Depending on the solution, thicknesses of deposited layers vary from about $1\mu m$ to $5\,\mu m$, and much thicker (about $25\,\mu m$) for fully additive printed circuit board manufacturing techniques.

Plate 2.7 *Wessel printed circuit board drilling machine (Astro Technology)*

Etchback

When multi-layer boards are drilled (Figure 2.14) **resin smear**, created by the drill bit heating and softening the prepreg, can cover the copper layers. Following metallization will result in layers being insulated from the plating through the holes. By dipping the board into a suitable etchant solution the base material between copper layers is etched back slightly, exposing the copper. Good contact is ensured when subsequent metallization by electroless copper deposition takes place. Typically, concentrated sulphuric acid is used as the etchback etchant for epoxy-based boards, other base laminates require other etchants.

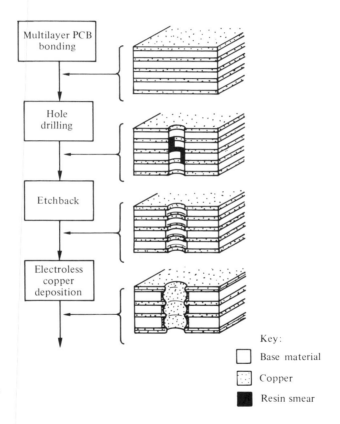

Figure 2.14 *Resin smear is created when multi-layered printed circuit boards are drilled. This is removed by etchback*

Etching

The etching process requires that unwanted copper is removed from the board. This can be done simply, where small quantities of printed circuit boards are required, by dipping the board into a bath where the etchant is agitated in some way. For larger quantities it is usual for boards to pass between nozzles, through which etchant is pumped as a spray.

The etchant used depends largely on board type. Simple print and etch boards are usually etched with ferric chloride, or cupric chloride where a regeneration of etchant is required. Boards which are tin/lead plated, particularly those with plated-through holes, require the tin/lead to be unaffected by the etchant, so ammoniacal etchants are normally used.

One effect of etching which should be noted is that of undercut, shown in Figure 2.15, where the copper layer under the tin/lead plating is etched away to a significant degree.

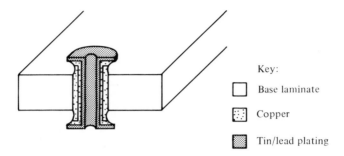

Figure 2.15 *Undercut, created by etching*

Key:

☐ Base laminate

▨ Copper

▨ Tin/lead plating

Making holes

The making of holes in printed circuit boards is one of the most time consuming of processes and can absorb as much as 40% of production costs, so much work has gone into automation. Generally, holes are drilled, though occasionally may be punched. Where drilling is undertaken, numerically-controlled or computer-numerically-controlled drilling machines are a necessity for complex double-sided and multi-layer boards, as well as for high-volume single-sided boards.

Metallization

Metallization is the collective name given to the processes involved in selectively building up layers of metal onto a board. Two main techniques of metallization have been used in printed circuit board manufacture:

- Panel plating (Figure 2.16). The board, which has been metallized by electroless copper deposition to a thickness of about 1 μm, is electroplated to a thickness of about 4 μm. Then, plating resist is applied, followed by tin/lead electroplate.
- Pattern plating (Figure 2.17). The board, metallized by electroless copper deposition, has plating resist applied. It is then copper electroplated, followed by tin/lead electroplate.

The main difference between the two techniques is the fact that pattern plating selectively builds up electroplated copper and tin/lead, while panel plating builds up copper over the whole board or panel – only selectively

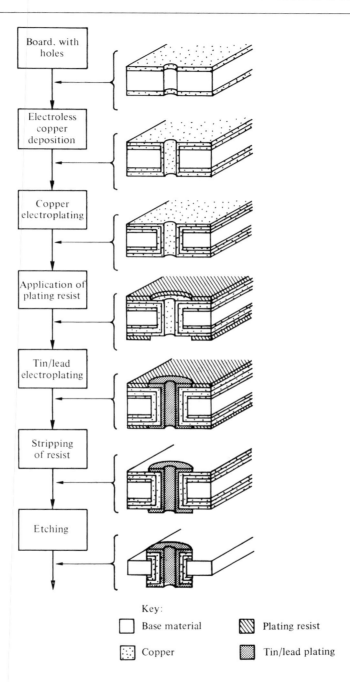

Board, with holes

Electroless copper deposition

Copper electroplating

Application of plating resist

Tin/lead electroplating

Stripping of resist

Etching

Key:

☐ Base material   ▨ Plating resist

▦ Copper   ▦ Tin/lead plating

Figure 2.16 *Illustrating the panel plating process*

plating tin/lead. As the majority of the copper on a panel plated board will be etched away anyway, this can be seen to be very wasteful. Consequently, pattern plating is the usual technique used, although it is a more difficult process to control and is harder to ensure even plating.

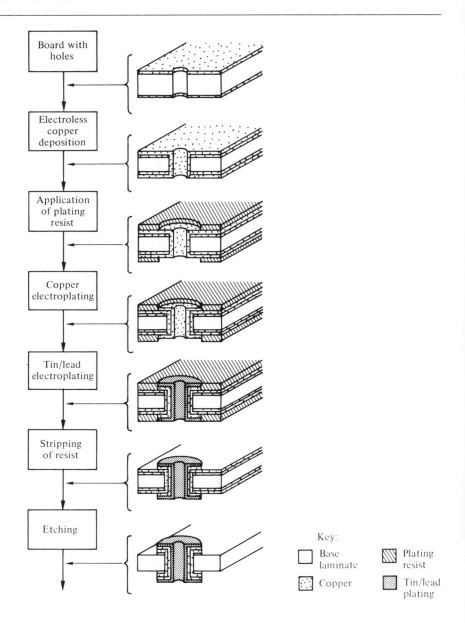

Figure 2.17 *Illustrating the pattern plating process*

Photo-resist

See *Application of resist*, page 30.

Placement of wires

Placement of wires of a multi-wired printed circuit board is an additive process, done with a numerically-controlled writing machine, the main

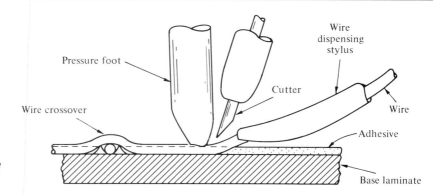

Figure 2.18 *Main principle of a multi-wired printed circuit board writing head*

principle of which is illustrated in Figure 2.18. A table allows movement in one direction, the wiring head moves in the other. The pressure foot is formed by an ultrasonic transducer and so, as wire is fed to the head from spools, the wire is ultrasonically bonded into the adhesive on the board.

A complete writing head is shown in Figure 2.19, where wire can be seen to be fed from a spool above the head, and an ultrasonic generator provides drive for the pressure foot transducer.

Plating of connector tracks

Plating is one of the processes which are collectively known as metallization. A number of metals can be, and are, plated on to printed circuit boards; copper, tin/lead, gold, and so on.

Copper is plated on to the conducting track mainly to reinforce the thin layer of copper deposited during electroless deposition of holes.

Tin/lead plating is used:

- To coat the track with an etch resistant material.
- To provide a solderable surface.

Gold plating provides a non-degrading surface, on to which edge connectors will always make good connections.

Screen printing

See *Application of resist*, page 30.

Stripping of resist

After the printed circuit board has undergone the process for which resist has been added, it is sometimes required that the resist be removed. This is referred to as **stripping**. Method of stripping depends, naturally, on the resist used.

With photoresists, where a solvent-type dry-film resist has been previously applied, the board is sprayed with a resist solvent and the solvent

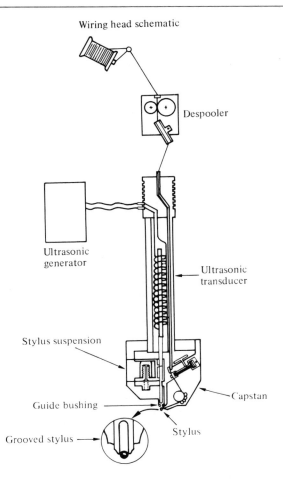

Figure 2.19 *A complete writing head for multi-wired printed circuit board manufacture*

reclaimed. For aqueous or semi-aqueous resists, sodium hydroxide solution is typically used.

Through-hole plating

Through-hole plating is the name given to the process of metallizing the barrels of holes through printed circuit boards, such that two or more layers of track on the board are electrically connected.

Standards

UK	USA	European
BS 1561	EIA208	DIN 40801
BS 4292	IPC D310	DIN 40802
BS 5658	IPC NC349	DIN 50960
BS 6096	IPC SM840	DIN LN9407

BS 6137	Mil Std 100	DIN VDE 3710
BS 6670	Mil T 10727	
BS 9760	Mil P 38510	
BS 9761	Mil G 45204	
BS 9762		
BS 9763		
BS 9764		
BS 9765		
BS 9766		

Design

In the basic design of through-hole assemblies, a number of factors should be taken into account by the engineer. The main ones are:

- The restrictions inherent in the components used in the circuit – their sizes, shapes, spacings.
- Dimensions and shapes of the conductors – hole, land, track.
- The generation and dissipation of heat by the circuit – heat management.
- Special electrical requirements as a result of using boarded assemblies – power distribution, decoupling.
- Physical restrictions, created by the assembly process – designing the PCB so that zero defects occur on component insertion and soldering.

Computer-aided systems are available to help in through-hole design and, in many instances, designers can produce adequate layouts merely by feeding in circuits to the system. Nevertheless, an understanding of the main factors listed here is still essential.

Component restrictions

Sizes and shapes of the components in the circuit must be known. Usually a suitable reference book is a worthwhile tool, although regularly used components and standard IC package sizes will probably be remembered.

Component spacing

Spacings between components depends largely on three things. First, components or circuit parts likely to create interference must be located away from components or circuit parts likely to be affected by interference.

Second, the number of tracks and, for that matter, track dimensions between components may restrict how close the components can be positioned. For modern manufacturing techniques, however, this is a minor concern.

Third, the closeness of components has a direct relevance to the soldering process chosen. Certain processes are more likely to create solder bridges between components and tracks, for any given dimensions, than others.

The soldering process used, and the components, effectively define the limits of closeness in through-hole assemblies.

Conductor dimensions

Typical dimensions which must be considered are:

- Minimum track width.
- Minimum spacing between adjacent tracks.
- Minimum land size around a hole.
- Hole sizes.

Generally, all these will be standardized within a company. They are set by the printed circuit board technology and soldering process used.

Minimum track width

Conductor widths should be as large as practicable, given the overall size requirements of the printed circuit board. Necessary conductor width depends largely on the proposed current which it is to carry, but its own thickness will influence width, too. A current through a conductor will create heat, which if excessive will damage the track itself. Figure 2.20 shows graphs of temperature rises for different track widths and currents, for a foil thickness of 35 µm. Thinner foils will exhibit greater temperature rises for equivalent currents, thicker foils exhibit lower temperature rises.

Minimum track spacings

Spacings between track conductors are defined largely by the soldering process used in production: if the tracks are too close together solder bridges may occur.

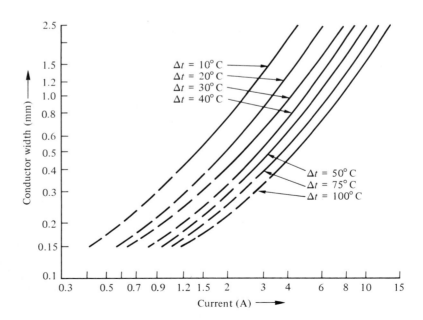

Figure 2.20 *Temperature rises for different track widths and currents, for printed circuit board with a copper foil thickness of 35 µm*

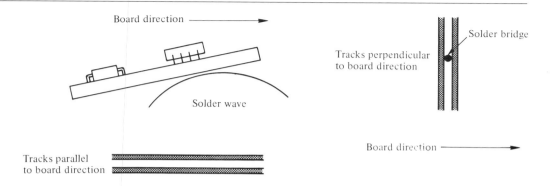

Figure 2.21 *For the same track spacing, tracks running parallel to the board direction in the soldering machine will suffer fewer solder bridges than those running perpendicular*

For the following discussion, readers are referred to Chapter 5 for an understanding of soldering processes. In this book, two distinctly separate types of soldering process are categorized:

- SC processes, where solder is applied first, in the form of solder paste or similar, then the component is added; finally heat is applied.
- CS processes, where the component is first applied, followed by molten solder.

As far as through-hole assemblies are concerned, soldering processes will be CS processes; where the components are inserted, then mass soldered, for example wave soldering.

Spacings when such CS processes are used, depend on track width, board direction through the soldering machine, and whether a solder resist (see later) is used prior to the soldering process.

Generally, the larger the track widths, the larger must be the corresponding spaces between tracks. This is owing to surface tension of the solder, and the effects of wetting, which cause a certain amount of solder to accumulate on a track as the board passes through the CS soldering machine. The larger the track, the more solder accumulates; and where adjacent tracks are separated by an insufficient gap, solder accumulated will bridge to the next track. Tracks running parallel to the direction of the board in the soldering machine will suffer fewer solder bridges than those running perpendicular to the direction of the board for the same track spacing (Figure 2.21), as the solder's surface tension between tracks has less effect in this direction. It follows that tracks running parallel to the direction of the board may be more closely spaced than perpendicular tracks.

BS 6221 specifies a minimum design spacing of 0.25 mm if the track direction is within 15° of board direction in the soldering machine (Figure 2.22(a)). Above 15° the spacing should increase to 0.6 mm (Figure 2.22(b)). Where a solder resist is used, which prevents solder from reaching tracks, the smallest spacing dimensions may be used for all tracks, irrespective of direction.

Spacing between lands are as this except that, even where solder resist is used, spacings over 15° from parallel must be at least 0.6 mm – solder resist cannot be applied to a land, as the land cannot then be soldered.

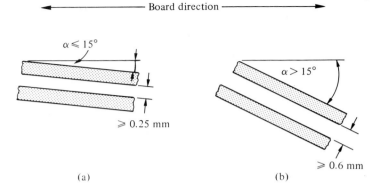

Figure 2.22 *Minimum track spacing for tracks. (a) Within 15° of board direction in the soldering machine is 0.25 mm. (b) Above 15° is 0.6 mm*

Another consideration which defines track spacings is the voltage which will be present across adjacent tracks, during operation. Table 2.9 lists safe track spacings for a selection of working voltages, while Table 2.10 lists spacings for a selection of instantaneous surge voltages.

Table 2.9   Safe conductor track spacings for a selection of working voltages across adjacent tracks

Working voltages peak AC or DC (V)	Track spacing (mm)
290	0.20
315	0.25
370	0.50
435	0.75
500	1.00
640	1.50
775	2.00

Table 2.10   Safe conductor track spacings for a selection of instantaneous surge voltages

Instantaneous surge (V)	Track spacing (mm)
600	0.50
800	0.67
1500	1.20

Minimum land sizes

Land sizes depend on whether the hole is plated-through or not. For a plated-through hole, the land diameter should be at least 1 mm larger than the hole diameter. For a non-plated-through hole, it should be at least 0.5 mm larger than the hole diameter.

Hole size

For obvious manufacturing reasons, the number of different hole sizes in a printed circuit board should be kept to a minimum. Where possible, preferred sizes should be used. Preferred hole sizes specified in BS 6221 are listed in Table 2.11, together with their hole codes and tolerances.

Table 2.11 preferred hole sizes, vodes and tolerances (BS 6221)

Finished hole diameter (mm)	Hole code	Tolerance (mm)
0.85	a	+0.15 −0.00
0.95	b	+0.15 −0.00
1.20	c	+0.15 −0.00
1.40	d	+0.15 −0.00
1.60	e	+0.15 −0.00
1.80	f	+0.15 −0.00
0.50	g*	+0.25 −0.00

* Hole code g is the preferred minimum hole size for a via.

Heat management

The design of assemblies where potential problems of heat are catered for, and excess heat is safely dissipated, is known as **thermal management**, and is discussed, in depth, in Chapter 4. For the sake of completeness, however, thermal management is briefly discussed here, in relation to through-hole printed circuit boards.

Although not normally a problem in the majority of individual through-hole assemblies, closely packed boards can generate significant amounts of potentially dangerous and damaging heat. Designers must always allow adequate heat dissipation. This **thermal design** of through-hole assemblies can be tackled in three main ways:

- At component level. To a large extent, engineers can design-in adequate heat dissipation, correctly selecting a low thermal resistance package design. Significant differences in thermal resistance occur between device packages. Use of certain low thermal resistance packages, however, could require a change in manufacturing capabilities which may not be cost-effective.

- At board level. Heat sinking with the use of what are known as **thermal planes** is a common solution, and two methods are available. First, a metal plate may be bonded to the component-side of the PCB, before component insertion (Figure 2.23(a)). Second, a metal plate can be laminated within a board to create a **metal-cored PCB** (Figure 2.23(b)). In either method, the plate must be shaped to accommodate the leads of components. In certain problem cases **thermal bridges** (essentially a metal cover jumping between two parts of the thermal plane over a sensitive component, or a component at a particularly high temperature) can be added after component insertion (Figure 2.23(c)).

  Thermal planes are typically of copper, or where weight is at a premium, aluminium. Where the planes require electrical insulation epoxy (for copper) or an anodized finish (for aluminium) can be applied.

- At package level. External heat-sinks may be added to the assembly to create forced heat dissipation. Cooling fins, cooling fans, and the metal housing of the assembly itself can be used for this purpose, too. (See also Chapter 4 where a liquid heat-sink is described.)

Thermal management problems more often than not arise, however, not in simple through-hole assemblies, but in hybrid and surface mounted assemblies, where packing density at board level is considerably greater. Fortunately, the substrates and bases typically used as boards in these assemblies have often been developed and chosen with heat management in mind. Use of, say, alumina or porcelain-enamelled steel substrates, together with correctly chosen component packages and carriers often gives the thermal solution sought. In problem cases PTH vias, from the board surface to a metal or other thermally conductive layer (say, when a porcelain-enamelled steel substrate is used – from the porcelain surface to the steel), can be used as **thermal vias** to improve heat dissipation around or underneath components.

Power distribution

Power and earth connections to components on printed circuit boards can pose some problems, particularly if large numbers of components are involved, or especially high packing densities are sought. Given that each device needs an earth connection and at least one power connection it can be easily understood that these connections will form a fairly complex layout arrangement, even before signal connections are considered.

The power and earth arrangement may more or less define the packing density which can be obtained. On a single-sided circuit board, for example, the restrictions posed by the arrangement may define that components cannot in any way be regarded as closely packed. On a double-sided board, however, the packing density may be increased significantly. Without doubt, the closest packing will be obtainable with a multi-layered

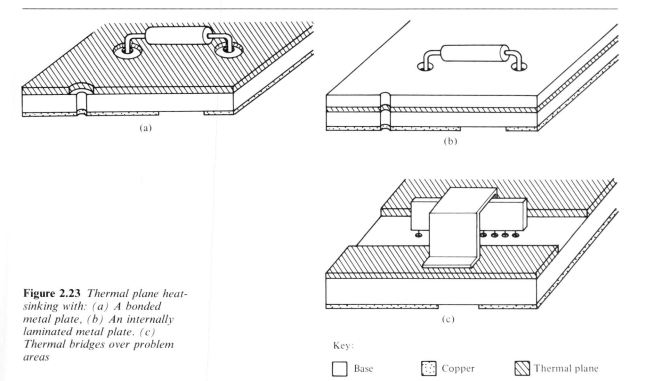

Figure 2.23 *Thermal plane heat-sinking with: (a) A bonded metal plate, (b) An internally laminated metal plate. (c) Thermal bridges over problem areas*

Key:

☐ Base   ▣ Copper   ▧ Thermal plane

circuit board of some description, separate power and earth tracks being internally layered in the board. If these tracks are formed by more or less solid planes, the benefit of a distribution decoupling of power supply to earth can also be realized.

Nevertheless, the much higher costs of multi-layered circuit boards may not be justified on the pure grounds of achieving what will amount to only a slightly increased packing density.

Component spacing and placement

Usually, a company will standardize on spacings and placements of components. These should be derived from requirements which include the following:

- Quality standards.
- Approval standards.
- Tolerances of component dimensions.
- Tolerances of hole positions and diameters.
- Specifications to avoid interference to other components.
- Tolerance of component positioning (particularly where surface mounted).

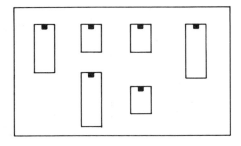

Figure 2.24 *Aligning all integrated circuits can reduce human errors on assembly*

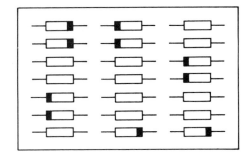

Figure 2.25 *Axial components should be mounted parallel*

- The possibility of vibration or shock.
- The soldering process.

Other factors which should influence a company's standards on this subject should regard method of board assembly. For instance, if components are to be manually inserted it pays to specify that all integrated circuits must be aligned (Figure 2.24). Potential human errors on assembly owing to reverse-placement of integrated circuits can thus be reduced. Similarly, other specifications could ensure that axial components be mounted parallel (Figure 2.25), polarized components be orientated in the same direction (Figure 2.26), and so on.

These considerations are beneficial for automated component insertion, also. Insertion of all components in a single axis means that relatively simple, single-axis, insertion heads are sufficient. If *all* components are to have the same span (Figure 2.27), too, only one single-axis head is required.

If components with different axes are unavoidable, it is advisable to limit the axes to 90° (Figure 2.28), as relatively simple mechanisms may be used to rotate the board to such angles. Printed circuit boards in which components are to be inserted with many axes and many spans (Figure 2.29) should, in fact, be positively avoided. Each axis change, and each span change, requires a new insertion head.

Once these standards have been defined within the design company, they must be adequately maintained and updated, whether printed circuit board design is manual or computer-aided.

Physical restrictions

Quite apart from the restrictions placed by the components on the design of the printed circuit board, the engineer should always have an understanding of the remainder of the assembly process, namely; component insertion and soldering. A number of points must be borne in mind:

- Hole size depends on printed circuit board technology. If conventional single-sided board is used (that is, without PTHs), hole diameter must

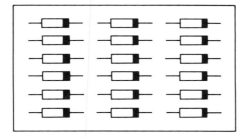

Figure 2.26 *Orientating polarized components in the same direction*

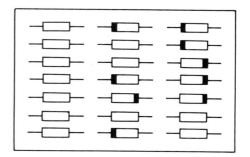

Figure 2.27 *Ensuring all components have the same span requires only one insertion head*

be less than about $+0.2$ mm over lead diameter to ensure adequate joint strength. This means (given a typically wide range of components and corresponding lead diameters) that many different hole diameters are usually required – making the printed circuit board more expensive to produce. An alternative is to standardize diameters using, say, preferred hole sizes in Table 2.11, and bend component leads after insertion (clinching, see page 63), although the engineer must be aware that holes may then need to be further apart to prevent bridging on soldering.

Where PTHs are used (double-sided and multi-layer printed circuit boards) hole diameters can be greatly increased and standardized, to less than about $+0.5$ mm over lead diameter, as solder flows into the hole to produce a strong joint.

• Track aspects affect quality of soldering. Track width, gap between parallel tracks, track direction and so on, can all affect the quality of assembly soldering. Where tracks are too close together, for instance,

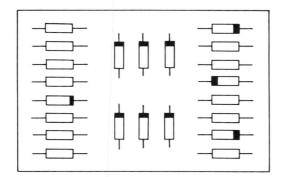

Figure 2.28 *If components cannot be mounted parallel, limiting the axes to 90° reduces the complexity of the assembly machine*

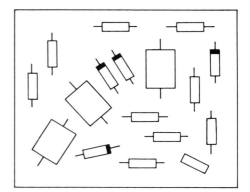

Figure 2.29 *Avoid printed circuit boards with many axes and many spans*

solder may bridge between them. This is especially so if parallel tracks run perpendicular to soldering machine conveyor direction (see page 42. The same gap between tracks running parallel to conveyor direction may allow perfect soldering. Sharp changes in parallel track direction create the same effect, so radiused corners may give the solution. DIL packaged integrated circuits should be orientated perpendicular to conveyor direction for the same reason.

- A good joint requires sufficient heat. Heat must be applied to all parts if the solder is to create a good joint. So, for instance, a thermal plane (or any local large areas of track, such as a ground plane) may absorb so much heat that joints in the vicinity are underheated and dry (as well as creating a possibility of warped PCBs). Similarly, a large component body can do the same for isolated joints.

Packing density

Economics of close packing depend largely on the product being designed, as well as the type of component packages to be used. A small (say, 10,000 off) run of product for consumer applications will probably not be able to justify the expense of high-density miniaturization further than general double-sided, or simple multi-layer, PCBs allow. The same product in its millions, however, may. Similarly, a product which uses DIL integrated circuit packages will probably be positively *uneconomical* if a multi-layer PCB is used – whatever the numbers involved. Flat-pack and higher density forms of integrated circuit packages, meanwhile, will probably never form an economical solution if used with conventional double-sided PCB.

On the other hand, a batch of even just a handful of products for satellite or missile applications, where space is at a premium (pun intended), may be impossible to justify *without* high-density close packing. Here, economy is warranted purely as a decrease of pay-load – not as a decrease of product cost.

Standards

UK	IEC	USA	European
BS6221	IEC321	EIA213	DIN40803
		IPC D300	
		IPC D350	
		IPC D351	
		IPC D352	
		IPC DW425	
		IPC SM782	
		IPC ML910	
		IPC D949	
		Mil Std275	
		Mil Hdbk338	

Layout

The design of a PCB really starts when layout of the track commences. It is here where all the rules and standards noted earlier are used, to produce artwork corresponding to track shapes, component overlays, silkscreen overlays, solder masks, etc.

Up until a few years ago, all drawings were produced manually, usually by drawing office staff. In this case the rules and standards were written down and followed methodically. However, with more and more complex layouts being required for boards with greater and greater component densities, computer-aided PCB design systems are becoming popular.

And, while many single- and double-sided PCB designs can still be (and still are) designed manually, developments of some densely packed PCBs are reaching the stage where manual design is no longer economically feasible or humanly possible. Multi-layer PCBs are produced with many, typically over eight, layers of interrelated tracks. Entering the realm of surface mounted assemblies, components will probably be mounted on each side of the board or substrate, too. In such cases producers will probably opt for a computer-aided design (CAD) system. Currently around 75% of PCB designs are generated on CAD systems.

In general, there are two main types of PCB CAD systems: those which are self-contained and purpose-built; those which are simple software packages to run on standard personal computers.

Manual drafting

Generation of artwork by manual means falls into three main stages:

- Rough track layout, when hand-drawn sketches are used to make preliminary pencilled layouts. Many erasings and revisions are prevalent here.
- Final production of track layout, when crepe tapes, transfer lands, tracks, integrated circuit pads, etc., are used to produce final track layout drawings. These are usually at twice or four times full size, to ensure accuracy.
- Production of ancillary drawings. Component overlays, silkscreen overlays and solder masks are now produced, usually at the same scale as the final track layout.

The aim of any PCB layout drawing system is to produce master films of individual track layouts. To aid discrimination between track layers, and allow accurate registration at later production stages, each track artwork may be coloured.

Standards

UK	IEC	USA
BS 5830	IEC97	EIA208

Through-hole PCB assembly

PCB assembly comprises two main processes:

- Inserting the components, often called stuffing.
- Soldering the component leads to the PCB track.

However, to these may be added some others:

- Testing.
- Cleaning the flux and its residues from the assembly.
- Coating the assembly for protection.

Soldering, in itself, is a vast topic. Vast enough, in fact, to warrant its own chapter (see Chapter 5). For this reason no attempt is made to explain it in detail here. Instead, the remainder of this chapter discusses component insertion as being the main process of through-hole PCB assembly, and notes the other processes with their involvement in the whole.

Process methods depend largely on the numbers of assemblies being produced. For low-volume assembly, that is, from single prototype to just a handful of boards, component insertion (and soldering) by hand generally provides adequately economic production methods. However, for assembly numbers higher than this, it rapidly becomes economic to use more automatic methods. Even semi-automatic methods can greatly improve production times, without too much extra expense. At all times, of course, initial outlay for machinery must be weighed against labour costs.

Where surface mounted assemblies are being produced, the manufacturer has little option but to automate, at least to a semi-automatic level. Components in such an assembly are, of course, not inserted into the substrate, but are placed *on* the surface. Indeed, a new term, **onsertion**, has been used, to describe the act of **placement** of surface mounted components, and the required assembling techniques are therefore considered separately in Chapter 3. Furthermore, the accuracies with which some surface mounted components must be placed are usually far greater than manual assemblers are capable of.

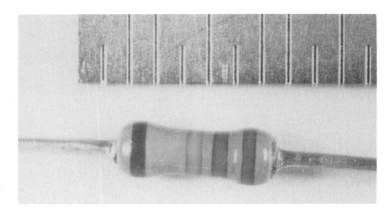

Plate 2.8 *Axial-leaded resistor – scale in millimetres (RJ)*

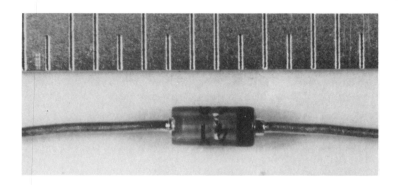

Plate 2.9 *Axial-leaded semiconductor diode – scale in millimetres (RJ)*

General assembly considerations

Most considerations regarding component insertion into through-hole printed circuit boards are generated by the components themselves. Often, these considerations are ideals, which may or may not be attainable in practice. Typical considerations include:

- Shape of component.
- Position of component wire leads.
- Special requirements in the positioning of components.
- Damage to sensitive components during handling.
- Heat dissipation during operational life.
- Mechanical stress the assembly may be subjected to.

In the following discussion, considerations should be taken as guidelines only, and are by no means exhaustive.

Shape of component

A component's shape often defines how it should be mounted in a board. Axial-leaded components are best mounted with their axes parallel to the board surface (Figure 2.30). As a rule, they can be mounted touching the board surface, unless otherwise specified.

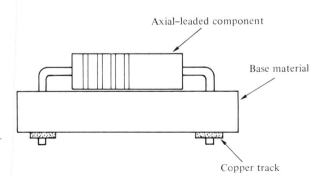

Figure 2.30 *Preferred method of mounting axial-leaded components*

A metal-bodied component must not come into contact with track, nor be sufficiently close that later short-circuit caused by, say, moisture, may occur.

Where two or more tracks run underneath an axial-leaded component, on the component side of the board (Figure 2.31), the component should not touch the board, as a safeguard against later short circuit caused by, say, moisture.

A vertically mounted axial-leaded component should be spaced between about 0.5 mm and 3 mm from the board surface, as shown in Figure 2.32, to prevent strain on the soldered joint.

Position of component wire leads

To prevent strain on vertically mounted radial-leaded components, they should be positioned so that the leads are parallel to each other, and perpendicular to the component base, with a clearance of between about 0.5 mm and 3 mm between the base of the component and the board surface (Figure 2.33).

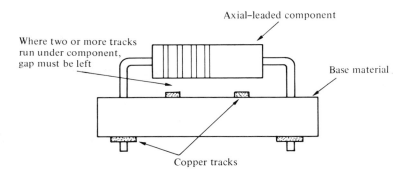

Figure 2.31 *Mount an axial-leaded component so that the body does not touch the board if tracks run underneath*

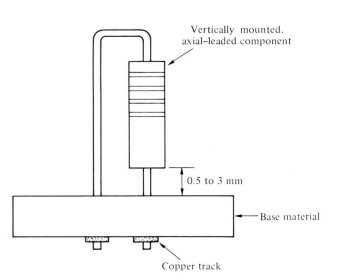

Figure 2.32 *Preferred method of mounting a vertically mounted axial-leaded component*

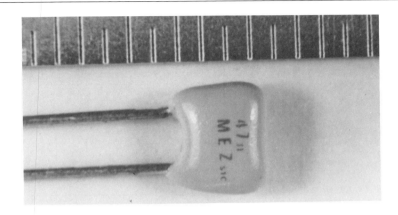

Plate 2.10 *Radial-leaded capacitor – scale in millimetres (RJ)*

Safeguards should be taken to ensure that components which are moulded or encapsulated with sealing materials have a clearance of at least 1.5 mm between the end of the lead coating and the surface of the board, as shown in Figure 2.34. This is to prevent the coating or sealing material from entering the joint area and preventing acceptable solder joints. Clearance can be reduced to 0.75 mm where holes are not plated-through.

Special requirements in the positioning of components

Component markings should be in the same direction for all similarly shaped components. Thus, all horizontal components should be mounted so that marking are read from, say, left to right. Vertical components should all be mounted so that markings are read from, say, top to bottom. This may not be possible with polarized components, however, which should always be mounted so that their polarization symbols (that is, + or −) are visible.

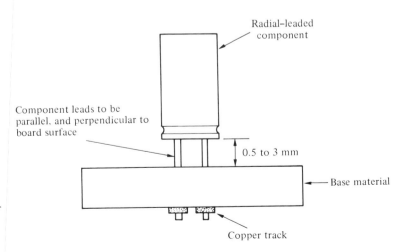

Figure 2.33 *Preferred method of mounting vertically mounted radial-leaded component*

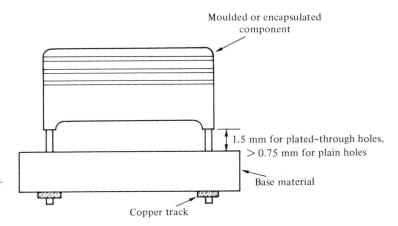

Moulded or encapsulated
component

1.5 mm for plated–through holes,
> 0.75 mm for plain holes

Base material

Copper track

Figure 2.34 *Preferred method of mounting a sealed or encapsulated component*

Components should be mounted on only one side of the printed circuit board (this requirement does not hold for surface mounted components, however, see Chapter 3).

Damage to sensitive components during handling

Components with seals must be handled carefully, in order that seals are not damaged. Leads should not be bent closer than, say, 2 mm from a seal.

Certain components are susceptible to damage by electrostatic discharge from, say, the assembler, or local equipment. Table 2.12 lists some types of components which are known to be susceptible, along with typical discharge voltages which have been recorded as causing damage. Generally, every attempt to keep static voltages down to less than, say, 100 V, should be made. Typically, this can be done by using equipment which maintains an electrical path to earth potential. Earthed floor mats, table mats, and wrist straps can all be used if static is a problem in any particular environment. Once boards are assembled, damage by electrostatic discharge is much less of a problem.

Plate 2.11 *Miniature horizontally mounted preset potentiometer (RJ)*

Table 2.12 Some components susceptible to damage by electrostatic discharge

Component type	Electrostatic discharge range (volts)
Bipolar transistors	Over 380
CMOS integrated circuits	Over 250
ECL integrated circuits	Over 500
EPROM memory integrated circuits	Less than 100
Film resistors	Over 300
GaAsFET devices	Over 200
JFET devices	Over 140
MOSFET devices and integrated circuits	Over 100
Op-amp integrated circuits	Over 190
SAW filters	Over 150
Schottky diodes	Over 300
Schottky TTL integrated circuits	Over 1000
SCR devices	Over 680
VMOS devices	Over 30

Heat dissipation during operational life

Every attempt should be made to ensure that the maximum allowable operating temperature of the board is not exceeded. In practice, this means that components which dissipate sufficient heat to be able to do this must be positioned so that:

- The component body does not come into contact with the board (Figure 2.35).
- A heatsink or similar dissipation aid dissipates heat from the component, away from the board.

Mechanical stress

Depending on application, assemblies may be subjected to severe shock and vibration during operation. If this is to be so, special precautions should be taken to ensure that any component or its related soldered joints

Figure 2.35 *Mounting a component capable of dissipating sufficient heat to damage the material of a printed circuit board*

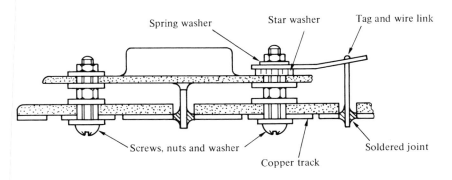

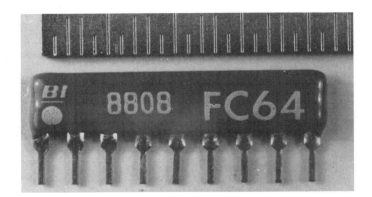

Plate 2.12 *Single-in-line (SIL) resistor network – scale in millimetres (RJ)*

Plate 2.13 *Single-in-line integrated circuit (SILIC) – scale in millimetres (RJ)*

are not damaged. This can entail fixing components to the board with brackets, clamps, or clips. Many types are available.

Manual insertion

Insertion of components into a PCB can take as much as 50% of the total production time. It is thus a bottleneck, representing considerable expense to the manufacturing organization. Also, as the PCB assembly can be made up of literally hundreds of component parts, incorrect insertion creates secondary problems of rework and even scrap.

The simplest and most time-consuming method of assembly uses manual component insertion, as shown in Figure 2.36, along with the following soldering and trimming stages. First, where necessary, the assembler bends the component leads by hand to fit the PCB (Figure 2.36(a)). Next, the component is inserted (Figure 2.36(b)). These two steps are repeated until all components have been inserted. A cushioned plate is pressed over the components to hold them in place (Figure 2.36(c)), and the whole structure is turned upside-down to allow the assembler to hand solder components

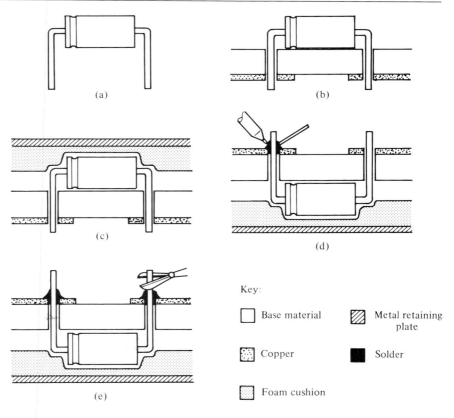

Key:

☐ Base material   ▨ Metal retaining plate

▨ Copper   ■ Solder

☐ Foam cushion

Figure 2.36 *Manual printed circuit board assembly. (a) Component leads are bent to fit the board. (b) Component inserted. (c) Cushioned plate maintains component position. (d) Components are hand soldered. (e) Excess leads are trimmed*

(Figure 2.36(d)). After this, excess component leads are cut or trimmed off with side-cutters (Figure 2.36(e)). The completed board is removed and a new assembly commenced.

Dual-in-line (DIL) packaged integrated circuit insertion

DIL packages form a separate concern when assembling. Packages have two rows of pins, spread so that they are wider at the bottom than at the component body (Figure 2.37(a)). The distance apart at the bottom is greater than the distance between the rows of holes in the printed circuit board. To insert them into the board, therefore, requires that the pins are squeezed together before insertion, after which the natural spring in the rows of pins holds the component in place (Figure 2.37(b)). In hand assembly, DIL insertion handtools are common.

If the board is fairly simple, assemblers will be able to memorize the layout. Where more complex boards are manually assembled, it may be necessary to divide the board into smaller areas, and have a production line of assemblers, each of whom have memorized their own areas.

Components for such manual assembly or boards are best sorted into marked, sequenced storage bins, located in easy reach for each assembler.

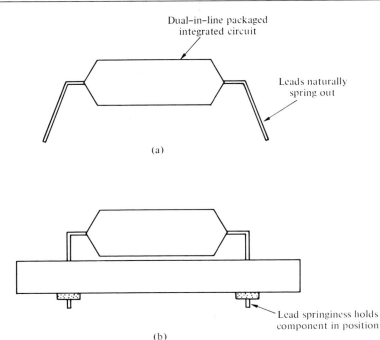

Figure 2.37 *Dual-in-line packaged integrated circuits. (a) The two rows of pins are wider at the bottom than at the top. (b) The rows' natural spring holds the integrated circuit in position prior to soldering*

Semi-automatic insertion

Some excellent improvements can be made to the previous completely manual assembly method, with semi-automatic insertion methods. There are three areas in which semi-automation can help:

- Bending the leads, known as **preforming** or **prepping** (an abbreviation of *preparing*) – machinery can be used which bends the leads to the correct shape to fit the board (an alternative to this is to buy and use components with preformed leads).
- Locating the holes through which the leads are to be inserted – machinery can be used which shows the assembler where to put the component. Typically, without such machinery, PCBs are screen-printed with a masked legend, showing component and lead locations.
- Trimming the component leads – trimming machinery can be used.

Preforming

The preformed shape can vary greatly, depending on personal preference and component type or shape. A number of typical shapes are shown in Figure 2.38. Components can be **dimple** preformed so that when inserted into the board the shaped leads themselves hold the component in, as shown in Figure 2.39. Dimple preforming, however, requires special tool dies, and the hole size tolerance must be strictly limited.

THROUGH-HOLE PCB ASSEMBLY 61

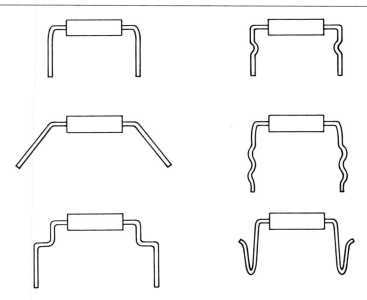

Figure 2.38 *Typical preform shapes for components*

Preforming can be undertaken by hand, before assembly, and special pliers as well as other handtools are available for such purposes. In general, however, preforming is done using machinery.

As a precaution against component damage, preform bends should not occur within about 1.5 mm of the component body.

Location aids

A screen-printed mask legend on the component side of the PCB is, of course, a location aid, helping the assembler find component mounting holes. The legend also has the advantage of assisting component location at later rework or service stages in an appliance's life.

Many other more sophisticated location aid techniques are used in PCB assembly, however. One of the most straightforward uses a slide projector arrangement to project a mask legend on to the board. Main advantage over a screen-printed legend is that different slide legends may be used: say, one for each type of component. This may be coupled to lamps illuminating component storage bins. Assemblers may thus be shown which components to put in which holes in the board.

Simple lamp arrangements may be used underneath the PCB to selectively illuminate holes corresponding to component types. When all

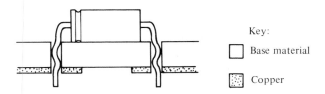

Key:

☐ Base material

▦ Copper

Figure 2.39 *Dimple preforming*

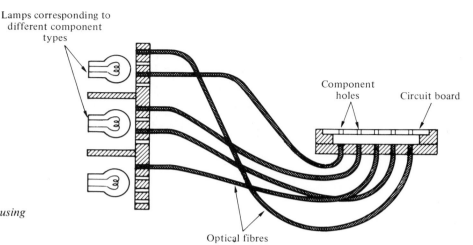

Figure 2.40 *Assembly aid, using optical fibres and lamps to illuminate component holes*

components of one type have been inserted, the assembler merely turns those lamps off, and turns the lamps corresponding to another component type on, thus illuminating the next set of holes. This hardwired lamp system suffers from two main disadvantages: changing from assembly of one PCB to another requires a complete rewiring: a single lamp failure may not be noticed. The technique can be greatly improved, however, if optical fibres link lamps to the component holes (Figure 2.40). A change from assembly of one PCB to another is more easily done, simply by rearranging fibres. Further, lamp failure is obvious, as all holes for a component type are not illuminated.

Sophisticated aids exist, similar to the side projector principle mentioned

Plate 2.14 *Panasert AVB axial-leaded component insertion machine (Panasonic Industrial)*

Plate 2.15 *Panasert RH6 radial-leaded component insertion machine (Panasonic Industrial)*

earlier, in which a laser beam of visible light is projected on to the board, pinpointing the location of the next component to be installed. Simultaneously, a digital display may present alphanumeric information regarding the component, say, component number, component type, and component value.

Lead trimming

In pure hand assembly, component leads are trimmed after soldering. But semi-automation (and automation) of the assembly processes mean that leads can be trimmed *before* soldering. In such operations, as part of the trimming process, leads are bent underneath the PCB, clinching the components to the board (Figure 2.41). The component is inserted through the board in the usual manner (Figure 2.41(a)), after which the lower clinching plate is moved (Figure 2.41(b)) in an operation which cuts off the excess component leads. Finally, the upper clinching plate is moved (Figure 2.41(c)) to clinch the leads to the bottom of the circuit board. In such assemblies, dimple preforming is made unnecessary as a component holding method.

Clinching to an angle from the horizontal of no less than 45° (Figure 2.42(a)) is usually considered ideal, as clinching, in general, may damage plated-through holes, so a restriction in the angle is necessary. Further, clinched leads with clinching angles from the horizontal of less than 45° require asymmetrical lands (Figure 2.42(b)). Boards may require rework, too, where components may need to be removed – the smaller the clinch angle from the horizontal, the harder it is to take components out.

Some degree of control must be exercised over the length of component lead remaining under the board after cutting and clinching. Lead length is a function of lead diameter, and Table 2.13 lists recommended minimum and maximum lengths after clinching. Care also must be taken that close

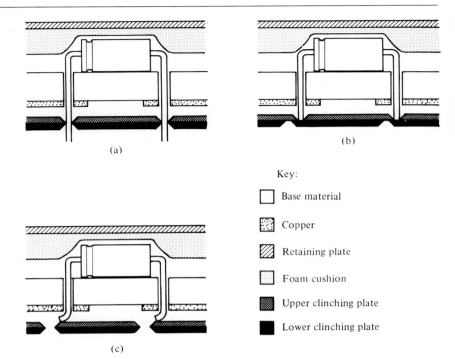

Key:

▫ Base material

▫ Copper

▨ Retaining plate

▫ Foam cushion

▪ Upper clinching plate

■ Lower clinching plate

Figure 2.41 *Component clinching. (a) Component is inserted. (b) Lower clinching plate cuts off excess leads. (c) Lower clinching plate clinches the leads*

components do not have leads clinched in closing directions or solder bridges may occur (Figure 2.43(a)). By specifying that leads must be clinched inwards for any single component (Figure 2.43(b)), or that all leads are clinched in the same direction (Figure 2.43(c)) this can be avoided.

Semi-automatic machinery to *trim* leads, on the other hand, can be as simple as a cutting wheel or grinder, over which the PCB is conveyed. Normally, such trimming would be used *after* initial soldering. Further soldering would, however, be required as the trimming operation may cause damage to the soldered joints. Secondary soldering is normally undertaken as a routine measure against this, with a wave soldering machine.

Table 2.13 Recommended lengths of clinched component leads after cutting

Component lead diameter (mm)	Lengths remaining (mm) Minimum	Maximum
0.5	0.8	2
0.8	1	2
1	1.3	2
1.3	1.5	2

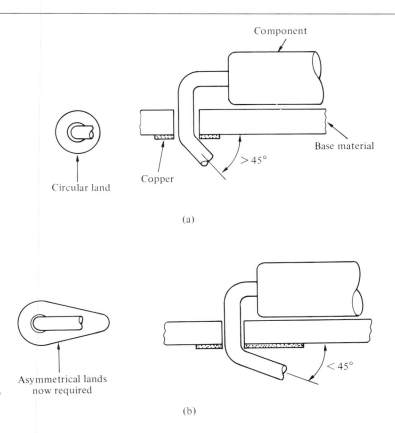

Component

Base material

> 45°

Copper

Circular land

(a)

Asymmetrical lands
now required

< 45°

(b)

Figure 2.42 *Clinching angles.
(a) Preferred. (b) Less than 45°
requires asymmetrical lands*

Automatic insertion

Semi-automatic insertion machinery still demands the considerable atten-
tion of human assemblers. The aim of **automatic component insertion** (ACI)
is to reduce the human involvement to a minimum, thereby eliminating, or
at least severely reducing, labour costs.

There are significant difficulties in attempting full automation of PCB
assembly. First, there is such a wide range of components required to be
inserted into the PCB that it is not always possible to automate every
component's insertion. Some component shapes: axial, DIL integrated
circuits, and so on, are fairly easy to handle but insertion of others:
transformers, power transistors and so on is extremely difficult to
automate. Where assemblies require insertion of such components, the
components must usually be hand soldered in, at the end of the assembly
stage, after mass soldering of the printed circuit board.

Second, even within component types, large differences in actual
component dimensions can occur. Generally, three different inserters are
required to automate through-hole printed circuit board assembly, to
insert:

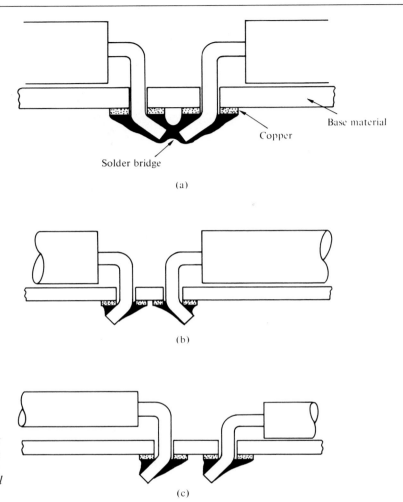

(a)

(b)

Figure 2.43 *Clinched leads may cause solder bridges where leads are clinched in closing directions (a); where clinched inwards (b) or in the same direction (c), will prevent this*

(c)

- Axial components.
- Radial components.
- DIL packaged components.

These inserters may be completely different machines, or may be different (may be manually interchangeable) insertion heads on the same machine.

Whatever the difficulties, however, a manufacturer committed to automation of PCB assembly can usually get round them. Naturally, everyone involved needs to be aware of individual responsibilities. Designers, for example, should be aware of the necessity to use easily manageable components in circuits, and accurately specify standard sizes and shapes. Component manufacturers, too, must ensure that specified tolerances in component shapes are not exceeded.

Plate 2.16 *Close-up of Panasert RH6 radial-leaded component insertion machine head (Panasonic Industrial)*

Automatic insertion machines feature a number of basic facilities, including:

- A programmable controller, which can control all following aspects of the machine.
- A horizontally-movable platform on which the board is fixed. The platform must move in the two horizontal axes (this feature is not critical if the insertion head is totally movable in the two horizontal axes).
- One or more insertion heads, which can insert component leads into their respective holes in the board.
- Some means of **loading**, that is, supplying, the insertion head with components.

Programmable controllers may be numerically controlled or, more likely, computer-controlled. Horizontally-movable platforms are fairly easily constructed, and robotic arm insertion heads are now quite commonplace.

Loading of the insertion head, on the other hand, is the main mechanical problem which insertion machines must tackle. There are two basic answers to the problem:

- The components must be sequenced in order of insertion and fed to the head.
- The insertion head must go to the supply of components and select the required one.

Where axial components form the great majority, sequencing of components is the simpler solution, but where large numbers of radial components, or DIL packaged components prevail, selection is best.

For insertion heads using component selection, axial components are available from manufacturers in taped and reeled form, as shown in Figure

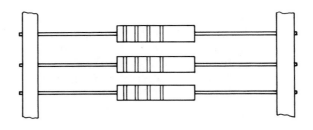

Figure 2.44 *Taped and reeled axial-leaded components*

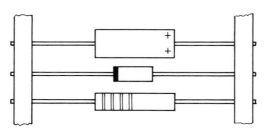

Figure 2.45 *Pre-sequenced taped and reeled axial-leaded components can aid automatic component insertion*

2.44. DIL packages are supplied in magazine tubes, which usually slot directly into the insertion machine.

Where component sequenced insertion heads are used, on the other hand, it is usual to supply the machine with pre-sequenced taped and reeled axial components, as illustrated in Figure 2.45.

Choice of automatic insertion machine

There are a large number of automatic insertion machines available. Choice depends largely on assembler's demands.

Differences between machines include:

- The number of insertions they make in a unit of time (normally quoted as so many per hour).
- Absolute **accuracy**, sometimes called **addressability**, which refers to how accurately the insertion head moves the component to its board position.
- The number of component types it can insert.
- The range of board sizes it can accommodate.
- Whether **vision**, that is, camera and monitor, is incorporated.
- How automatic the machine *really* is.

Choice often involves a trade-off.

Standards

UK	USA
BS 6221	EIA 467
Def Stan 00–10	EIA 468
	IPC CM770
	Mil Std2000

Testing

Boards can be tested before, during and after assembly. Tests can range from fairly straightforward visual tests, to in-circuit and full-function tests of fully assembled boards. Environmental and stress testing can also be undertaken on assemblies. Chapter 6 discusses aspects of testing, in depth.

Cleaning of assemblies

Assemblies are cleaned, primarily, to increase reliability and quality. **Post-assembly cleaning**, that is, undertaken after soldering, is covered in detail in Chapter 5.

Conformal coatings

Where it is known that assemblies will be subjected to certain environmental stresses, **conforming coating** is usually undertaken to help maintain performance. Conformal coating processes and materials are discussed in Chapter 4.

Total automatic assembly

As this chapter has shown, assembly of a through-hole printed circuit board comprises many separate processes, at the least including:

- Component insertion.
- Soldering (see Chapter 5).
- Testing (see Chapter 6).
- Cleaning.
- Coating.

Equipment for each process is available with conveyorized chain systems, which means that boards are simply entered at one end of the machine, and removed from the other, having undergone the process. For *total* automatic assembly, some form of conveyor system must move the boards from the output of one process to the input of the next. Many types are available and, in general, feature similar facilities, including:

- Adjustable width, to cater for different sizes of printed circuit board.
- Different speed sections, to cater for the different rates at which the equipment at different stages in the production line can take up boards.
- Automatic magazines, to load and unload boards at different stages.
- Ability to interface between equipment with work levels at different heights.
- Ability to change directions, to enable wrap-around production lines.

3 Electronics assembly: the SMA

Surface mounted assemblies

There are a number of terms and abbreviations for surface mounted assemblies, which are sometimes interchanged, correctly or incorrectly. The term **surface mounted assembly** (SMA) refers to the complete board, comprising base, conductive track and attached components. The principle which surface mounted assemblies follow is known as **surface mount technology** (SMT). Finally, the components used in a surface mounted assembly are known as **surface mounted components** (SMCs) or, sometimes, **surface mounted devices** (SMDs).

Many of the basic criteria regarding printed circuit boards apply equally to surface mounted assemblies. Surface mounted assemblies can, for instance, be built on conventional printed circuit base materials, such as phenolic-resin paper, or epoxy-resin glass fibre, reinforced laminates. Surface mounted components may be surface mounted on to conventional, through-hole printed circuit boards, too. So, in many areas, there is considerable overlap between through-hole printed circuit and surface mounted techniques.

Indeed, it is not just that surface mounting is a new technique. Surface mounting of components into a circuit has been around for a long time (around twenty years) in production of hybrid assemblies. Such hybrid assemblies tend to be quite specialized in applications. It is merely a coincidence that surface mounting, as a technique for constructing assemblies in its own right, has only comparatively recently evolved as a viable technique for general appliances.

Nevertheless, significant differences between conventional, holed, printed circuits and surface mounted, non-holed, assemblies exist. These differences are sufficient in number and importance to warrant a fresh consideration.

Comparing through-hole, hybrid and surface mounted assemblies

The main differences between through-hole, hybrid and surface mounted assemblies are illustrated in Figure 3.1. Through-hole assembly principle (Figure 3.1(a)) is seen to comprise a base with conductive track, through which holes are drilled, and component leads inserted and soldered. It is because of this, in comparison with surface mounted assemblies, that conventional printed circuit boards are known as *through-hole* assemblies

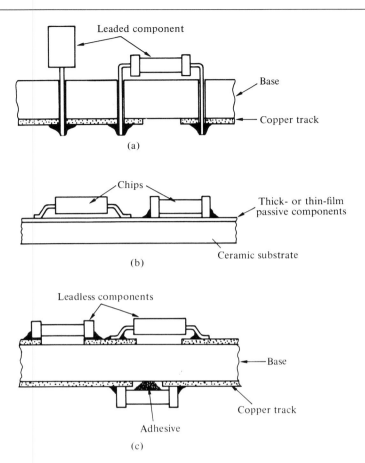

Figure 3.1 *Differences between through-hole, hybrid and surface mount printed circuit boards. (a) Through-hole. (b) Hybrid. (c) Surface mount*

and the components used are known as **leaded** components, that is, they feature wire leads – not that they are metal-coated. Conductive track may be on both sides of or within the base but, generally, components are mounted only on one side and soldered on the other.

Hybrid assembly principle (Figure 3.1(b)) is seen to comprise a substrate base, film passive components, and surface mounted passive and active components. Again, components are only on one side of the base and, although not shown, sometimes the added components may be attached using the through-hole technique.

Surface mounted assembly principle (Figure 3.1(c)), however, typically uses a conventional printed circuit base (but without holes), conductive track and only surface mounted components, on one or two sides of the board. Sometimes, depending on the application, a substrate base is used, similar to those of hybrid assemblies. Whatever the base, components are attached by either adhesive or solder paste, prior to soldering. In direct comparison with through-hole assembly, surface mounted components are **leadless**, that is, they have no wire leads – not that they use unleaded petrol.

Whereas through-hole components are *inserted* into the board, surface mounted components are often, in slang, said to be **onserted** on to the board.

Several similarities exist, too, between through-hole and surface mounted assemblies. Often, the bases on which components are surface mounted are also called printed circuit boards. They are, of course, often made in the same way as through-hole circuit boards (although no holes are incorporated – with certain exceptions). However, where the surface mounted assembly has a substrate base, it is not recommended that it be known as a printed circuit board, thus saving possible confusion.

It is also possible to mount leaded components together with leadless components on a single base – either on the same side of the base or, more usually, on opposite sides. Owing to the fact that not all types of components are yet available in leadless form, such **mixed assemblies** or **mixprints** will be a normal occurrence for the next few years, at least. Figure 3.2. illustrates some of the many possibilities of printed circuit assembly variations using leaded and leadless components. Assembly and manufacturing techniques of these and other variations are considered later.

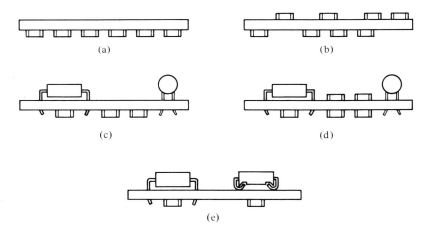

Figure 3.2 *Some of the many assembly variations using leaded and leadless components*

Advantages and disadvantages

Two major advantages of surface mounted assemblies are well documented:

- Miniaturization. A number of factors go towards the consequent size reduction realized with surface mounted assemblies. Surface mounted components are much smaller than their leaded counterparts and, as a result, are lighter. High-density integrated circuits are able to have a considerably greater number of connection pins, more closely spaced. The ability to mount components on both sides of the board means that boards can be reduced in size – in fact, by more than the expected 50%.

- Rationalization. Several cost reductions are apparent. Components have no leads, so lead cutting and lead bending is eliminated. Smaller printed circuit bases, with no through-holes, mean cheaper production. In many cases no expensive base material is required – phenolic-resin paper or epoxy-resin fibre glass reinforced base materials are often suitable. Often, only one automatic placement machine is required (compared with, typically, three automatic insertion machines required for component insertion into through-hole assemblies). Use of automatic placement machines may reduce labour costs.

On the other hand, disadvantages concerning surface mounted assemblies appear few and far between. Assembly can only be effectively undertaken by automatic means – sizes, and closely-packed pin arrangements, of some components means they cannot be hand-assembled or hand-soldered. Low-volume electronics assembly generally remains the province of through-hole printed circuit boards, therefore.

Capital outlay of the assembly equipment is another disadvantage, but is one which may be effectively offset by the greater product throughput and hence cheaper appliance.

Surface mounted components

A number of component types has been developed specifically for use in surface mounted assemblies. New types are frequently being developed, too, so any categorization of those available must change equally frequently.

Types

The main types, some known simply by their abbreviation, include:

- Chips. In this context, the term *chip* does not refer to an integrated circuit, but to a type of passive component (for example, resistor, capacitor, inductor), rectangular prism shaped.
- MELF. Metal electrode face bonded components, cylindrical shape.
- MIFI. Miniature ferrite inductors, rectangular prism shaped.
- SO. Small outline components, generally integrated circuits, rectangular prism shaped.
- SOD. Small outline diodes, cylindrical shape.
- SOIC. Small outline integrated circuits, rectangular prism shaped.
- SOT. Small outline transistors, rectangular prism shaped.
- Quad flat-pack. Integrated circuits having four rows of terminals, rectangular prism shaped.
- TAB. Tape automated bonding, sometimes called **mikropacks**, film integrated circuits in taped form, without protecting packaging.
- Tubular. Passive components, cylindrical shape.
- VSO. Very small outline components.

In addition, some integrated circuits are mounted into chip carriers,

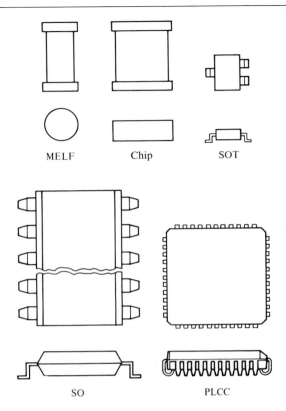

MELF   Chip   SOT

SO   PLCC

Figure 3.3 *Various types of leadless components suitable for surface mount assembly*

where the term *chip* does now refer to an integrated circuit, for assembly purposes. These carriers include:

- LCCC. Leadless ceramic chip carriers, square prism shaped.
- PLCC. Plastic leaded chip carriers, square prism shaped.

General outline shapes of some of these components are shown in Figure 3.3. Dimensions of versions of surface mounted components and chip carriers are found in manufacturers' literatures.

Other components

In some cases, lead component types may be adapted for surface mounting. For instance, a standard DIL IC can be adapted by bending the leads to form connecting feet.

Inductive components are often difficult to adapt to surface mounted assembly, but the general move away from analog circuits to those of a digital nature has reduced the need for their use, anyway.

Variable, presettable, resistors and capacitors are often needed in appliances, so a number of types have been developed, the smallest of which are only a fraction of a square centimetre in area.

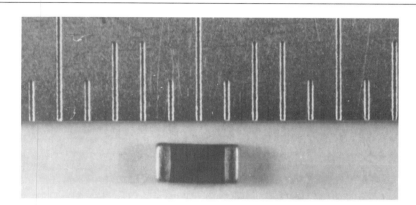

Plate 3.1 *Typical chip surface mount component – scale in millimetres (RJ)*

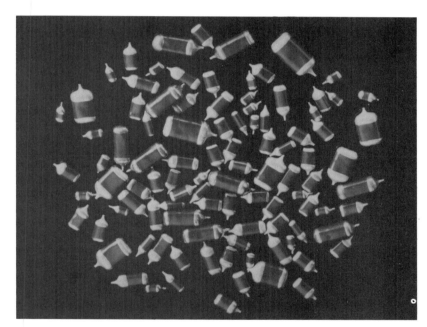

Plate 3.2 *Tantalum chip capacitor surface mount components (HB Addon)*

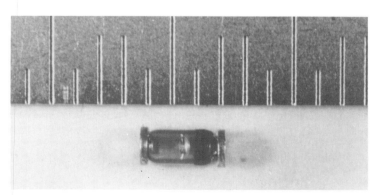

Plate 3.3 *Metal electrode face bonded (MELF) semiconductor diode – scale in millimetres (RJ)*

Plate 3.4 *A 24-pin small outline integrated circuit – compare with Plate 2.3 (RJ)*

Plate 3.5 *Small outline transistor – scale in millimetres (RJ)*

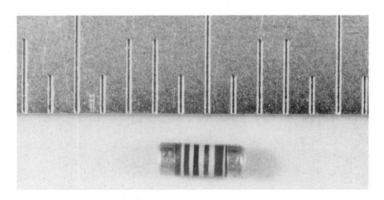

Plate 3.6 *Tubular surface mount component – scale in millimetres (RJ)*

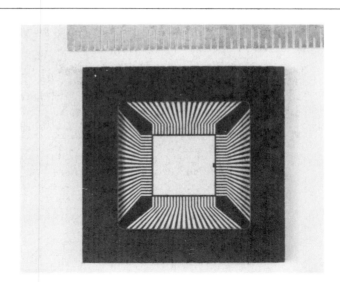

Plate 3.7 *Internal view of a leadless ceramic chip carrier – scale in millimetres (RJ)*

Plate 3.8 *Plastic leaded chip carrier (RJ)*

Plate 3.9 *Ceramic leaded chip carrier – scale in millimetres (RJ)*

Chip-on-board, and tape automated bonding

Tape automated bonding (TAB) integrated circuits illustrate how assemblies of all types (through-hole, hybrid and surface mounted) are moving towards miniaturization which will result, ultimately, in the mounting of bare semiconductor dice (that is, *real* semiconductor chips) on to the assembly board, with simple production techniques. Such **chip-on-board** (COB) technology is also sometimes called **bare chip-and-wire** (BCW).

Correctly, the terms chip-on-board and bare chip-and-wire refer to an assembly method which attaches a bare die to a board with adhesive, then bonds each terminal to the board with thin wires, and completes the assembly by encapsulating it.

Wire-bonding using aluminium or gold wires is accomplished using one of three methods:

- If aluminium wire is used, ultrasonically scrubbing the wire through the gold plating of a die's connecting terminal. The heat generated by the scrubbing action welds the wire to the terminal.
- If gold wire is used, thermosonic bonding (using both heat and ultrasonic scrubbing) bond the wire to the gold plating of the die's terminal.
- If gold wire is used, thermocompression bonding (using heat and pressure).

Two bonds are required for each connecting wire: one at the die terminal, one at the circuit board land, as shown in Figure 3.4.

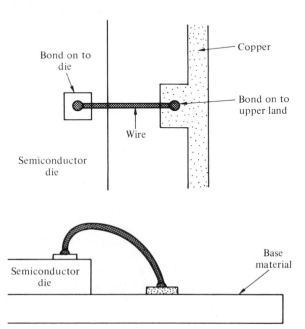

Figure 3.4 *Chip-on-board bonding of die terminal and circuit board land*

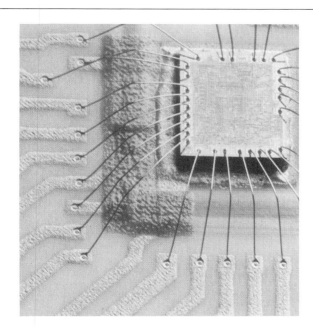

Plate 3.10 *Wire-bonded semiconductor die, directly mounted on a printed circuit board (Du Pont Electronics)*

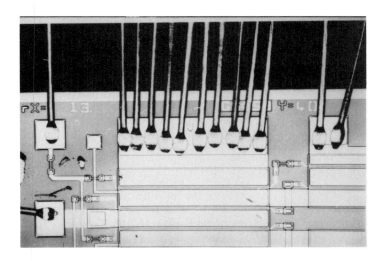

Plate 3.11 *Wire-bonded joints on a semiconductor die (RJ)*

Encapsulation is required to protect the die from the environment, and epoxy-based or silicone-based compounds are frequently used for the purpose. The resultant **glob-top** encapsulation forms a secure, fairly robust housing for the die, although hermetic sealing is not possible.

Generally, such a procedure is beyond the capabilities of most electronics assemblers. Tape automated bonding, on the other hand, is simply one of the latest miniaturization offerings of the semiconductor industry which allows assembly using relatively simple production tech-

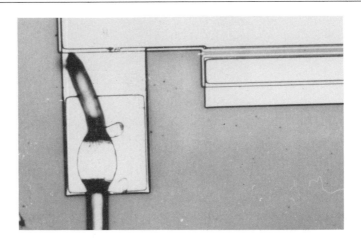

Plate 3.12 *Close-up of a wire-bonded semiconductor die joint (RJ)*

niques. The semiconductor die is mounted, complete with wire leads already bonded to the die terminals, in a taped film form, such that the arrangement is punched out of the tape on to the board and the outer ends of the connecting wires are soldered to the board lands in a single operation. This is followed by covering the device with a glob-top encapsulation of epoxy or silicone, for protection. Figure 3.5 illustrates the typical taped format of a TAB integrated circuit on a film base.

Figure 3.6 shows a cross-section through a typical TAB integrated circuit, illustrating its basic make-up. A layer of glass covers the die, and the glass has been etched through to expose the aluminium die terminals at contact holes. These holes are closed by solderable overlapping metal electroplated layers, known as **bumps**. Although it is possible to construct TAB integrated circuits with bumps on the tape, rather than on the die, few examples exist.

The copper connecting leads to the die terminals are formed from a copper foil which is bonded on to the polyimide film, and coated with a photoresist. Photoprinting, tin electroplating, and etching are then undertaken to leave the copper leads ready for bonding to the die bumps. This **inner lead bonding** (ILB) is done by thermocompression bonding, and all bumps and leads are bonded in a single operation.

At this stage, the TAB device is ready for board mounting and the necessary **outer lead bonding** (OLB) of the leads is performed by the assembler simply by soldering them on to the board lands.

Advantages in use of TAB integrated circuits over COB devices are that:

- The inner bonds, to the die terminals, are already made.
- Wires are actually tinned copper conductors, which can be easily soldered to the printed circuit board lands.
- Soldering of the outer connections to the board lands may be in a single operation.

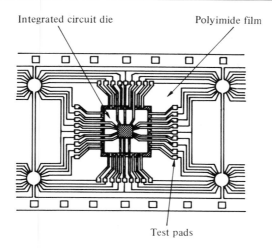

Integrated circuit die   Polyimide film

Test pads

Figure 3.5 *Typical taped format of a TAB integrated circuit*

- The die is hermetically sealed by the glass layer (the glob-top is simply for general protection).
- Prior to board mounting, individual devices may be fully tested in tape form, and failed devices discarded.

Although the preferred method of soldering TAB integrated circuits on to boards is, individually, by heated collet (see Chapter 5), under certain circumstances they may be mass soldered by other methods. Electrically conductive adhesive may also be used. Hand soldering may also be attempted, if a controlled-temperature soldering iron (to maintain a temperature below the 220°C limit of TAB integrated circuits) is used.

Base materials

In many surface mounted assemblies the base material may be a simple, single-sided, epoxy-resin fibre glass reinforced, or even a phenolic-resin paper reinforced, laminate, just as through-hole printed circuit boards. Indeed, this may be a specific requirement. However, double-sided or multilayer laminates and, indeed, other base materials altogether, may be used if the assembly requires it. Flexible and flexi-rigid boards may be used, just as through-hole printed circuit boards, too.

On the other hand, substrates may be specified which are not used for through-hole assemblies. Generally, these are required for thermal matching purposes (see page 83).

Three categories of base material for surface mounted assemblies exist:

- Organic printed circuit bases. Those laminate materials used, conventionally, for through-hole printed circuit boards; epoxy-resin, glass fibre; phenolic-resin, paper; silicone-resin, glass fibre; polyester film, polyimide film (see Chapter 2, for details).

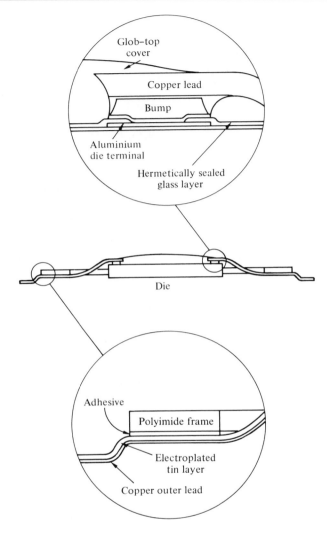

Figure 3.6 *Cross-section of a typical TAB integrated circuit*

- Ceramic substrates. These were first developed as base materials for hybrid assemblies, so the common ones (alumina and beryllia) have been around for a while. Some others have been developed more recently.
- Metal-cored substrates. Bases, comprising a metal-core, coated with insulating material. The insulator layer may be of a ceramic or an organic nature, that is, of one of the two previous categories.

Ceramic substrates, historically, were the first base materials used for surface mounted assemblies. Generally, the conductive track is formed by printing a mixture of conductive material and glass on to the ceramic surface, followed by firing the assembly before mounting components. This is the conventional thick-film technique.

Standards

UK	IEC	USA	European
BS 3953	IEC249	IPC L108	DIN 40802
BS 4584		IPC L109	DIN LN9407
BS 5102		IPC L112	
BS 6673		IPC L115	
		IPC L125	
		IPC AM361	
		Mil P13949	

Thermal design of surface mounted assemblies

The reasons for using base materials other than the relatively cheap organic printed circuit bases are largely owing to thermal considerations.

Differing thermal coefficients of expansion between base and component

When a temperature change occurs, a material expands or contracts according to its **thermal coefficient of expansion** (TCE). If two bonded materials have different thermal coefficients of expansion, then a stress will be created between the materials which will cause solder creep (see Chapter 5) and, if sufficiently large, will fracture the bond, or damage the component itself. When discussing the different thermal coefficients of expansion between surface mounted components and the base material the difference is often loosely called a **thermal mismatch**.

If there is a thermal mismatch between component and base material, stress occurs on soldering, immediately an assembly begins to cool after the solder has solidified, and continues at an increasing rate until its maximum at the assembly's ambient temperature.

The problem is specifically a surface mounted assembly one, because thermal mismatches between leaded components mounted on a through-hole printed circuit board do not usually create problems as the wire leads themselves are compliant and so flex to make up the difference, even though considerable difference in lengths may occur. Many surface mounted components, on the other hand, have no such in-built compliancy, as they are leadless.

Reducing thermal mismatch problems

A number of alternatives exist:

- Ignore it. For simple surface mounted components such as chip resistors, chip capacitors and small leadless chip carriers, thermal mismatch can usually be ignored, as the difference in lengths is usually absorbed by the solder joints. Low complexity circuits, that is, without complex integrated circuits, should suffer no bond fractures.
- Use plastic leaded chip carriers or tape automated bonding packages for complex integrated circuits – the leads will form compliant links to

absorb the differences in length – and ignore thermal mismatch for lower complexity components.

- Use a flexible base material, or a base material with a flexible top layer to absorb the length differences.
- Use a thermally matched base material. Large leadless chip carriers (such as leadless ceramic chip carriers) are prone to thermal mismatch problems, and so use of a different base material often forms a solution. A base material with identical or similar thermal coefficient of expansion to the ceramic-based components will eliminate the length differences caused by temperature changes.

A final alternative using a thermally matched base is, of course, the ultimate but is, as you may expect, the most expensive. However, where extreme miniaturization of the product is critical, it may be the only viable answer.

Heat dissipation

Lack of adequate heat dissipation from complex and high-density packed components may cause the other main thermal problem – component damage owing to excessive heat. An answer to this is to make plated-through holes in the base around and under components – **thermal vias** – to act as heat-sinks, dissipating heat away through conductive tracks. Another solution is to use a base material with good thermal conductivity. Metal-cored substrates are, of course, ideal for this purpose, and provide a perfectly adequate short-term solution.

In the long-term, however, as components become more complex and are more closely packed (which, inevitably, they will be as surface mounted technology progresses) alternatives may be to use full heat-sinks, directly connected to the sources of heat, forced cooling methods such as substrates with cooling fins, cooling fans, liquid immersion and so on.

Such **heat management** techniques will become commonplace, and are considered in Chapter 4.

Design

As in the design of through-hole assemblies, a number of factors should be taken into account when designing surface mounted assemblies. These factors are discussed in the equivalent section of Chapter 2 and readers are referred to them.

The fact that surface mounted components are leadless, however, means that certain extra factors should be borne in mind. For instance, more so than in the assembly of through-hole printed circuit boards, surface mounted boards are affected by the soldering process used – basically because of the different thermal coefficients of expansion between components and base material of the board, but also because the components *are* leadless. So an understanding of the effects of the various soldering processes which a surface mounted assembly may undergo is essential.

Influence of soldering process

For the following discussion, readers are referred to Chapter 5 for an understanding of soldering processes and later in this chapter, for an understanding of surface mounted assembling processes.

As far as surface mounted components and the following are concerned, component/solder (CS) processes generally involve fixing the component to the base with adhesive, before soldering. Wave soldering is a typical CS process used for soldering of some types of surface mounted components. On the other hand, solder/component (SC) processes involve the application of solder, in one form or another, *before* the component is mounted. SC soldering processes are often known, not quite correctly (see Chapter 5), as reflow soldering processes.

Surface mounted assemblies and mixed assemblies have some very different extra layout requirements to those of plain through-hole assemblies. The very fact that a component is to be surface mounted, for example, may automatically define the soldering requirements. Certain surface mounted components cannot be soldered by CS processes, and so require soldering by SC processes. Mixed assemblies, on the other hand, must be soldered by CS processes, unless the through-hole components are to be manually soldered after the surface mounted components have been soldered by an SC process.

Surface mounted components can be divided, broadly, into two groups of soldering processes:

- Those suitable for CS process soldering *and* SC process soldering; these include chip passive components and small outline integrated circuits.
- Those suitable for *only* SC process soldering; these include all other integrated circuits.

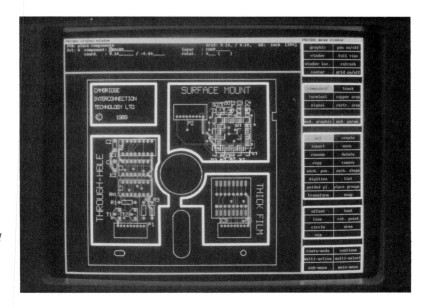

Plate 3.13 *Computer-aided design (using* Prisma *software) of a printed circuit board to hold through-hole, surface mount and thick film components. Design was used at Internepcon 1989 (Calay Systems)*

CS process soldering may be unsuitable for a number of reasons, including:

- The high temperatures which inevitably occur may damage the components, or may cause significant stress on the soldered joint.
- Unsealed packages, preventing complete immersion in flux or solder.
- Packages which do not allow an adhesive to be used as a fixing method.
- Packages which have finely spaced connecting pins – CS process soldering has a tendency to produce solder bridges.

On the other hand, SC soldering processes are usually considered suitable for *all* surface mounted components. However, more conventional SC processes may not be the best method to solder tape automated bonding integrated circuits. Instead a pulsed soldering head may be the best option.

Conductor dimensions

As with through-hole printed circuit boards, surface mounted boards have minimum restrictions on track dimensions. The dimensions which must be considered are:

- Minimum track width.
- Minimum spacing between adjacent tracks.
- Minimum land size and shape.
- Minimum hole size (holes in surface mounted boards are for via purposes alone).

Generally all these will be standardized within an organization, and will be primarily set by the technology used to produce the board and the soldering process. Following dimensions of tracks and lands are suggestions which, if followed, should allow successful assembly layout design (Siemens).

Minimum track width and spacings

Minimum track width and spacings depend totally on etching technique. Basically there are three grades of etching technique, listed in Table 3.1, along with minimum track widths and spacings which should be allowed with these techniques.

Table 3.1 Minimum track widths and spacings recommended for three etching techniques

Etching technique	Minimum track width (mm)	Minimum track spacing (mm)
Normal – A	0.6	0.60
Fine – B	0.3	0.30
Super-fine – C	0.2	0.15

Minimum land size and shape

Lands of a surface mount board are not drilled for component lead insertion, they are present purely to provide a soldering anchorage for the component terminals. Accordingly, surface mount land design depends more on the components than through-hole land design. Also to be considered is the soldering process used. As a rule, lands for boards which are to be soldered by a SC soldering process (such as vapour phase reflow) may be smaller than lands for boards to be soldered by a CS soldering process (such as dual wave).

Two-terminal component lands

For two-terminal components of rectangular prism (*wrongly called cubic*) and cylindrical shapes, land dimensions are illustrated in Figure 3.7. To allow for tolerances in component sizes and placement tolerances in the placement machine, lands should be at least 0.25 mm larger in both directions than the component terminals for SC process soldering, and 0.5 mm larger for CS process soldering. Distances between lands depend

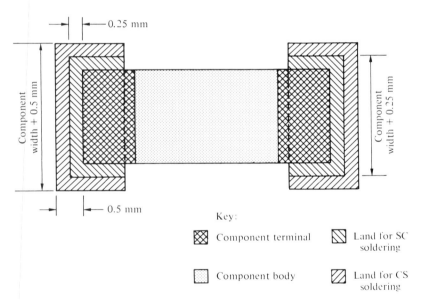

Figure 3.7 *Two-terminal component lands*

directly on individual component dimensions, and manufacturers' literature should be referred to for details. Numbers of permissible tracks which are allowed under two-terminal components are listed in Table 3.2, for the three etching techniques.

Small outline transistor lands

Small outline transistor (SOT) packages are fixed in size and land dimensions, together with track positions, are shown in Figures 3.8, 3.9 and

Table 3.2   Recommended maximum number of tracks under two-terminal components

Distance between lands (mm)	Etching techniques		
	A	*B*	*C*
1.0	0	1	2
1.8	1	2	4
2.0	1	2	5
2.3	1	3	6
3.0	2	4	8
3.1	2	5	8
4.2	3	6	>10
4.7	3	7	>10
5.7	4	9	>10
6.2	4	10	>10
6.8	5	10	>10

Note: recommended maximum numbers of tracks under certain component types may be lower than this generalized list suggests. Check with manufacturers' specifications.

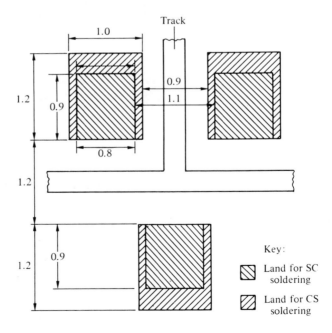

Figure 3.8 *Land dimensions for basic SOT package*

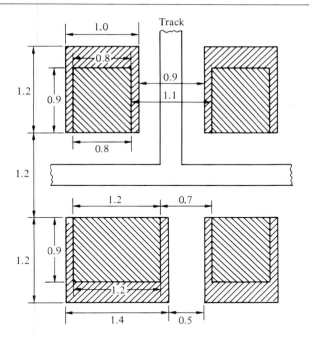

Figure 3.9 *Land dimensions for SOT143 package*

3.10. Numbers of tracks allowed under components should be restricted to those listed in Table 3.3, for the three etching techniques.

Small outline IC lands

Small outline integrated circuit (SOIC) package lands are shown in Figure 3.11. The widths of SOICs depend on the number of pins (SO4 to SO16 = 4 mm; SO20 to SO28 = 7.6 mm), so land positions vary accordingly. Pin spacing for all SOICs is 1.27 mm. Note that only super-fine etched tracks should be routed underneath SOICs. Land centre-to-centre spacings for SC and CS process soldering are listed in Table 3.4.

Solder thieves

Note the use of solder thieves in Figure 3.11 is only for mass CS process soldering (for example, wave). A **solder thief** is an additional solder land,

Table 3.3 Numbers of recommended maximum tracks under small outline transistors

Etching technique	Number of tracks in x direction	Number of tracks in y direction
A	0	0
B	1	1
C	3	2

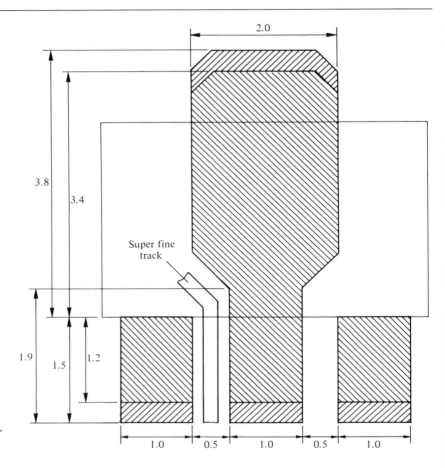

Figure 3.10 *Land dimensions for SOT89 package*

positioned to follow the last component mounting land through a mass CS process soldering machine. Surface tension and the effects of wetting cause a certain amount of solder to retain on any solder joint after CS soldering. When a number of lands in line are soldered, the solder will accumulate, and the last land will gather this accumulation. Undesired solder bridges may occur, as shown in Figure 3.12(a). Enlarging the last land to act as a solder thief (Figure 3.12(b)) will alleviate the problem, or the addition of a **dummy land** will do the same (Figure 3.12(c)).

Table 3.4   Numbers of recommended maximum tracks under small outline integrated circuits

Package	Land centre-to-centre spacings	
	SC soldering	*CS soldering*
S06 to S018	5.080	5.715
S020	9.525	10.106

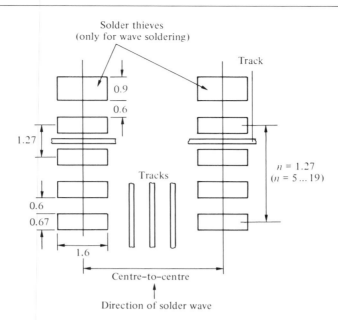

Figure 3.11 *Small outline integrated circuit land dimensions*

Plastic leaded chip carrier lands

With terminals on all four sides, plastic leaded chip carriers (PLCCs) normally should not be soldered by CS soldering processes – with occasional exceptions (see Chapter 5). Figure 3.13 shows the lands and track arrangement together with internal dimensions. External dimensions A, B, E and F depend on the number of terminals the chip carrier has. Only super-fine etched tracks should be routed under PLCCs.

Tape automated bonded package lands

Tape automated bonded (TAB) integrated circuits vary in number of terminals, spacing and sizes, so no overall fixed dimensions can be specified. To further complicate the issue, different mounting techniques should be used depending on soldering process (see Chapter 5).

TAB integrated circuits cannot be soldered by mass CS soldering processes. Generally, therefore, they will be soldered by vapour phase or infra-red (that is, mass SC soldering processes), or by heated collet SC soldering processes.

Figure 3.14 shows land sizes with vapour phase or infra-red soldering. Generally, land widths should equal terminal widths plus 0.1 mm, while land lengths should be 1.5 mm.

Similarly, Figure 3.15 shows land sizes with heated collet soldering. Where terminal spacings are over about 1 mm, land width should equal terminal width plus 0.1 mm. Land sizes for terminal spacings less than this

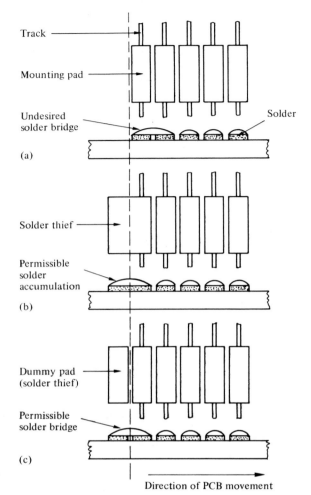

Track

Mounting pad

Undesired
solder bridge

Solder

(a)

Solder thief

Permissible
solder
accumulation

(b)

Dummy pad
(solder thief)

Permissible
solder bridge

(c)

Direction of PCB movement

Figure 3.12 *Use of solder thieves. (a) Undesired solder bridges between adjacent lands. (b) Alleviating solder bridging by enlarging the last land through the soldering machine. (c) Adding a dummy land to do the same*

should equal terminal widths. Land lengths should be about 1.5 mm longer than terminal lengths.

The reason for the different land sizes, when different soldering processes are used, is the different mounting methods, shown also in Figures 3.14 and 3.15. On initial placement (whether standard SC mass soldering or heated collet soldering is to be undertaken), terminals merely push into the solder paste. Mass SC soldering melts the solder paste and the terminals are fixed. When soldering by heated collet, on the other hand, the terminals are distorted by the collet such that they are flattened against the land. The collet is heated until the solder paste melts, then allowed to cool before removal – allowing time for the solder to solidify.

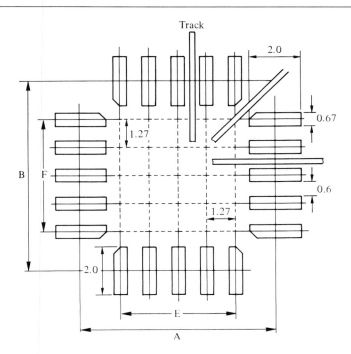

Figure 3.13 *Lands and track arrangements for PLCCs*

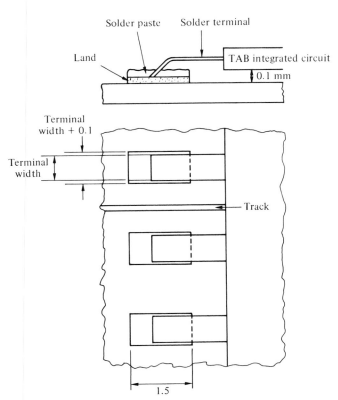

Figure 3.14 *Land dimensions for TAB integrated circuits, when vapour phase or infra-red soldering*

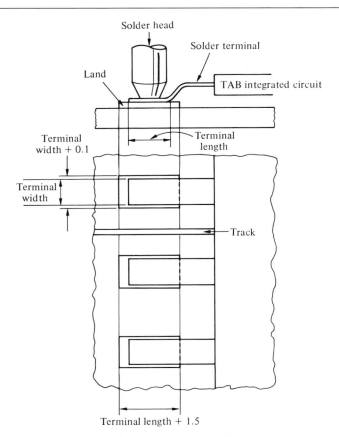

Figure 3.15 *Land dimensions for TAB integrated circuits when soldering by heated collet*

Component spacing and placement

Unlike through-hole component spacings, where the soldering process and the components themselves effectively limit how close components may be positioned, spacings between surface mounted components do not have that limit. Components are considerably smaller than their through-hole counterparts, and the lack of leads means that CS soldering can be dispensed with. Instead, the spacings between the miniature components, which are soldered using an SC soldering process, are effectively limited by the circuit board technology.

Packing density

As surface mounted components are very much smaller than through-hole counterparts, because they can be mounted on both sides of a board, and because miniaturized components can be manufactured which are simply not feasible in through-hole form, surface mounted assemblies have a corresponding increase in packing density possibility. Where through-hole assemblies have to resort to multi-layered printed circuit boards to increase packing density to the limits imposed by the soldering processes and component sizes, surface mounted assemblies can surpass that limit without the requirement of a multi-layer structure.

Designing for test

Although the test points specified in the following section relate to surface mounted assemblies, they are by no means specific, and may be incorporated into through-hole assemblies, too. Chapter 6 looks at the principles of testing in electronics assembly in greater detail.

Testing of assemblies is done by means of test points, located at nodes in the circuit. Therefore, by measuring electrical aspects of the assembly, faults can be located, and repaired in the rework stage of production.

Assemblies are tested by locating sharp pointed pins, one at every selected nodal test point. Because of this test-pin nature, a jig to perform interconnections to the assembly is usually called a **bed-of-nails** adaptor.

For complex and high-density assemblies, many hundreds of test pins will be required – one per circuit node – in order that a full test may be performed. This large number of test points and the physical aspects of the bed-of-nails adaptor, mean that various considerations must be taken into account when designing the assembly, including:

- Minimum size of test points, usually 0.9 mm in diameter, although extended lands and vias may be used (Figure 3.16).
- Soldered test points, or a plated solder layer, are essential to ensure good electrical contact between the test point and test pin.
- All test points should be brought to one side of the board (top or bottom) using vias where necessary, to ease the complexity of the bed-of-nails adaptor.
- Test points should be a minimum distance from components. 2 mm where the component has a height of 3 mm, 4 mm where the component height is more than 3 mm (Figure 3.17).

It is unacceptable to allow a component's terminals to be used as a test point for a number of reasons, including:

- Damage to the component.

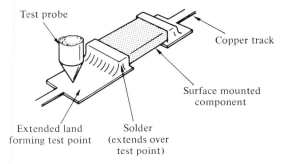

Figure 3.16 *Minimum size of test points*

Test probe

Copper track

Surface mounted component

Extended land forming test point

Solder (extends over test point)

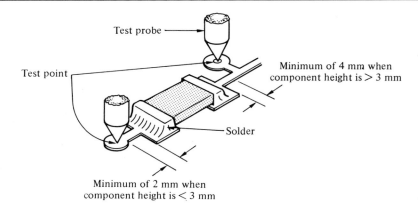

Figure 3.17 *Minimum distance of test points from components*

- Defective solder joints may appear perfect owing to the test pin's pressure.
- Small terminals may be missed entirely by the test pin.

It is advisable to use bed-of-nails adaptors with test pins located on a grid spacing no closer than 2.54 mm (that is, 0.1 in). Adaptors located on a grid spacing of 1.27 mm (that is, 0.05 in) are available, but suffer problems owing to the fragility of their required small diameter test pins. Location of large numbers of test points, while maintaining a 2.54 mm grid, can be achieved by using staggered or fan-shaped test point arrangements, as illustrated in Figure 3.18.

The use of test adaptors on a 2.54 mm grid is, in fact, another reason why component terminals must not be used as test points – surface mounted components have terminals which do not correspond with a 0.1 in grid spacing (that is, they are sized metrically), so a non-standard bed-of-nails adaptor would be required.

Standards

UK
BS 6221

USA
EIA 213
IPC SM 782

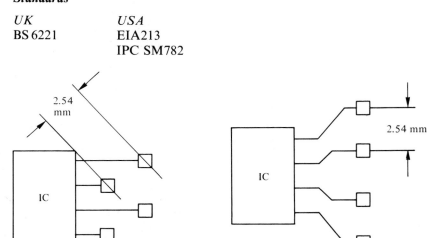

Figure 3.18 *Staggered or fan-shaped test point arrangements allow a 2.54 mm grid to be maintained, even for large numbers of test points*

Assembly

Like through-hole printed circuit board assembly, surface mounted assembly comprises two main processes: component placement on to the board; and soldering the component terminals or pins to the board track. Component placement is often referred to by the term **pick and place**, owing to the way some semi-automatic and automatic equipment choose (that is, pick) then place each component, one at a time, on to the board. The term, however, strictly refers to only one type of placement machine (see page 110).

However, where components may be manually inserted, and manually soldered, to a through-hole board, surface mounted component placement and soldering are normally only undertaken as parts of a semi-automatic or fully automatic process. Mainly owing to components' small size and finely spaced connecting pins, manual assembly is generally impossible on any large scale.

Plate 3.14 *Adhesive dispenser for electronics use such as surface mount component bonding (EFD)*

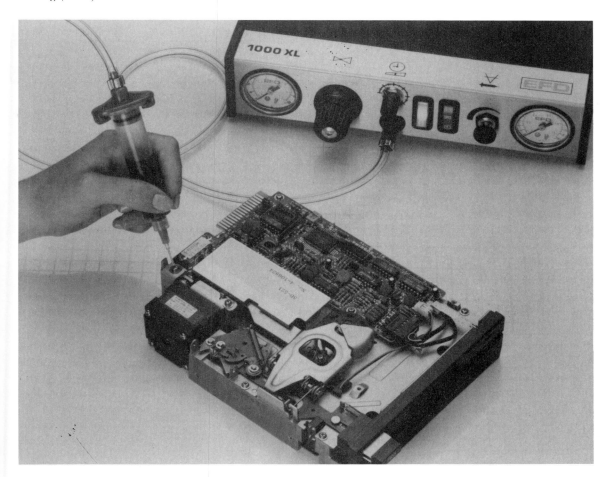

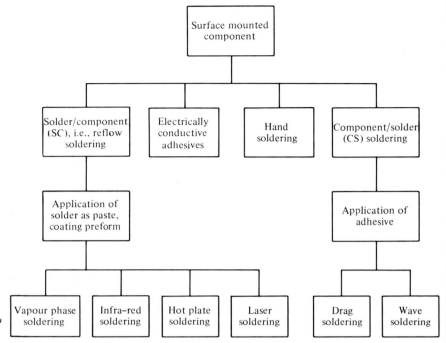

Figure 3.19 *Illustrating the mounting of surface mount components to the board prior to soldering*

Where an *inserted* component can be clinched to a through-hole PCB assembly, holding it until the soldering operation has been completed, such a mechanical retention of the component has been eliminated in a surface mounted assembly. Surface mounted components, therefore, must be first fixed to the board or substrate, before soldering. This situation is illustrated in Figure 3.19, where the soldering processes involved are included. Usually the surface mounted component is fixed to the board or substrate with some sort of adhesive, and at this point two main methods of fixing surface mounted components can be categorized, depending on the type of adhesive:

- Pure adhesive, where the adhesive used must set before the following application of molten solder.
- Solder paste, powdered solder and flux-based cream, sufficiently tacky to hold the components in place, before heating to melt the solder.

Both methods are illustrated in Figure 3.20. Processes for component fixing by hand soldering, electrically conductive adhesives, or application of solder by solid preform or coating are generally few and far between; mostly used in design, development, laboratory or rework stages.

Adhesive

In general, pure adhesive is typically used where components are to be mounted on the bottom of a board or where the board is to be turned

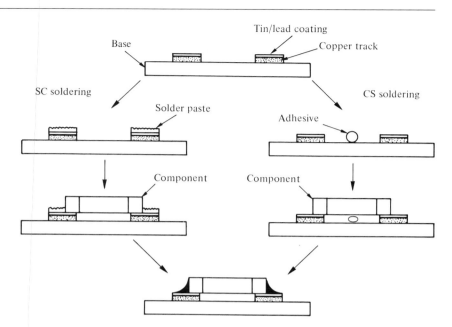

Figure 3.20 *Surface mount components are fixed to the board by (left) solder paste or (right) adhesive, prior to soldering*

upside down in any subsequent operation (as solder paste will not prevent components falling off by gravity). A number of features are important in any adhesive used in mounting of components, including:

- It must not react with either the component or the board material.
- It must not conduct electrically.
- It must be tacky enough to retain the component until cured.
- It must be capable of withstanding the heat of soldering.
- It must allow removal of the component, for later repair or servicing.
- It must be non-toxic and solvent-free.
- A short curing time is desirable, for a rapid throughput of assemblies.

Some acrylate or epoxy adhesive meet these criteria, and many more adhesives are currently in development to improve upon them. Adhesive curing is of two main types: heat and ultraviolet (UV) light.

Heat curing is usually performed in an oven, while ultraviolet cured adhesives must undergo exposure to ultraviolet light. Either can be done with the boards moving through the heat or light source on a conveyor belt to maintain production volume. Sometimes, an ultraviolet light cured adhesive's curing time can be shortened upon application of supplementary heat. This is only a little problem and, in fact, could be incorporated into the preheating stages of a soldering process.

Where adhesive is heat cured, the strongest bond will occur when the adhesive is applied as a spot underneath the components, in the centre, as illustrated in Figure 3.21(a). However, where the adhesive is ultraviolet light cured, the component's body will prevent light from striking the

Plate 3.15 *Close-up of 4713 adhesive dispensing head used in high-volume surface mount assembly (Universal)*

Plate 3.16 *Ultraviolet adhesive curing machine (Ultra-violet Products)*

adhesive in this position, so application of a spot of adhesive on each side of the component, as in Figure 3.21(b), provides the optimum bond.

Size and volume of the adhesive spots depend largely on the adhesive used, although diameters of between 1 and 2 mm, and volumes between 0.5 and 4 mm³ are common.

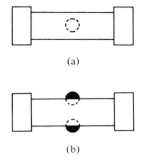

Figure 3.21 *Application of adhesive depends on curing process. (a) Heat cured adhesive is best applied to the centre of the component. (b) Ultraviolet light cured adhesive must be applied to the edges of components*

Figure 3.22 *Amount of adhesive depends on the type of component. (a) Chip components require only a small amount. (b) Small outline components sit further from the board, requiring more adhesive. (c) A dummy track underneath the component aids adhesion and reduces the amount of adhesive*

The amount of adhesive to be applied depends, too, on the type of component, as illustrated in Figure 3.22, according to the gap between the component body and the base. Small chip passive components require only a small amount of adhesive, as the gap is merely the thickness of the conductor track plus the thickness of the component's metallized terminations (Figure 3.22(a)). Small outline integrated circuits, on the other hand, sit far more proud of the board, and the gap now comprises the thickness of the conductor track plus the leg height of the component. Naturally, this will require more adhesive (Figure 3.22(b)), which may not be possible if the application method is by screen-printing. Often, better bonding of components can be obtained, together with a reduction in adhesive, by running a **dummy track** underneath the component as in Figure 3.22(c).

An alternative answer is to use a higher viscosity adhesive, as shown in Figure 3.23, where the adhesive sits more proud from the board (Figure 3.23(a)) prior to component placement (Figure 3.23(b)). Higher viscosity adhesives, however, may not be suitable for application by the simpler methods low viscosity adhesive allows (see page 102).

The number of spots required by components depends not only on the adhesive, but on the size of components, too. Small passive components will need a single spot, while larger components, say, SO–28 and bigger, will require three or more. It is important to note that the bond required is not large, merely sufficient to maintain the component in position until the soldering process is completed. Indeed, if too much adhesive is applied, when the component is placed on the board adhesive may be squeezed out to cover the conducting track pads, as shown in Figure 3.24, thus preventing effective soldering of the component terminations.

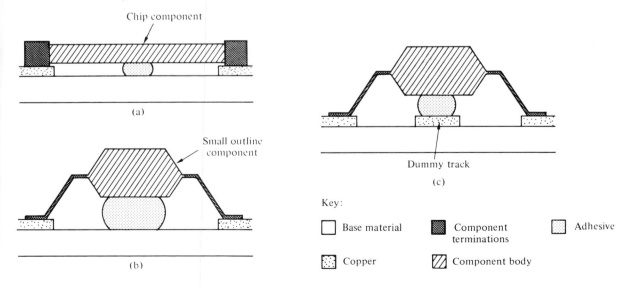

Chip component

(a)

Small outline component

(b)

Dummy track

(c)

Key:

☐ Base material	■ Component terminations
▦ Copper	▨ Component body
☐ Adhesive	

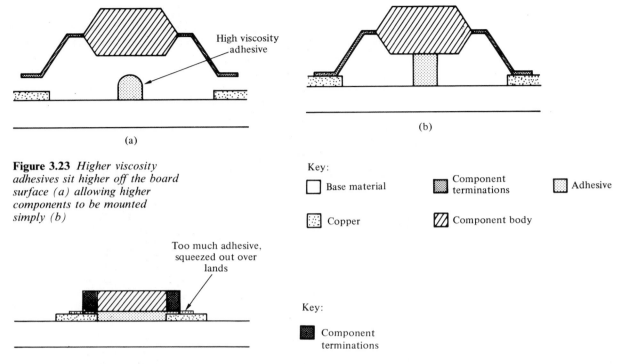

(a)

(b)

Figure 3.23 *Higher viscosity adhesives sit higher off the board surface (a) allowing higher components to be mounted simply (b)*

Key:

☐ Base material

▦ Component terminations

▨ Adhesive

▦ Copper

▨ Component body

Key:

■ Component terminations

Figure 3.24 *Too much adhesive will be squeezed out on mounting of component, and may cover the joint to be soldered*

Solder paste

Solder paste is typically used where components are only mounted on the top of a board and where the soldering process does not require the board to be inverted.

They comprise solder alloy in powdered form, together with flux and a solvent.

Application

Whatever the method, adhesive or paste must be applied to the board before the component. A number of ways to do this are used, including:

- Screen-printing (Figure 3.25). See Chapter 2 for a detailed discussion on screen-printing as a method of applying resist to a printed circuit board. Instead of resist ink, adhesive or solder paste is used. Suitable for low viscosity adhesive.
- Pin transfer (Figure 3.26), where a number of pins are first dipped in a reservoir of adhesive or solder paste then lowered on to the board surface. Suitable for low to medium viscosity adhesive.

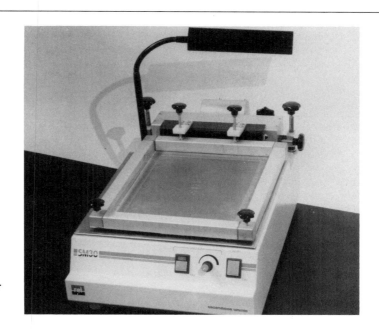

Plate 3.17 *SM30 screen printer for solder paste application (Groatmoor)*

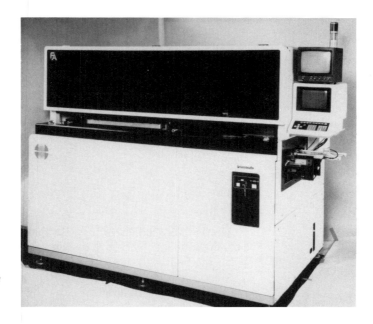

Plate 3.18 *Panasert SPP screen printer with vision (Panasonic Industrial)*

- Dispensing from nozzles (Figure 3.27). Syringe-type nozzles are connected with tubing to a pump, which forces adhesive or solder paste from a reservoir out onto the board. Suitable for high viscosity adhesives.

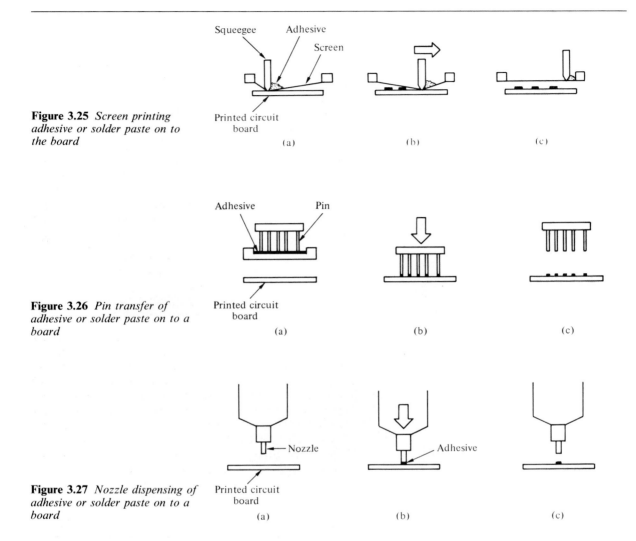

Figure 3.25 *Screen printing adhesive or solder paste on to the board*

Figure 3.26 *Pin transfer of adhesive or solder paste on to a board*

Figure 3.27 *Nozzle dispensing of adhesive or solder paste on to a board*

Alternatively, adhesive may be applied individually to the bottom of each component, by nozzle dispensing or pin transfer, before placement on to the board.

After component placement, the adhesive or solder paste must be dried (cured, in the case of adhesive) and the assembly is then soldered. Unlike PCBs, however, where solder is usually applied to the opposite side of the board to the components, surface mounted assemblies must be soldered on the same side as components. Where pure adhesive has been used, soldering using reasonably straightforward techniques used in PCB assembly is possible. Where solder paste is used, it is only necessary to heat the assembly to the point where the solder particles melt together. Soldering processes are covered in detail in Chapter 6.

Standard

UK
BS 6221

Assembly variations

Because surface mounted components may be used alone or alongside through-hole components there exists a number of possible assembly variations (Figure 3.28). Further, because certain surface mounted components may be soldered by either CS or SC soldering processes, there is a corresponding number of manufacturing variations, too, depending on whether the surface mounted components are mounted on one or both sides of the board, and the actual soldering process. The assembly and consequent manufacturing variations are:

- Surface mounted components on one side, SC soldering process.
- Surface mounted components on one side, CS soldering process.
- Surface mounted components on both sides.
- Mixed assembly, surface mounted components on one side.
- Mixed assembly, surface mounted component on both sides.

Any SC soldering process may be used to solder surface mounted components. Generally, however, CS soldering of surface mounted components may only be by the wave soldering process. (Readers are referred to Chapter 5 for descriptions of SC and CS soldering processes.)

Further, not all surface mounted components *can* be CS soldered – only two-terminal chip components and small outline devices. With only minor exceptions (noted in Chapter 5), chip carriers, TAB integrated circuits, and so on, may be soldered only using SC methods. Consequently, unless otherwise stated, following descriptions of assembly and manufacturing variations apply to chip and small outline surface mounted components, only.

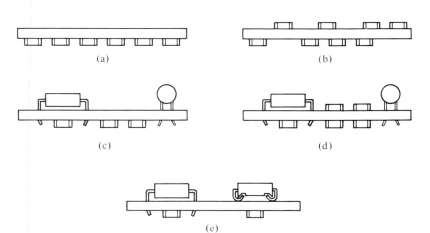

Figure 3.28 *Possible assembly variations when using surface mounted components*

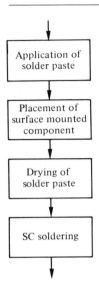

Figure 3.29 *Assembly of surface mounted components on one side of the board, SC soldered*

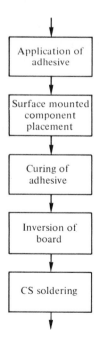

Figure 3.30 *Assembly of surface mounted components on one side of the board, CS soldered*

Surface mounted components on one side, SC soldered

This is, in terms of the number of steps, the most straightforward method of manufacturing surface mounted assemblies, shown in Figure 3.29. For this reason, it forms an entry point into the manufacture of surface mounted assemblies for many companies.

Solder paste is applied to the board, generally by screen-printing method but, occasionally, pin transfer or dispensing nozzles may be used. Components are then placed on to the board, the paste is dried, and the board is heated in one of the SC soldering processes.

Surface mounted components on one side, CS soldered

Although slightly more complex than the previous variation, the use of a CS soldering process means that companies with existing through-hole production facilities (which include a wave soldering machine) may be able to adapt production lines to manufacture limited-complexity surface mounted assemblies. Consequently, this variation (shown in Figure 3.30) forms another popular entry point into the manufacture of surface mounted assemblies, without too great an expense.

Adhesive is first applied, either as spots (using pin transfer or dispensing nozzle methods) or screen-printed. This stage is followed by component placement. The adhesive is cured, the board is inverted, and wave soldering of the assembly follows.

Surface mounted components, on both sides

Double-sided surface mounted assemblies require soldering by both SC *and* CS soldering processes, in sequence. Thus, for a company contemplating entry into surface mounted assembly manufacture, it is comparatively expensive.

As shown in Figure 3.31, the method of manufacture for this type of assembly is simple addition of the two previous variations. Initially, components on the top of the board must be soldered first. Application of solder paste is followed by component placement, paste drying and SC soldering.

Next, the components on the other side of the board are mounted and soldered. So, the board is inverted, adhesive is applied, components are placed, and the adhesive is cured. Following another board inversion, wave soldering is undertaken.

Mixed assembly, surface mounted components on one side

Here, there are three manufacturing variants. The first is shown in Figure 3.32, where leaded components are first inserted into the board, the board is inverted, adhesive is applied, surface mounted components are placed, and adhesive is cured. Note that, as leaded components have been inserted (their leads now stick out of the bottom of the board) adhesive cannot be

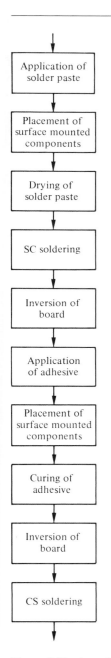

Figure 3.31 *Assembly of surface mounted components on both sides of the board*

applied to the bottom of the board by screen-printing – pin transfer or dispensing nozzle methods must be used. Following a second inversion, the board is wave soldered.

A second variant simply places surface mounted components before insertion of leaded components (Figure 3.33).

Both of these variants solder both leaded and surface mounted components in a single, wave, soldering process. A third variant, however, completely separates soldering of each type of component, as shown in Figure 3.34. Surface mounted components are initially SC soldered, then leaded components are CS soldered.

Although marginally longer production times are required in this variant, it does give the advantage that complex surface mounted

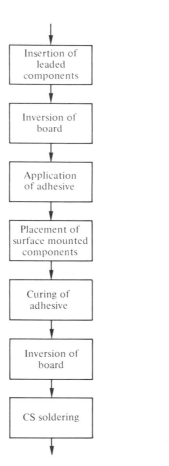

Figure 3.32 *Assembly of mixed components with surface mounted components on one side of the board, CS soldered*

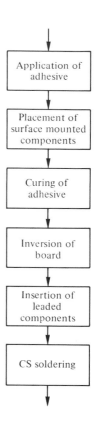

Figure 3.33 *Variant of Figure 3.32*

Figure 3.34 *Assembly of mixed components, separating CS and SC soldering processes*

components, such as leaded and unleaded chip carriers, or TAB integrated circuits, may be placed on a mixed assembly. None of the previous methods allows this.

Mixed assembly, surface mounted components on both sides

Where surface mounted components are to be placed on both sides of a mixed assembly, there is no option but to separate soldering of components on the top and bottom sides of the board.

The procedure is illustrated in Figure 3.35. First, after the usual application of solder paste, surface mounted components are placed on the top of the board, the paste is dried, and the components are SC soldered.

Next, leaded components are inserted, the board is inverted, adhesive is applied, surface mounted components are placed, and the adhesive is cured. Again, as leaded components have been inserted, adhesive application cannot be by screen-printing. After final board inversion, wave soldering completes the process.

This method, like the previous, allows mixed assemblies to contain complex surface mounted components, such as leaded or leadless chip carriers, or TAB integrated circuits.

Cleaning of assemblies

Whatever manufacturing method is undertaken, whether assemblies are purely of surface mounted form, or are mixed, cleaning will be necessary after soldering. Such **post-assembly** cleaning is described in Chapter 5.

Testing assemblies

Surface mounted assemblies lend themselves to high levels of testing. Details of the tests and procedures generally undertaken on surface mounted components and assemblies are found in Chapter 6.

Component placement

The three main processes – application of adhesive, placement and soldering – are usually automated, at least to the point of semi-automation. Many semi-automatic and automatic equipments are available.

Manual placement

Where components are to be surface mounted, either in true surface mounted assemblies, or in mixed assemblies on PCBs where other components are inserted, manual placement (or manual onsertion, if that term is preferred) is not usually possible on any large scale. Nevertheless, occasions do arise where manual assembly is desired. Typically these are in design and development, or where mixed assemblies with only a few surface mounted components are to be placed.

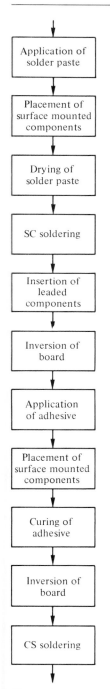

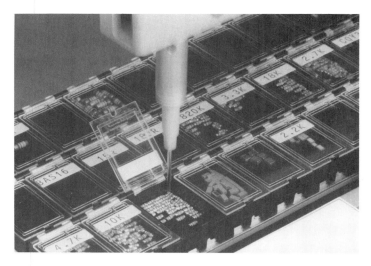

Plate 3.19 *Fritsch surface mount component container system, with vacuum pick-up nozzle (Groatmoor)*

Apart from the small size of the components, the problems associated with hand placement of surface mounted components include the fact that few components are marked as to their value. Aids to help overcome the problems of manual surface mounted component assembly may be simple labelled storage bins and a pair of tweezers.

Semi-automatic placement

There are many semi-automatic placement machines, ranging from container systems with spring-loaded lids and hand-held vacuum pick-up nozzles, which merely assist the operator to choose the correct component and position it on the board; through to computer-controlled placement arms, which dispense adhesive or solder paste and pick up the components from bins before a placement.

Also, equipment similar to that for through-hole printed circuit board assembly: to indicate the component position and orientation on the board, using slide projector, optical fibre, or laser light beam techniques exist.

Such semi-automatic equipment may provide an adequate assembly environment for low- to medium-volume assembly production.

Automatic placement

There is little doubt that surface mounted technology comes into its own when the assembly processes are automated. Where through-hole assembly technology is difficult to automate – simply because the components *are*

Figure 3.35 *Where surface mounted components are to be on both sides of a mixed assembly*

The flow chart in Figure 3.35 reads:

- Application of solder paste
- Placement of surface mounted components
- Drying of solder paste
- SC soldering
- Insertion of leaded components
- Inversion of board
- Application of adhesive
- Placement of surface mounted components
- Curing of adhesive
- Inversion of board
- CS soldering

Plate 3.20 *Fritsch LM901-500 semi-automatic surface mount component placement machine, based around a personal computer (Groatmoor)*

leaded and *do* need to be inserted through holes – surface mounted technology lends itself wholeheartedly to automated production.

Leadless components can be easily fed to a placement machine which, under computer-control can, in turn, easily place the component on to a board with considerable accuracy. Elimination of the requirements to preform leaded components leads, then cut the excess leads off afterwards, have simplified automatic assembly enormously.

Indeed, the very fact that through-hole printed circuit board assembly requires such complicated procedures effectively limits the ease of automatic assembly which surface mounted components provide. Through-hole assembly, too, limits the reductions in size which surface mounted assembly components, and the boards themselves, are currently enjoying.

These two factors give the assemblers who choose the surface mounted route an added benefit: while miniaturization continues in surface mounted components and boards, the assemblers can reap the rewards. In through-hole assembly, the limits of miniaturization and automated production have been reached.

Automatic assembly is in two main forms: sequential and simultaneous. Sequential assembly means that components are chosen one at a time, then placed on the board before the next component is chosen. This is the classic **pick and place** assembly method.

On the other hand, simultaneous assembly means that many components are placed on the board together.

Simultaneous assembly is, of necessity, a high performance, high speed process, suitable for large volume production. Sequential assembly, however, does not have the high performance requirement, is not so fast, is correspondingly cheaper and more suited to low- to medium-volume production.

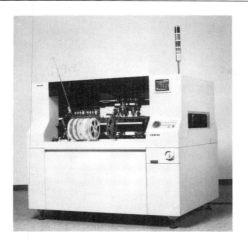

Plate 3.21 *CSM60 surface mount component placement machine (Philips Scientific)*

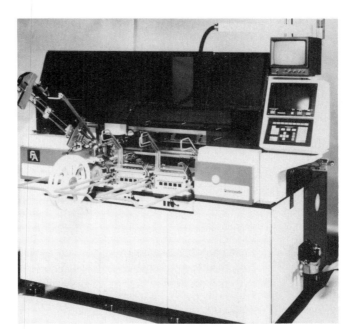

Plate. 3.22 *Panasert MPA80 surface mount component placement machine (Panasonic Industrial)*

Machines

In terms of complexity, the machines which place surface mounted components have a simpler job than insertion machines for through-hole assemblies. They do not need to preform component leads, insert leads through holes, then cut and clinch excess leads. Instead, their job is merely to apply adhesive or solder paste then place components.

This ease of job function has meant that the process is generally more

Plate 3.23 *Fuji CP-III surface mount component placement machine, used at Philips Dunfermline printed circuit board assembly factory (Phil. Components)*

Plate 3.24 *Close-up of Fuji CP-III component placement head (Astro Technology)*

Plate 3.25 *Close-up of MS-90 component placement head (Siemens)*

Plate 3.26 *Close-up of Omniplace II 4621B component placement head – for colour version see book cover (Universal)*

quickly performed than component insertion. In turn, the extra speed requires that components are supplied to the placement head or heads far more rapidly.

To allow this, manufacturers supply surface mounted components in three forms:

- Bulk.
- Magazine.
- Tape.

Plate 3.27 *Surface mount components: loose; taped; reeled (Murata Electronics)*

Bulk is the simplest and cheapest, and is suitable for passive components and small semiconductors. It is hopper-fed into the placement machine, where a vibratory feeder directs the components to the placement head's pick-up position.

Magazines are available in many forms (Figure 3.36), depending on individual machines, and hold only, say, 200 or so components. A vibratory feeder feeds the components from a magazine to the pick-up position of the placement head. The relatively small numbers of components held in magazines may be considered a disadvantage, but the method can be useful where components which cannot be bulk-fed (such as integrated circuits) and which are not available in taped and reeled form need to be placed. Lack of standardization on shapes and sizes of magazines means that magazines are usually machine-specific.

Tapes, on the other hand, are standardized to fit any tape-fed placement machine (Figure 3.37), and are available in 8 mm, 12 mm, 16 mm, 24 mm and 44 mm widths. Tape automated bonded integrated circuits are only available in tape form of 8 mm, 16 mm or 35 mm widths. Not by coincidence, tape widths and positions and sizes of sprocket holes are the same as those for corresponding sizes of movie-type films. Tape reels can hold many thousands of components.

Many machines can accept only one form of supplied components, while others can accept two or all three. The most complex (and expensive)

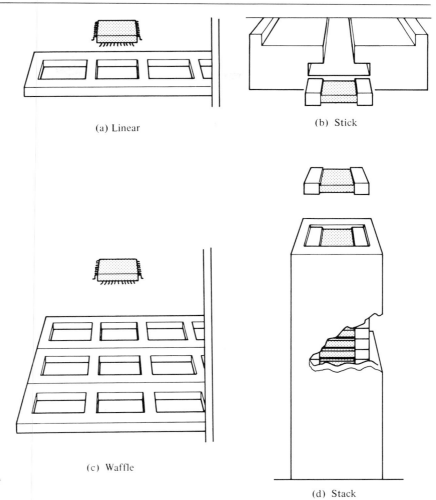

(a) Linear

(b) Stick

(c) Waffle

(d) Stack

Figure 3.36 *Forms of component magazines*

placement machines will accept all three types, as well as having many hoppers, many magazine stacks and many tape reels. Often, a selection of over 100 different components can be made on a machine.

Adhesive or solder paste is applied in any one of the ways noted earlier. If by screen printing, usually before the board is positioned under the placement head. If by dispensing nozzle or pin transfer, while in position.

All parts of the machine are typically computer-controlled, such that a simple software change will enable the machine to place components on to a totally different design of board.

Placement rates of machines vary according to the machine complexity. Some sequential pick and place machines have rates of, say, up to 2000 components per hour. Top-of-the-range simultaneous placement machines often have rates of up to 50,000 components per hour.

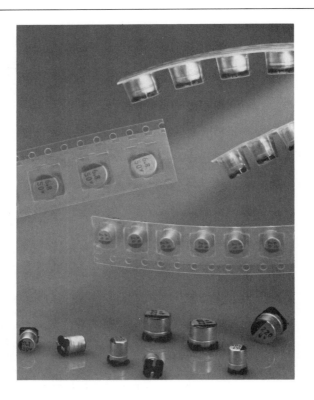

Plate 3.28 *Chip aluminium electrolytic capacitors in plastic tape (Panasonic Industrial)*

Placement, and the placement heads themselves, form the most mechanically complex part of the machine. Also, for obvious reasons, they must be extremely accurate. Placement of two-terminal devices is a relatively inaccurate process, so machines specifically for two-terminal component placement need not be as complex as those for multi-terminal devices, where extreme accuracies may be important. In terms of placement accuracy, it is common to divide all surface mounted components up into three main groups (Universal). These along with the approximate placement accuracies required in the two horizontal axes for each group are:

- A, two-terminal components, and small outline transistors (± 0.2 mm to ± 0.4 mm).
- B, small outline, and smaller flat-pack and chip carrier, integrated circuits (± 0.08 mm to ± 0.12 mm).
- C, large flat-pack and chip carrier integrated circuits, and TAB integrated circuits (± 0.05 mm or less).

From these figures of required accuracies, it should be fairly obvious that even simpler group A component placement machines are pretty accurate. Group C component placement machines have to be *extremely accurate*. A further problem can affect the placement of group C components owing to the extremely close positions of their terminals, where the components

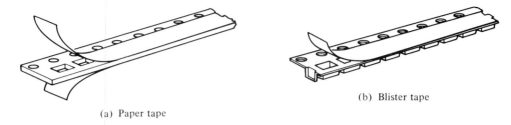

(a) Paper tape

(b) Blister tape

Figure 3.37 *Surface mount component tapes*

suffer a rotational misalignment, illustrated in Figure 3.38. Here (Figure 3.38(a)), an 80-terminal quad flat-pack is shown, which has an overall size of approximately 25 mm by 18 mm. Terminals are approximately 0.35 mm wide, with centre-to-centre dimensions of 0.8 mm. In Figure 3.38(b), horizontal placement errors of 0.05 mm in both X and Y axes are shown, together with a rotational error of 1°. In Figure 3.38(c), however, horizontal errors have been halved, which may lead you to believe that placement has improved. Yet, because the rotational error has increased (by only 50%) to 1° 30′ the actual placement accuracy has drastically been reduced. Placement accuracy, in fact, is a major characteristic of any given system, and it affects complexity, cost and speed.

Placement heads often allow fairly accurate movement in both horizontal axes, although sometimes the printed circuit board is moved underneath a stationary head. Typically, the head holds a vacuum pick-up nozzle mounted on a spindle assembly, which can be moved up and down,

Figure 3.38 *Rotational alignment of group C components is important. (a) An 80-terminal quad flat-pack integrated circuit. (b) With rotational error of 1°. (c) With halved horizontal errors but a rotational error of 1° 30′*

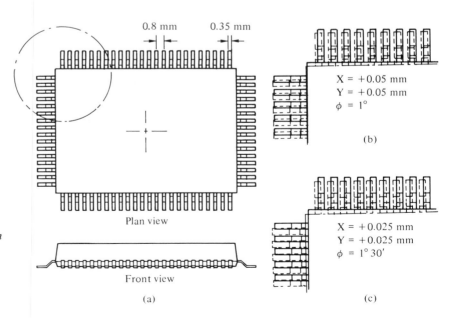

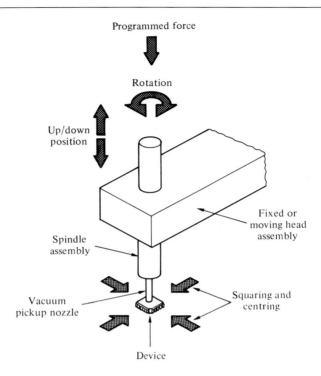

Figure 3.39 *Typical surface mount component assembly head*

as well as being rotatable, as shown in Figure 3.39. Some heads allow rotational increments of as low as 0.01°; important where group C components are to be placed. The force with which the head's spindle is moved up and down is usually programmable, such that various consistencies of solder paste or adhesive may be catered for as the machine places the component.

After the head has picked up a component, the component must be centred so it is in an absolute position. This can be done using mechanical arms which move in on the component, as shown in Figure 3.39. Alternatively, the head can move the component to a fixed jig, comprising (in its simplest form) two straight edges at 90°. Centring by a jig method is usually referred to as taking the component to a **placement centre**. Centring using either of these methods usually allows repeatability of the component on the placement head to within 0.025 mm. But, that does not mean the component will be positioned to that accuracy on the board. Factors such as the machine's mechanical tolerances, as well as the sliding effect solder paste or adhesive can have on the component as it is placed, may not allow placement to the accuracy required on the circuit board. Although this type of machine will usually place group A and group B components sufficiently accurately, it is not really capable of accurately placing group C components.

Higher accuracies of placement are achieved with machines which use optical recognition to aid centring of components as they are ultimately

Figure 3.40 *Typical fiducials printed on to surface mount boards, to allow vision-aided placement of components*

positioned on the circuit board. These systems, known as vision systems, incorporate a camera mounted on the placement head which monitors the position of the head in relation to the circuit board. Optically recognizable location marks on the circuit board known as **fiducials** are detected, using the camera, by the machine's computer-controller, so that extremely fine adjustments may be made, prior to final placement. Typical fiducials are shown in Figure 3.40.

Accuracies of vision placement systems may be as small as ± 0.02 mm, with rotational inaccuracies within 0.2°. Most machines using vision are capable of high-accuracy placement to ± 0.1 mm.

Standard

USA
EIA481

References

Universal, *Guidelines for surface mount technology*, New York: Universal Instruments Corporation.
Siemens, *PCB Layout Recommendations*, Munich: Siemens Aktiengesellschaft.

4 Electromechanical assembly: packaging

Complete production and manufacture of electronic appliances may simply be thought of as a collection of solutions to the many problems of interconnection – interconnection between a component package and its printed circuit board, interconnection between the circuit board and its housing, and so on. In this respect, a total of six levels of interconnection have been documented (Samtec). These are:

- Level 1. On-the-device, where the individual connections between the semiconductive component parts of integrated circuits are made as minute etched wires (Figure 4.1(a)).
- Level 2. Device-to-package, where the semiconductor die is permanently attached, with thin aluminium or gold wires, to the terminals of its package (Figure 4.1(b)).
- Level 3. Package-to-board, where flat, round or square package terminals are connected to a printed circuit boards, as permanent or separable connections (Figure 4.1(c)).
- Level 4. Board-to-board and on-board, where components are interconnected with the conductive track of the circuit board, and where circuit boards are connected to each other by permanent or separable connectors and cables (Figure 4.1(d)).
- Level 5. Board-to-cabinet, where connections between a circuit board and its cabinet (a distinct chassis may be involved between circuit board and cabinet) are made with separable connectors (Figure 4.1(e)).
- Level 6. Cabinet-to-cabinet, where separable connections between cabinets are made with multiple contact cables (Figure 4.1 (f)).

Many other methods of looking at the various interconnection levels are possible, of course, and they are fairly arbitrary anyway, but the classification does provide a good introduction to the problems of electrical assembly.

Chapters 2 and 3 have been concerned largely with the various methods of interconnections at levels 1, 2 and 3. Those chapters discussed the various methods available to manufacturers to combine electronic components on a printed circuit board, using either through-hole or surface mounted components. This chapter is about the remaining three levels of interconnections (though particularly level 4), in which assembled boards are connected, housed in cabinets, and presented to the customer. In other words, we are concerned here with the electromechanical packaging of completed assemblies.

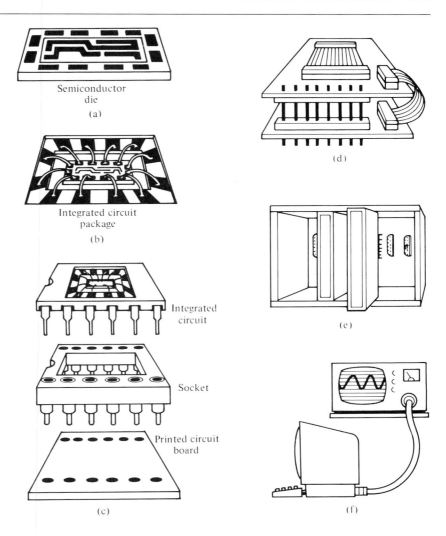

Semiconductor
die
(a)

Integrated circuit
package
(b)

Integrated
circuit

Socket

Printed circuit
board

(d)

(e)

(f)

(c)

Figure 4.1 *Illustrating the six levels of interconnection in any electronic assembly (after Samtec)*

Packaging engineering

Electromechanical packaging of assemblies is not merely a question of interconnection, though. Packaging is a form of design which affects all stages of the appliance's life: from initial concept, through design of the circuit itself, assembly layout, overall appearance and, last but not least, reliability. Good packaging design will benefit the appliance, the customer and, of course, the manufacturer. Poor packaging design, on the other hand, is detrimental to all.

Many of the packaging processes and techniques used to house electronic assemblies (sheet metal work, casting, drilling, cutting and so on) are fairly conventional, and are described comprehensively in many other texts. Also, many metal and plastic cabinets are available off-the-shelf;

assembly manufacturers merely design the circuit board to fit the cabinets' internal mountings.

However, there are many important aspects on which details are more difficult to ascertain. Main aspects, covered in this chapter, are:

- Adhesives.
- Thermal management.
- Environmental considerations.
- Electromagnetic interference.

Adhesives

Adhesives are substances, often called glues or cements, used to stick things together. Glue is a popularly used name for adhesives, but applies particularly to animal-based products.

There are many areas in electromechanical packaging where adhesives may be used effectively. It is true to say that adhesives could be used successfully in many more applications than they currently are. But, choosing the adhesives best suited to the job is no mean feat; probably the reason why more adhesives *are not* used in many more applications. Even the adhesive manufacturers themselves find it difficult to provide straightforward and consistent guides to selecting an adhesive for any particular application – so what chance has the packaging designer got? (Saying that, at least one manufacturer, Permabond, has developed a computer program (*EASel*) to run on Apple, BBC and IBM-compatible computers to ease the problems of adhesive selection.)

The problems arise because of the wide range of families of adhesive, as well as the wide range of **adherands** – the materials to be stuck together. Adhesives suitable for one adherand may not be suitable for the other in a proposed joint. Further, adherands and adhesives perfectly matched in one type of joint may be unsuitable in another. Even after adhesives have been theoretically determined for any given pair of adherands in a joint, it still remains a trial-and-error task to discover which particular adhesive gives the best bond. Indeed, some adherands (glass, polyethylene, polypropylene, PTFE, silicone) are extremely difficult to bond, and it may prove impossible to find suitable adhesives for use in certain types of joints.

Main families of adhesives (there are many others) include:

- **Acrylics**. Although forming the base for the following two families acrylics are adhesives in their own right, particularly in toughened form. Toughened acrylics are generally two-part, that is, a catalyst must be added to cure the adhesive.
- **Anaerobics**. Adhesives in this family are often labelled *locking compounds* or *sealants*, and are typically used to lock threaded parts. They are based on acrylic resins which set in the absence of oxygen (hence their name) and in the presence of metal. High viscosity variants can be used to form gaskets.
- **Cyanoacrylates**. So-called *super glue* adhesives, cyanoacrylates harden because of the catalytic effect of adherands' surface moisture. In use,

hardening takes place in just a few seconds – so care must be taken.

- **Epoxides**. Based on epoxide resins, these adhesives usually are of two-part form although one-part, heat-cured epoxides are available, too. Toughened versions are available giving greatly increased performance.
- **Phenolics**. Based on phenol-formaldehyde resins, and one of the oldest man-made adhesives.
- **Polyurethanes**. Generally two-part, like epoxides, with similar performance but greater susceptibility to moisture.

Further, adhesives are found in many applicatory guises (emulsion, solution, powder, stick and so on) and grades within each family.

Finally, as a general guideline, Table 4.1 lists a large number of adherands and possible adhesives. This has been compiled from a range of manufacturers' data, where considerable overlap as well as disagreement exists.

Table 4.1   Adherands, with suggested adhesives

Adherand	Suggested adhesives
ABS	Cyanoacrylate, two-part epoxide, two-part polyurethane, pressure-sensitive tape, toughened acrylic two-part non-aerobic, toughened epoxide.
Butyl rubber	Cyanoacrylate, rubber solution, pressure-sensitive tape.
Cement (asbestos sheet, concrete, mortar, and so on)	Cyanoacrylate, latex emulsion, two-part epoxide, hot-melt stick, two-part phenolic, two-part polyurethane, rubber solution, pressure-sensitive tape, toughened acrylic two-part non-aerobic, toughened epoxide.
Ceramic (masonry, pottery, tiles)	Cyanoacrylate, latex emulsion, one-part epoxide, two-part epoxide, hot-melt stick, two-part polyurethane, rubber solution, pressure-sensitive tape, toughened acrylic anaerobic, toughened acrylic two-part non-aerobic, toughened epoxide.
Chloroprene rubber	Cyanoacrylate, two-part epoxide, two-part phenolic, two-part polyurethane, rubber solution, pressure-sensitive tape, toughened epoxide.
Chloro-sulphonated polyethylene rubber	Cyanoacrylate, rubber solution, pressure-sensitive tape, toughened acrylic two-part non-aerobic.
Cloth	Latex emulsion, two-part epoxide, hot-melt stick, two-part phenolic, two-part polyurethane, rubber solution, pressure-sensitive tape, toughed acrylic two-part non-aerobic, toughened epoxide.
Cyclized rubber	Cyanoacrylate, two-part epoxide, two-part phenolic, rubber solution, pressure-sensitive tape, toughened epoxide.
Epoxide (including glass reinforced)	Cyanoacrylate, one-part epoxide, two-part epoxide, two-part polyurethane, rubber solution, pressure-sensitive tape, toughened acrylic two-part non-aerobic, toughened epoxide.

Table 4.1   (cont.)

Adherand	Suggested adhesives
Fluorinated rubber	Cyanoacrylate, rubber solution, pressure-sensitive tape.
Glass	
Leather	Latex emulsion, two-part epoxide, hot-melt stick, two-part polyurethane, rubber solution, toughened epoxide.
Metal	Cyanoacrylate, latex emulsion, one-part epoxide, two-part epoxide, hot-melt stick, two-part phenolic, two-part polyurethane, rubber solution, pressure-sensitive tape, toughened acrylic anaerobic, toughened acrylic two-part non-aerobic, toughened epoxide.
Neoprene rubber	Cyanoacrylate, two-part epoxide, hot-melt stick, two-part phenolic, two-part polyurethane, rubber solution, pressure-sensitive tape, toughened epoxide.
Nitrile rubber	Cyanoacrylate, hot-melt stick, rubber solution, pressure-sensitive tape.
Paper (including board)	Cyanoacrylate, latex emulsion, two-part epoxide, hot-melt stick, two-part phenolic, two-part polyurethane, rubber solution, pressure-sensitive tape, toughened acrylic anaerobic, toughened acrylic two-part non-aerobic, toughened epoxide.
Phenolic (including laminated)	Cyanoacrylate, one-part epoxide, two-part epoxide, hot-melt stick, two-part polyurethane, rubber solution, pressure-sensitive tape, toughened acrylic two-part non-aerobic, toughened epoxide.
Polyacetal	Cyanoacrylate, two-part epoxide, two-part polyurethane, rubber solution, pressure-sensitive tape, toughened acrylic anaerobic, toughened acrylic two-part non-aerobic, toughened epoxide.
Polyacrylate	Cyanoacrylate, two-part epoxide, pressure-sensitive tape, toughened acrylic anaerobic, toughened acrylic two-part non-aerobic, toughened epoxide.
Polyalkyd	Cyanoacrylate, two-part epoxide, rubber solution, pressure-sensitive tape, toughened epoxide.
Polyalyphthalate	Cyanoacrylate, two-part epoxide, rubber solution, pressure-sensitive tape, toughened epoxide.
Polyamide	Cyanoacrylate, hot-melt stick, two-part phenolic, rubber solution, pressure-sensitive tape, toughened epoxide.
Polyamino	Cyanoacrylate, two-part epoxide, rubber solution, pressure-sensitive tape, toughened epoxide.
Polycarbonate	Two-part epoxide, hot-melt stick, two-part polyurethane, pressure-sensitive tape, toughened epoxide.
Polyester	Cyanoacrylate, one-part epoxide, two-part polyurethane, rubber solution, pressure-sensitive tape, toughened acrylic two-part non-aerobic, toughened epoxide.
Polyethylene	Two-part epoxide, rubber solution, pressure-sensitive tape, toughened epoxide.
Polyimide	Cyanoacrylate, one-part epoxide, two-part epoxide, hot-melt stick, two-part polyurethane, rubber solution, pressure-sensitive tape, toughened epoxide.

Table 4.1   (cont.)

Adherand	Suggested adhesives
Polymethyl methacrylate	Cyanoacrylate, two-part epoxide, pressure-sensitive tape, toughened acrylic anaerobic, toughened acrylic two-part non-aerobic, toughened epoxide.
Polypropylene	Two-part epoxide, rubber solution, pressure-sensitive tape, toughened epoxide.
Polystyrene	Cyanoacrylate, latex emulsion, two-part epoxide, pressure-sensitive tape, toughened epoxide.
Polysulphone	Rubber solution, pressure-sensitive tape, toughened acrylic anaerobic.
Polytetrafluoroethylene (PTFE)	Two-part epoxide, rubber solution, pressure-sensitive tape, toughened epoxide.
Polyvinylchloride (PVC)	Cyanoacrylate, rubber solution, pressure-sensitive tape, toughened acrylic two-part non-aerobic.
Polyurethane	Two-part polyurethane, pressure-sensitive tape.
Rubber (natural)	Cyanoacrylate, two-part polyurethane, rubber solution, pressure-sensitive tape.
Structural rubber	Cyanoacrylate, two-part epoxide, two-part phenolic, two-part polyurethane, rubber solution, pressure-sensitive tape, toughened epoxide.
Wood	Cyanoacrylate, latex emulsion, two-part epoxide, hot-melt stick, two-part phenolic, two-part polyurethane, rubber solution, pressure-sensitive tape, toughened acrylic anaerobic, toughened acrylic two-part non-aerobic, toughened epoxide.

If two different adherands are to be used in a joint, make sure suggested adhesives are compatible. After selection of as many adhesives as possible, tests should be performed to determine the ideal.

Standards

UK	European
Def Stan 01–6	DIN 16920

Thermal management

There is a trend towards higher packing densities on circuit boards, mainly owing to the effects of surface mount technology, but also owing to the increasing complexities of integrated circuits. Generally, the closer together components get, the warmer the assembly gets, as the same power is dissipated from a smaller area.

Where packing increases sufficiently, heat will reach the level where a number of problems arise. For instance, the components themselves may be damaged by the heat. Reliability also becomes questionable. Methods to overcome heat-related problems are classified under the banner **thermal management**, or simply **heat management** methods.

In the short-term, small heat-related problems may be (and often are) successfully tackled by using fairly simple cooling methods, such as heat-sinks or cooling fans. Use of heat-sinks and similar natural techniques is known as **passive** thermal management while *forced* heat dissipation, by cooling fans and so on, is often referred to as **active** thermal management.

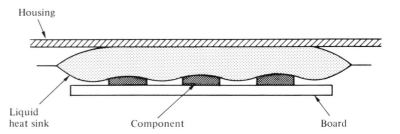

Figure 4.2 *3M's fluorinert liquid heat-sink principle*

Apart from run-of-the-mill solutions using these methods, some novel applications are available, too. One such product is a **liquid heat-sink** (LHS), comprising bags of fluid, mounted between board or substrate and the assembly's metal housing, as illustrated in Figure 4.2. The *fluorinert* system made by 3M is an example. Heat is dissipated from the components, by convection through the fluid, to the housing. Because the heat-sink conforms to the surface of the assembly, it makes thermal contact with components easily. A metal heat-sink, on the other hand, must be specifically shaped to fit the component.

Methods all rely on the fact that the medium directly in contact with the hot component will dissipate heat sufficiently, to maintain an acceptably low temperature. There are, thus, a number of variables which can all affect performance, including:

- Temperature of the component's surface.
- Ambient temperature.
- Thermal resistance of the junction between the component and the medium.
- Ability of the medium to dissipate heat.

Where the medium is metal, say, a typical heat-sink, a further variable is electrical conductance – is there a possibility of short circuits? Most methods, however, are well documented by manufacturers, and the packaging designer merely inserts the assembly's own figures into the manufacturer's formulae to obtain the solution.

As components become more complex and are more closely packed (which they inevitably will be as surface mounted technology progresses), however, such straightforward solutions may not be sufficient to guarantee acceptable thermal operation. New active techniques, therefore, have been developed to dissipate large amounts of heat, including heat exchange systems and refrigeration systems (where an evaporating liquid absorbs heat). Such drastic techniques are cumbersome and costly.

Somewhere in between, however, some relatively simple passive solutions have been recently developed to aid heat dissipation, including:

- Thermal vias.
- Base materials with good thermal conductivity.
- Thermal planes.

Thermal vias are plated-through holes in the circuit board, underneath and around a component (Figure 4.3), with the express purpose of dissipating heat away from the component through the copper track on either side of the board.

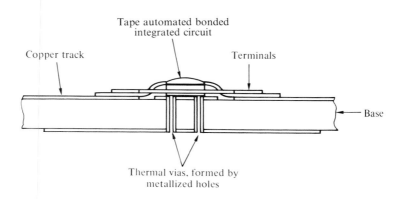

Figure 4.3 *Thermal vias under and around component can aid heat dissipation*

Most base materials in both through-hole and surface mounted assemblies are of epoxy-resin with a glass fibre reinforcement – thermal resistance of such boards is high. A solution to thermal problems can therefore be made with circuit boards made from materials which have a low thermal resistance. The board effectively acts as a heat-sink, dissipating heat from components. This solution is not, in reality, new because hybrid assemblies (that is, those with thick- or thin-film passive components and integrated circuit dice) have used thermally conductive substrates for many years. Examples include alumina, beryllia and porcelain-enamelled steel. Conventional circuit board base materials are also available, bonded around a metal sheet, forming **metal-cored** circuit boards. However, although the elegance of this solution may be appealing, hybrid-type substrates and metal-cored circuit boards are expensive.

A technique which combines the effectiveness of thermally conductive base material with that of cheapness and simplicity (Hamilton, 1987a; Printed Circuit Association, 1988) is that of the bonding of **thermal planes** to conventional circuit boards. Thermal planes are usually of copper or aluminium – copper having the lowest thermal resistance, aluminium having the lowest weight. Where matched coefficients of thermal expansion are of extreme importance, though, invar is used.

Plate 4.1 *Thermal planes, thermal bridges, and thermal modules (Enco Industries)*

Thermal planes are bonded to the component side of the circuit board. So, a plane must conform to the circuit board, in that component terminations have to be made through the plane. Chemical milling, or CNC machining, therefore, is used to machine thermal planes to fit the circuit board. Once machined, the thermal plane is bonded on to the board, using no-flow prepreg (see Chapter 2) under heat and pressure.

Design of thermal planes is usually undertaken by computer-aided **thermal path analysis** (Hamilton, 1987b). Figure 4.4(a) shows the starting point for thermal path analysis, where a single component is mounted on

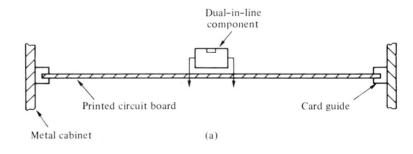

Figure 4.4 *Design of thermal planes by computer-aided thermal path analysis. (a) Starting-point; where a single component is mounted on an epoxy-resin circuit board. (b) The eighteen thermal resistances of this arrangement*

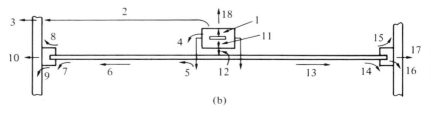

an epoxy-resin circuit board. The board is mounted in card guides, attached to a metal cabinet. The cabinet is sealed, with no cooling by convection means. The first step is to itemize all possible thermal resistances and paths in the cabinet, and show how they interact. There are, in fact, eighteen thermal resistances in the configuration shown in Figure 4.4b. These are related in four separate thermal paths, as shown in Figure 4.5. The eighteen resistances are listed along with methods of reduction in Table 4.2.

By adding a thermal plane to the configuration, as shown in Figure 4.6, thermal resistances 6, 7, 12, 13, and 14 are reduced, and so thermal conductivity of paths 3 and 4 are increased. Often, addition of a single thermal plane can aid heat dissipation sufficiently. Figure 4.6 shows the two methods of bonding thermal planes to circuit boards, such that the plane and board overlap inside the card guide (on the right in Figure 4.6) or no overlap occurs at the edge and the plane itself fits in the card guide (on the left in Figure 4.6). The left-hand side configuration provides greatest thermal conductivity.

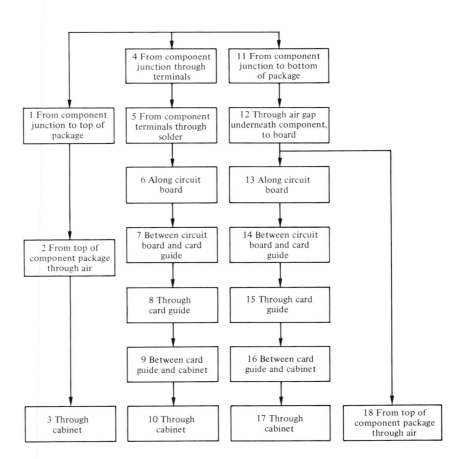

Figure 4.5 *The four thermal paths of the arrangement of Figure 4.4*

Table 4.2   Thermal resistances in the circuit board configuration of Figure 4.4

Resistance number	Description of thermal resistance	How to reduce
1	From component junction to top of package.	Inherent to component package type.
2, 18	From top of component package through air.	Use more thermally conductive medium.
3, 10, 17	Through cabinet.	Make cabinet of high thermally conductive medium.
4	From component junction through terminals.	Inherent to component package type.
5	From component terminals through solder.	Inherent to solder.
6, 13	Along circuit board.	Replace with, or add, thermally conductive medium.
7, 14	Between circuit board and card guide.	Ensure high pressure contact over largest possible area.
8, 15	Through card guide.	Use thermally conductive card guide.
9, 16	Between card guide and cabinet.	Ensure high pressure fixing, or integrate card guide and cabinet.
11	From component junction to bottom of package.	Inherent to package type.
12	Through air gap, underneath component, to board.	Fill air gap with thermally conductive medium.

If small numbers of components' temperatures are still too high, however, there are two further enhancements which may be made to the configuration. First, a **thermal bridge** (patented by Enco) may be added, over an individual component, to channel the heat from the top of that component down to the thermal plane, as shown in Figure 4.7(a). The annealed legs of the extruded thermal bridge deform easily so that the bridge comes into direct thermal contact with the top of the component. In this way, thermal resistance 2 is reduced, increasing thermal conductivity of path 1.

Thermal bridges may be used in another way – to protect a thermally sensitive component, by ensuring the thermal path of the plane bypasses

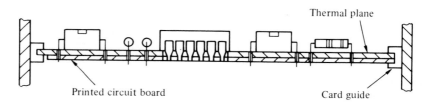

Figure 4.6 *Adding a thermal plane*

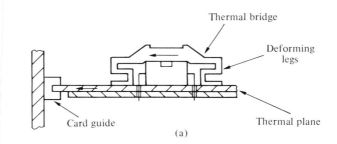

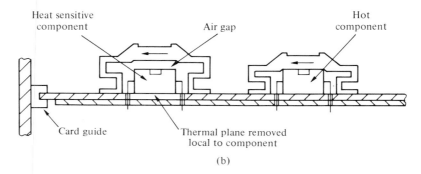

Figure 4.7 *Thermal bridges. (a) Principle of heat dissipation from a hot component. (b) Bypassing a heat-sensitive component*

the component, as shown in Figure 4.7(b). The thermal plane is removed (that is, machined prior to bonding) from underneath the component, but to ensure a thermal path still exists, the thermal bridge takes the path over the top of the component. An air gap is left between the component and the thermal bridge to ensure thermal insulation.

The second enhancement of the thermal plane to ensure individual component temperatures remain sufficiently low is the **thermal module**, as shown in Figure 4.8. Here the module forms a thermal bridge over a number of components (rather than just one) and **thermal springs** (made of beryllium copper). Thermal resistances 2 and 3 are lowered, increasing thermal conductivity of path 1.

Thermal modules are particularly useful in the case of surface mounted assemblies (where thermal planes cannot be placed underneath components). In such cases (Figure 4.9) heat dissipation may only be from above the component.

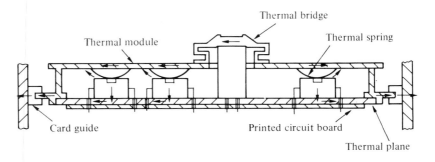

Figure 4.8 *Principle of the thermal module*

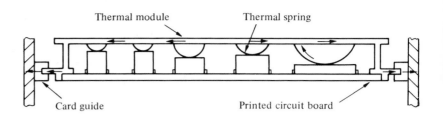

Figure 4.9 *Thermal modules used in surface mount assemblies, where heat dissipation can only be from above the component*

Environmental considerations

Some consideration must be given in design of any electromechanical packaging arrangement to the environment the appliance will be subjected to after it leaves the production line. Environments can have considerable effects, generally on assemblies within a housing but sometimes, too, on the housing itself, as well as connectors and leads. Generally, environmental protection is required in two areas: where corrosion or wear may occur; and where mechanical stress may occur.

Sometimes, the environment may not be that which the appliance was designed for. Where users subject the appliance to a **hostile environment**, which was not specified in the design brief, the manufacturer may rightly say that the user is to blame. But handling and transportation even, both manufacturers' concerns, may cause damage, too.

Environmental protection of cabinets and housings

In most instances, surfaces of cabinets and housings are protected by one or more of a number of methods against corrosion. In some instances, however, improvements in cabinet or housing surfaces are sought in terms of resistance to wear, electrical insulation or conductivity, thermal dissipation, or simply colour. Methods of protecting or improving surfaces of cabinets or housings are usually known as **finishes**. Finishes depend largely on the material to be protected or improved. To this end, most cabinets or housings are of only a few basic types: aluminium or aluminium alloy; ferrous metal; organic (plastic or wood).

Aluminium or aluminium alloy finishes

There are a large number of aluminium or aluminium alloy finishes, including:

- Aluminium, where an aluminium alloy is susceptible to corrosion, coatings of sprayed aluminium may be used to protect the alloy. The coating may need to be regularly renewed.
- Anodizing. Aluminium or aluminium alloys may be anodized to give a high level of corrosion protection. Aluminium anodized layers are electrically insulating.
- Blackening. This is an anodizing process which creates a black anodized layer.

- Plating. Aluminium may be plated with a number of metals (gold, tin, tin/lead, nickel, rhodium, silver) by conventional plating techniques, although electroless nickel plating is usually required initially.
- Zinc spraying. Used, like aluminium spraying, on aluminium alloys which are susceptible to corrosion.

Table 4.3 lists these finishes, together with characteristics relating to use.

Table 4.3 Aluminium and aluminium alloy finishes

Finish	Corrosion resistance	Abrasion resistance	Electrical conductivity
Aluminium and aluminium alloy (untreated)	3	4	2
Aluminium spraying	1	3	5
Anodizing	1	1	5
Blackening	2	2	5
Gold plating	3	3	2
Nickel plating	3	1	2
Rhodium plating	3	1	2
Silver plating	4	3	1
Zinc spraying	1	3	5

Note: Characteristics are recorded in descending scales of 1 to 5, that is, 1 is good, 5 is poor.

Ferrous metal finishes

Generally, ferrous metals require corrosion protection finishes. Certain stainless steels, however (not all), do not require finishing for corrosion protection purposes, although may still be finished for electrical or optical reasons. The main finishes for ferrous metals are:

- Aluminium spraying. See earlier section on aluminium and aluminium alloy finishes.
- Galvanizing, that is, dipping the ferrous metal in molten zinc.
- Phosphate treatment followed by a suitable number of coats of paint.
- Plating, generally of cadmium, chromium or zinc (although many metals may be plated).
- Zinc spraying. See earlier section on aluminium and aluminium alloy finishes.

Table 4.4 lists these finishes, together with characteristics relating to use.

Organic material finishes

Plastic and wood cabinets and housings are typically finished only to improve electrical conductivity for electromagnetic screening purposes,

Table 4.4   Ferrous metal finishes

Finish	Corrosion resistance	Abrasion resistance	Electrical conductivity
Aluminium spraying	1	4	4
Cadmium plating	2	3	2
Chromium plating	2	2	3
Corrosion-resisting steel	1	2	3
Galvanizing	2	4	3
Phosphate treatment and painting	1	5	5
Zinc plating	2	4	3

Note: Characteristics are recorded in descending scales of 1 to 5, that is, 1 is good, 5 is poor.

although improvements in solderability, heat dissipation, chemical resistance and mechanical properties may also result. Main methods of finishing include:

- Cathodic sputtering.
- Conductive paints.
- Electroless plating followed by conventional plating.
- Metal spraying.
- Vacuum evaporation of metals.

Environmental protection of assemblies and components

Assemblies and components may be subjected to either a corrosive environment or a mechanically stressful environment.

Effects of one or both of these environments may be reduced to acceptable levels (though never eliminated) by **encapsulating** assemblies. Assembly encapsulation is a generic term referring to techniques using resin-like materials to package the assembly. There are four main methods of encapsulation:

- Conformal coating.
- Embedding.
- Impregnation.
- Potting.

Conformal coating

By far the most common method of encapsulation, **conformal coating**, sometimes called **surface coating** or **surface sealing**, uses thin (between 0.005 mm to 0.075 mm) transparent coats of materials to provide an electrically insulating protective barrier against humidity, dirt, vaporous contaminants, and foreign bodies such as metal filings. Fully assembled

Plate 4.2 *Conformal dip coating machine (Electrolube)*

printed circuit boards are often conformally coated to help protect them during normal operating conditions, where hostile environments are not envisaged.

Typical coating materials include:

- Acrylic.
- Epoxy.
- Oleo resin.
- Parazylylene.
- Polystyrene.
- Polyurethane.
- Silicone.
- Silicone rubber.

Of these, acrylic, epoxy, polyurethane and silicone are the most common. A summary of the main characteristics of these four conformal coating types are listed in Table 4.5. When selecting a coating, the known use and environment of the assembly must be carefully considered. Manufacturers' precautions should be followed, and safety precautions regarding vapours and toxic materials observed.

Conformal coatings also may be applied to individual components, or subassemblies, in the case of, say, hybrid assemblies to be mounted on a through-hole printed circuit board. In this case, the conformal coating is to protect the subassembly during later processes, such as soldering, in the assembly's production.

Application of conformal coatings is usually by brushing, dipping, flow coating or spraying. Paraxylylene, is an exception, as it is applied by vapour phase deposition technique under vacuum. Note that application of a conformal coating by spraying may cause damage to electrostatically sensitive components.

It is sometimes thought that conformal coatings aid mechanical strength

Table 4.5   Summarized characteristics of the four main conformal coating types

Characteristic	Acrylic	Epoxy	Polyurethane	Silicone
Abrasion resistance	3	1	2	2
Acid resistance	1	1	3	2
Alkali resistance	1	1	3	2
Application ease	1	3	2	3
Cure time	1	4[1]	3[2]	4
Humidity resistance:				
short-term	1	2	1	1
long-term	2	3	1	2
Mechanical strength	3	1	2	2
Pot-life	1	4	2	4
Removal:				
burn	1	3	2	–
chemical	1	5	3	5
Solvent resistance	5	1	2	2
Temperature resistance	5	5	5	2

Notes: Characteristics are recorded in descending scales of 1 to 5, that is, 1 is good, 5 is poor.
[1]   Reduced to 3 if heat-cured.
[2]   Reduced to 2 if heat-cured.

and thermal insulation, providing protection against stresses such as vibration or thermal shock, but this is not true, and other encapsulation methods must be used where such stresses are envisaged.

Conformal coatings do, on the other hand, allow a measure of protection against damp environments, and where occasional condensation is met conformally coated assemblies may function satisfactorily. But where constantly damp environments are encountered, conformal coatings are not suitable.

Embedding

An **embedding** process completely envelopes an assembly or component within a protective material not less than 6 mm thick, filling free space in the assembly. A mould or container is required to confine the encapsulating material while hardening, after which the embedded assembly is released from the mould. The result is a self-contained assembly module.

Usually, mould-releasing agents are used to treat a mould prior to embedding an assembly, so that once cured, the embedded assembly can be easily released. Exceptions to this are where moulds are made of materials such as polythene or PTFE. These are self-releasing. Mould release agents may be non-drying liquid, or dry-film forms. Liquid forms may migrate to areas which require bonding, so as a rule-of-thumb, dry-film forms are normally preferred.

Impregnation

Impregnation methods rely on the injection of a material into all intervening spaces or voids of components to provide environmental protection. Impregnation may be used alone, or together with other methods of encapsulation.

Potting

Potting is an embedding method where the encapsulating material bonds to the mould or container becoming integral with the item. Release from the mould is therefore not wished for.

Encapsulation design considerations

Choice of encapsulation method depends on a number of factors, such as the need for later repair of assemblies. Where embedded, potted or impregnated encapsulation methods are used, assemblies generally cannot be repaired and must be considered expendable. Costly components, or components likely to fail and require repair or replacement therefore must not be embedded, potted or impregnated within such an encapsulated assembly. Within limits, however, conformally coated assemblies *can* be repaired.

Whatever encapsulation method is chosen, the necessity of a clean assembly is vital. There is little point in encapsulating an assembly to protect it, say, against corrosion, if contaminants in the form of flux, grease moisture and so on, are present. The topic of cleaning assemblies is covered in detail in Chapter 5.

Similarly, encapsulating materials and processes must be compatible with assemblies – any material or process which causes damage in any way to an assembly is self-defeating. A number of factors must be borne in mind here, including:

- Circuit change caused by encapsulation. Tuned, high impedance, or high frequency circuits may be significantly degraded by encapsulation.
- Chemical damage to components. Cleaning chemicals may damage certain components. Similarly, curing agents in the encapsulating materials may cause damage.
- Differential expansion. Thin-film carbon or metal resistors may expand so much as to cause a breakage in a conformal coating.
- Electrostatic discharge. Certain resins under mechanical stresses such as vibration generate voltages which may be large enough to damage electrostatically sensitive components.
- Fragile components. Stresses may occur as resins cure and these may be large enough to damage certain components, say, glass enveloped diodes.
- Heat-sensitive components. Curing resins may generate exothermic heat which raises the local temperature above the maximum specified for certain components.

- Lack of adhesion between encapsulation and assembly materials. Most encapsulation materials do not adhere to materials such as polythylene and PTFE.
- Thermal dissipation. There are two areas for concern. First, a component's effective thermal dissipation may be decreased by encapsulation, causing damage to the component. Second, dissipation from a component may be sufficient to damage the encapsulating material.

Standards

UK	European
BS 729	DIN group 3320
BS 1706	
BS 2569	
BS 4921	
BS 4950	
BS 5917	
BS 6221	
BS 6918	
Def Stan 00–7	
Def Stan 00–10	
Def Stan 00–29	
Def Stan 00–35	
Def Stan 00–50	
Def Stan 03–3	
Def Stan 03–5	
Def Stan 03–7	
Def Stan 03–8	
Def Stan 03–9	
Def Stan 03–10	
Def Stan 03–13	
Def Stan 03–20	
Def Stan 03–26	
Def Stan 59–47	

Electromagnetic compatability

Any electrical or electronic appliance should be able to operate without causing electromagnetic interference, and without being affected by electromagnetic interference. This concept of **electromagnetic compatability** has not had much legal binding in Europe. However, a directive currently in negotiation looks set to change all that within the next couple of years. Manufacturers of all electrical and electronic appliances will be required to ensure their products' electromagnetic compatibilities are within defined limits.

Packaging considerations

Electromagnetic interference (EMI) is, with a few notable exceptions, a totally man-made form of noise. Being man-made it is normally possible, therefore, to devise ways of reducing its effects to an acceptable, if not negligible, level. In theory, at least, we need only understand what electromagnetic interference is and what causes it to be able to formulate techniques to control it.

In practice, of course, life is not that simple. Electromagnetic interference is not easy, if at all possible, to predict at the design stage. Only when the appliance is fully built can a measurement be taken, so any action can only be corrective – not preventive – there is no perfect way of predicting electromagnetic interference. Further, there is only a limited number of corrective procedures which may be effectively and economically employed – if the appliance emits electromagnetic interference to a level which cannot be corrected by these, nothing else can be done to help.

Electromagnetic interference can be considered as being interference in the classic sense, that is, noise generated by a noise source, picked up by a noise victim, via a noise path (Figure 4.10). The noise path can be any form of transmission media. Consequently, there are three main points at which EMI can be reduced: at the noise source, in the noise path or at the noise victim. The problem, however, is that it is often difficult to differentiate between the three parts.

Figure 4.10 *Electromagnetic interference is generated by a noise source, picked up by a noise victim, via a noise path*

There are a number of main causes of electromagnetic interference, including:

- Radio transmitters. The ether is full of radio transmissions at frequencies from just a few kilohertz upto several gigahertz. These are at varying levels of saturation. Obviously, the greater the saturation, the greater the risk of significant electromagnetic interference taking place. At levels below $100\,\text{mVm}^{-1}$ there is negligible risk of interference. Between $100\,\text{mVm}^{-1}$ and $3\,\text{Vm}^{-1}$ there is a risk of interference, depending on the physical dimensions of the victim equipment. At levels above $3\,\text{Vm}^{-1}$ there is significant risk from electromagnetic interference.
- Non-radio, high frequency generators. Many items of electrical equipment are sources of high frequency electromagnetic interference. Computers, arc welders, microwave ovens etc., can generate electromagnetic interference by radiated and/or conductive means, and so are potential noise sources. Major sources of this sort of electromagnetic interference are clock-driven circuits, in the 30 to 200 MHz frequency range, and switched-mode power supplies with switching frequencies of 0.5 to 1.5 MHz.

- Electrostatic discharge. One of the main culprits of electrostatic discharge is the pure man-made carpet: simply walking over a carpet can create a static potential in the human body which will discharge as the person touches equipment maintained at a different potential. The situation is aggravated in dry atmospheres.
- Lightning. A lightning strike creates a huge electromagnetic field, which may induce voltage surges in power and communications lines.
- Transient electromagnetic interference sources. There is a vast range of sources such as dimmer switches, fluorescent lights, power tools, car engines, power supplies, all of which can act as interference sources.
- Power line interference. AC mains voltage is usually only nominal, minor and long-lived variations of up to $\pm 10\%$ are common. Transient spikes may also occur owing to the previous two electromagnetic interference sources.

An important point in all of these causes, is that electromagnetic interference falls into one of only two types: radiated or communicated. The methods to reduce electromagnetic interference, therefore, fall into one of only two corresponding categories.

Radiated EMI – reduction by screening

Primary prevention of radiated electromagnetic interference is always sought through the use of a grounded, or earthed, conductive enclosure: a **screen**, sometimes called a **shield**. (**Grounding** refers to the electrical connection, that is, **bonding**, of an electronic assembly or part of an assembly to a point of common potential. **Earthing** refers to bonding to the earth's common potential.)

A screen is typically in the form of a metal box, to house the potential victim, or potential source. Steel enclosures have better absorption loss than aluminium or copper for thicknesses above 1 mm. Below 1 mm thick, copper or aluminium have similar qualities. Enclosures which provide some 90 dB or so of electromagnetic interference attenuation are possible, and provide the ultimate in interference protection.

Ideally, the enclosure should be continuous, without holes, connectors or seams. Outside electromagnetic interference radiation can then not pass in through the enclosure to the victim inside; and, likewise, cannot pass out through the enclosure from a source inside. However, such an ideal enclosure is impossible in practice. Ventilation holes, cable-through holes, connectors, controls and so on, are always needed, and of necessity must pass through the enclosure, providing breaks in the shielding through which interference may pass.

So, usual steps to ensure maximum possible electromagnetic interference prevention is obtained with a metal enclosure are to:

- Make sure all through-holes are as small as possible, preferably using correctly sized cable glands.
- Use perforated grids to cover ventilation holes.

- Ensure all joints in the enclosure are adequately seamed, and allow good electrical bonding.
- Where covers are electrically separate (say, a painted metal box with separate lid is used) use braided copper jumpers bolted to both cover and main frame.
- Where covers are electrically joined, use conductive gaskets to ensure adequate sealing.

In the case of severe electromagnetic interference radiation, use a grid with perforation holes no greater than 2 mm in diameter, and ensure several copper jumpers are used, where the spaces between them never exceed one tenth the wavelength of the expected interference. So if the potential interference is known to be around a frequency of 27 MHz then jumpers should be no further apart than about a metre. If the interference is around 300 MHz than jumpers should be less than 10 cm apart.

In many cases a metal enclosure is unsuitable – for aesthetic or cost reasons, may be. Several electromagnetic interference reducing procedures can be followed when plastic or wood enclosures are used, fortunately. Plastic and wood provide no shielding whatsoever, of course, against EMI; so the procedures generally try to incorporate an internal screen of some description.

Plastic boxes are now available which are coated at manufacture stage with a metal acrylic layer, effectively allowing good screening (between 50 and 90 dB depending on interference frequency), with a good appearance and still cheap.

Aerosol sprays exist, which allow the user to incorporate a metallized conductive coating on to the inside of plastic enclosures. Electromagnetic interference attentuation up to about 50 dB is possible.

Alternative procedures usually incorporate internal screens over parts of the equipment: either over parts prone to electromagnetic interference pickup (printed circuit boards, cables), or over radiating parts (power supplies, cathode ray tubes and so on).

These internal screens and, indeed, full metal enclosures benefit from good seaming techniques, as shown in Figure 4.11 to ensure that electromagnetic interference does not pass through the seam itself.

Figure 4.11 *Seaming techniques to ensure adequate screening*

Cabling techniques

Much EMI can be caused by incorrect cabling within the enclosure. Electromagnetic interference in this context is simple crosstalk: radiation from one cable to another. This may be from one part of the system to another, or may be owing to external interference entering the equipment through cable inlets.

The first step is to organize all cables into three distinct groups:

- Power cables, carrying mains voltages. These are potential interference sources.
- DC control and power cables. These can be electromagnetic interference sources *or* victims.
- Signal and logic cables. These are generally interference victims, but may be sources, too.

Next, cables in the three groups must be routed round the equipment separately, and as far away from each other as space allows.

If signal and logic cables run parallel to cables of the other two groups (it is on parallel runs that crosstalk will be maximum), make sure that distances apart are at a maximum. As a rule-of-thumb allow a space of 25 mm between digital cables and power cables for every metre of parallel run. Similarly, ensure that analog signal cables are 250 mm away from power cables, for every metre of parallel run.

Where cables of more than one group enter the enclosure, separate entry holes must be made, and cable routes outside the equipment should follow the same separation techniques just prescribed.

Figure 4.12 *Interference and cable entries. (a) Even with screened cable, electromagnetic interference can enter a screened enclosure. (b) Method of ensuring interference does not enter*

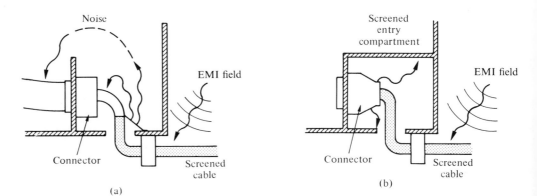

(a)

(b)

Regarding cable entries, it should not be assumed that outside radiated electromagnetic interference cannot enter the enclosure along the cable itself – even if the cable itself is screened. Figure 4.12(a) shows how radiated electromagnetic interference can enter the enclosure through the cable screen, while Figure 4.12(b) shows a method of cable entry which prevents this.

Cables carrying low-level digital or analog signals fall into three main wire types: ribbon cable, coaxial cable and twisted pair. In all, each signal wire should have its own return running beside it, thus reducing signal loop area. (The larger the loop area, the greater the risk of interference by inductive coupling.)

Types of cable

Figure 4.13 shows how signal wires within a ribbon cable should, ideally, have grounded wires between. The grounded wires create the effect of a screen between the various signals – reducing potential crosstalk.

Coaxial cable effectively allows an electrostatic screen or shield, much like the screen afforded by a metal enclosure. In many cases it can be extremely useful in reducing the effects of electromagnetic interference. However, problems – worse than the original interference – can occur if care is not taken. To work correctly, the screen must have zero resistance to ground; in this way any coupled electromagnetic interference is effectively shorted directly to ground. If, however, the screen has a finite resistance to ground (which is always the case when a long connecting lead is used between remote parts of a system – purely because the cable has resistance) then the electromagnetic interference will generate a noise voltage between the screen and true ground. Resultant interference may even be worse than without coaxial cable. With short lengths of screened coaxial connecting cable this is not usually a problem, however.

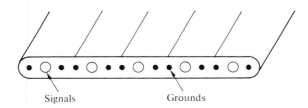

Figure 4.13 *Signal wires in a ribbon cable should be separated by grounded wires to reduce crosstalk*

Signals   Grounds

Interference may also be caused by sloppy use of coaxial cable, on the other hand, if the use of the term 'ground' is not fully understood. Figure 4.14 shows a transducer connected to an amplifier by coaxial cable, in which the cable's screen is grounded at the tranducer and at the amplifier. Grounding, however, is not a guarantee that voltage at two different ground points will be identical. If even just a tiny difference in potential between the two ground points exists then a current will flow along the screen, itself causing interference. This situation is known as a **ground loop**, or an **earth loop** where the ground is at earth potential. As a rule of thumb, when coaxial cable is used to connect low frequency parts (that is, less than,

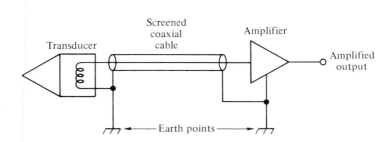

Transducer   Screened coaxial cable   Amplifier

Amplified output

Figure 4.14 *Grounding separate parts of a system may create a ground loop*

Earth points

say, 1 MHz) of a system the screen should be grounded at only one end (generally the transmitting end) of the cable run. Above this, however, coaxial cable should be grounded at both ends of the cable run.

Figure 4.15 shows a twisted pair, in which each signal wire runs with its return. These can be highly effective against electromagnetic interference produced in differential mode or balanced analog circuits, but is virtually useless in common mode circuits. The protection against electromagnetic interference is given simply because interference voltages induced in each turn of the twisted wire pair are equal and hence cancel each other out.

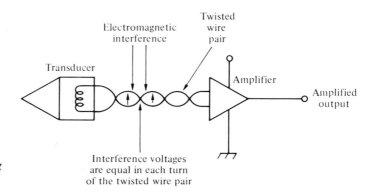

Figure 4.15 *Twisted pairs of wires can be effective in reducing interference*

Printed circuit board techniques

Many of the techniques used in electromagnetic interference reduction through cable routing and use can be adopted when designing circuit boards. Printed circuit board is, after all, just a connecting method between components of the system.

For example, ground loops can occur in analog circuits where two or more amplifying stages are in series (Figure 4.16(a)). The problem is that the two separate ground points may have slightly different potentials, and a noise current will flow – even if the two ground points are formed by the same conductor which may be a single piece of printed circuit track. In low amplification circuits this will probably cause few problems, but high amplification circuits will be unstable. The only solution is to provide a common grounding point for all parts of the circuit, as shown in Figure 4.16(b).

Circuits which require a high impedance input stage are more prone to crosstalk than low impedance circuits, so if a high impedance input is necessary the guard ring approach may be useful. Here, the high impedance amplifier is configured as a non-inverting buffer amplifier (Figure 4.17) in which the amplifier's output impedance is much lower than that of its input. The guard ring is linked to the amplifier's output, so that it forms a low resistance path to electromagnetic interference signals.

On power supply printed circuit boards, ripple and high frequency noise

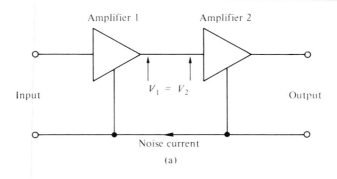

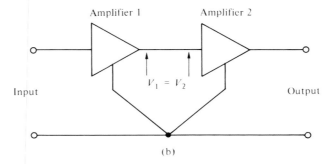

Figure 4.16 *Interference reducing techniques applied to printed circuit boards. (a) Separate ground point may cause ground loops. (b) Common grounding points will help prevent this*

can be reduced if connections are made as large as possible, using copper planes rather than individual tracks. This has the added benefit of making the circuit board slightly cheaper (less copper has to be removed at the etching stage).

Generally, and particularly on signal boards, it is advisable also to leave copper on any unused areas of board. These can then be grounded.

Communicated EMI – reduction by filters

Where electromagnetic interference reaches the victim through cables, as opposed to being radiated, the only real solution is to filter out the interference signal. Generally, electromagnetic interference will be in the

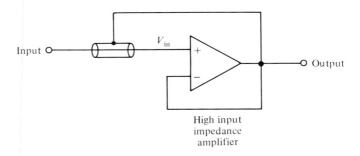

Figure 4.17 *Use of a guard ring, to provide a low resistance path for interference signals*

Plate 4.3 *D-type connector with internal interference filter (ITT)*

form of voltage spikes and transients on AC mains, power input leads, so the obvious course of action is to install a filter at the input to the equipment, and various types exist. Neatest are the chassis-mounted plug units, although many surface-mounted filters exist. Electromagnetic interference attenuation up to about 60 dB is a feature.

Mains filters have the double benefit of attenuating noise produced within a system, attenuating the level of electromagnetic interference going into the mains, thus reducing the likelihood of interference with other equipment, too. National regulations covering electromagnetic interference produced by equipment may necessitate the use of such filters. Low-level signal connectors may also be fitted with filters.

Transients spikes and surges on the AC power lead may reach peaks much higher than equipment can cope with, and filters cannot dissipate the extra energy which thus occurs. Suppressors must be used if large over-voltages are expected. Two main types are available: gas discharge tube arrestors and varistors. The former is connected across the input and under usual conditions remains open circuit. However, if the input voltage exceeds a sparkover voltage the gas inside the device becomes ionized and effectively short circuits the supply, until the surge ends.

The varistor clamps the AC power supply voltage to a preset value, rather like a zener diode does for DC supplies.

Standards

UK	IEC	USA	European
BS G100	CISPR11 to 23	ANSI C63	DIN VG95370
BS 613	IEC53	Mil Std461	DIN VG95371
BS 800	IEC315	Mil Std462	DIN VG95373
BS 905	IEC801	Mil E6051	DIN VG95374
BS 6527			DIN VG95375
BS 6667			DIN VG95376
Def Stan 59–41			DIN VG95377

References

Hamilton, Sheila, *Bonding Thermal Planes to PCBs*, Electronic Production, February 1987a.

Hamilton, Sheila, *Developments in Passive Thermal Management Systems for Electronics*, Printed Circuit World Convention IV, June 1987b.

Printed Circuit Association, *Cost-effective PCB Design*, Electronic Production, April 1988.

Samtec Electronics, *Samtec's Complete Interconnect Pocket Guide*, Scotland: Samtec Electronics.

5 Soldering

Soldering, in principle, is a reasonably straightforward process, used in the electronics industry to bond components together, forming one or more electrical connections. From this description, it is easy to see that soldering serves two functions:

- Mechanical support, holding the components of an assembly together.
- Electrical support, forming the required electrical connections of a circuit.

Most components in an assembly use the mechanical support of soldered joints alone to give adequate fixing into the assembly. A few isolated components (notably, larger, heavier components) may require additional mechanical support, such as straps, nuts and bolts, and so on.

On the other hand, all components may use solder as electrical support to form required electrical connections. No other method has yet been devised to take the place of solder in all assemblies to the same level of performance.

Changing face

For many years, soldering of assemblies has been undertaken by only one main form of soldering. Emergence of surface mounted assemblies, however, is altering the face of electronics assembly. So much is surface mount technology changing soldering that, at present, somewhere around 50% of all electronics assemblies use at least a few surface mounted components. Ten years ago this figure was, to all practical purposes, zero.

The change in assembly technology has only been possible with development of a change in soldering technology.

Soldering is unique in that it provides the two functions listed earlier cheaply and easily. Solders used for electronics assembly melt at temperatures around 185°C or so, therefore simple equipment (a soldering iron) can be used to create soldered **joints**. Joints are formed by metallic bonds between the metals (usually the copper track of a circuit board and component leads) and the solder. Solder is an alloy, usually of tin and lead (although other alloys can be used, and selected impurities may be added to a conventional tin/lead solder to create changes in properties, as required), which melts at a lower temperature than either of the metals to be joined – this means that joints can be made to metals which form the leads of otherwise quite fragile components. Further, the reasonably low melting point means that many joints may be soldered at the same time with little fear of damaging components.

Solder only adheres to certain surfaces, usually metallic, and does not adhere to insulating surfaces – this means that solder may be applied in excess. The alternatives to soldering – welding, conductive adhesives – require much more complex equipment. In the case of welding, the greater heat required to create a welded joint precludes welding many joints en masse. Even welding joints consecutively may damage the component being welded. In the case of conductive adhesives, accuracy is extremely important – adhesive will adhere to conductors and insulators alike.

In electronics assembly, by far the most typical of soldered joints is in printed circuit assembly, when component leads are soldered to the copper track of the board. Such a typical joint is illustrated, in cross-section, in Figure 5.1, where a component lead projects through a plated-through hole in the board and is bonded to the copper with solder. Note that, in this ideal joint, solder has been drawn inside the hole during the soldering operation. The solder between the copper track and the component lead is called the fillet.

Requirements of the soldering process

There are a few important points to be understood when studying the soldering process, considered here.

In its simplest form, soldering is uncomplicated. Production of a soldered joint requires only that the parts to be soldered are positioned to remain relatively immobile. The surfaces are then heated to allow wetting with molten solder, and the solder is allowed to cool and solidify.

Flux

In most cases, a substance called flux is used in the process, primarily to clean the surfaces to be soldered and so aid wetting. However clean they

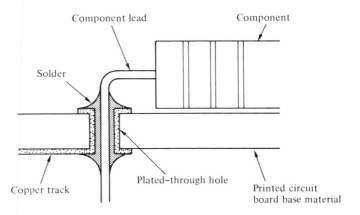

Figure 5.1 *A typical soldered joint of a through-hole printed circuit board*

are, all metals (with the exception of the noble metals) oxidize to form an oxide layer on their surfaces. Other tarnish products may occur, too. Presence of any tarnish layer will prevent wetting. Flux reacts with the tarnish layers, leaving a pure base metal surface for the solder to wet. A secondary function of the flux is to reduce the solder's surface tension, so increasing the solder fluidity and aiding wetting.

Heat

Application of heat is a prime requirement of the soldering process: the solder has a melting point of, typically, around 185°C. So, to enable its application, the solder has to be heated to at least this temperature. This can be done by either heating the joint before the solid solder is applied, or by heating the solder until molten before application to the joint. It is not a prerequisite that the *joint* be heated although, for convenience, it often is.

Wetting

Wetting is the process in soldering where the solder comes into direct metallic contact with the metals to be soldered together into a joint, forming a specific alloy of solder and metal at the junction. In turn, this implies that the joint's metallic surfaces be so clean that metallic contact can be made.

Often, the term *intermetallic* is used to describe the bond which occurs between solder and metal when the solder wets the metal (as in *intermetallic bond*). This is incorrect: it is, in fact, a strict metallurgic term referring to *intermetallic compounds*, compounds of elements whose atoms have an extremely high affinity for each other – so high an affinity that their presence denies bonding of other elements by other means. To appreciate the difference between intermetallic compounds and alloys it is important to realize that intermetallic compounds have fixed stoichiometric ratios. Alloys, on the other hand, have ratios of metals which can vary.

Wetting occurs when solder comes into intimate contact with the metal atoms. If the metal surface is perfectly clean and metal atoms are present, then the solder wets the metal, forming a bond with the metal atoms at the interface (Figure 5.2). Once this interfacing bond, an intermetallic compound as it happens, has been created it cannot be removed.

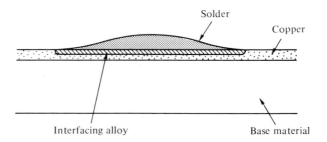

Figure 5.2 *Wetting occurs when solder comes into intimate contact with the metal surface atoms*

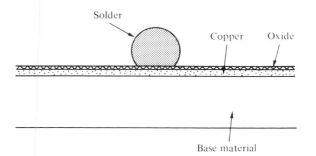

Figure 5.3 *Wetting cannot occur if the surface of the metal is unclean, say, oxidized*

If, on the other hand, the metal is unclean in any way, say, it is oxidized (Figure 5.3) such that metal atoms are not present on the surface, then wetting cannot occur – in a similar way to which a drop of water on a greasy surface will remain as a droplet.

In context with the wetting of metals, two other terms need to be defined. The first is **non-wetting**, where part or all of the metal to be soldered is devoid of solder. Usually this occurs where a contaminant or oxide has been left on the metal surface, so preventing the necessary alloy bond between metal and solder layer. The second is **dewetting**, where the alloy bond has occurred, but where the solder withdraws from the metal and forms dispersed, irregular droplets. Further solder cannot accumulate owing to the high surface tension formed. Where dewetting occurs, it is sometimes difficult to determine. A simple visual check may not show it.

Both of these problems are usually caused by lack of cleanliness, although dewetting can also occur when large amounts of intermetallic compounds form.

Cleaning

There are two areas in which cleaning may need to take place in the soldering process. First, the metallic surfaces to be soldered together must be perfectly clean, in order that solder can wet the metals involved. Second, the residues left after soldering may need to be removed. These may be separated, and termed **pre-assembly** and **post-assembly cleaning**.

Another pre-assembly area where cleaning is important, often out of the hands of the assembler, is cleanliness during board manufacture. Where an assembler simply buys in ready-made boards, problems of cleanliness during manufacture may be difficult to isolate, and even more difficult to eliminate.

Solderability and protective coatings

One of the most important terms in the subject of soldering, is **solderability**: the ability of a metal to be completely wet by solder. In other words, it refers to how well and how uniform the interfacing alloy bond between solder and metal is made.

It follows that solderability is concerned with *every* aspect of the soldering process (that is, wetting, fluxing, heating, cleaning), and the main aspects of board manufacture, too (that is, copper plating tin/lead plating, solder resist application). Further, solderability generally decreases with age, as tarnishing of the metals involved occurs naturally in normal atmosphere.

One of the major problems of guaranteeing adequate solderability is the difficulty in measuring exactly what solderability is. Not so very long ago, solder joint quality (and hence, solderability of the metals involved) was determined by an over-simple visual check: the joint's brightness and smoothness was thought an indicator of joint quality. However, modern joints on surface mounted assemblies, are rarely bright, and never smooth, yet are known to be joints of perfect quality.

Solder joint quality can never be determined by appearance of the outside layer of the solder. Actual quality is determined by what has happened at the interface between the solder and the metal. As this is impossible to view, visual inspection serves little purpose in assuring joint quality. More cohesive tests for solderability and for joint quality are discussed in Chapter 6.

Once a board is known to have an acceptable solderability, it is usual to coat it with a substance, in an attempt to maintain solderability. This is only an *attempt*, note, as no coating can maintain solderability indefinitely. The extent to which solderability decreases under storage conditions depends primarily on the protective coating used, but also on the storage conditions and the thicknesses of coatings, so estimates of solderable lifespans, that is, shelf-life, can only be approximate. Boards should be re-tested for solderability after each period, say, three months, of storage.

Although the addition of such **protective coatings** is specifically a manufacturing process, it is covered in this chapter for sake of completeness; as we shall see soon, in most cases the protective coating is of solder form. In the remaining few cases, however, organic compound and precious metal coatings are used.

Organic compounds

Two types of organic compounds are used:

- Monomolecular lacquers.
- Resin-based (see later section on *flux*).

These compounds have an approximate solderable lifespan of about three months (monomolecular) and six months (resin-based). Resin-based coatings give the advantage of aiding fluxing when the assembly is soldered. Lacquers will be dispersed by the soldering process.

Thickness is fairly important: too thin and susceptibility to damage or low shelf-life will result: too thick and coatings may crack or blister with the same result. A disadvantage, the reason for their limited use, is the fact that they are hygroscopic, so absorbing water, which with time will reach the metal underneath, causing oxidation.

The advantage of such coatings is their relative low cost. As long as the circuit board is to be used rapidly after storage, they can prove quite economical.

Metallic layers

Two forms of metallic layer are used to protectively coat circuit boards:

- Precious metal plating (gold, rhodium, platinum, palladium).
- Tin/lead alloy coating.

Precious metals are often used to protect edge-connection terminals of a circuit board. Their low oxidation rates and metallic softness help to ensure that push-on contacts maintain an adequate low resistance. Occasionally they are used to maintain solderability, however. Shelf-life of precious metal coated boards is up to twelve months. Thickness should be between $0.5\,\mu m$ and $1\,\mu m$.

A coating of pure tin, or tin/lead alloy (that is, solder itself), is the normal method of protectively coating printed circuit boards to maintain solderability. Three main methods are used to coat circuit board surface:

- Roller coating, using a solder-covered roller, partially immersed in a solder bath, shown in Figure 5.4. Boards coated in this way should have a coating thickness of $0.5\,\mu m$ to $1\,\mu m$, and will have a shelf-life of up to nine months.
- Dipping. The board is fluxed and dipped into a solder bath, then levelling of the solder layer, and clearing of plated-through holes, is accomplished with a hot-air knife, as illustrated in Figure 5.5. (Hot-air knives are also found in some machine soldering processes – see page 184.) Boards coated in this way should have a coating thickness from $1\,\mu m$ to $5\,\mu m$, and will have a shelf-life of at least twelve months.
- Plating. The board is plated with tin, or a tin/lead alloy, to a thickness of at least $10\,\mu m$, then the copper and plated alloy layers are fused with the application of heat. Even with the initial $10\,\mu m$ plated layer, thicknesses around holes or close to board edges will fall to as low as $1\,\mu m$, so hot-air levelling may be required. Shelf-life is a minimum of twelve months.

Technically, the process of **fusing** is one of heating a previously electroplated tin/lead layer to ensure an interfacing alloy bond, while

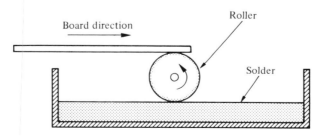

Figure 5.4 *Applying a protective metal coat to a printed circuit board, by roller coating*

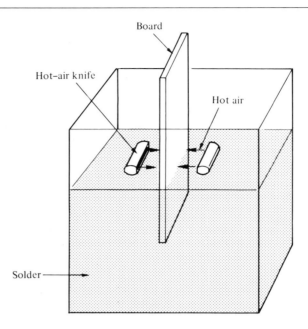

Board

Hot–air knife

Hot air

Solder

Figure 5.5 *Applying a protective metal coat to a printed circuit board, by dipping*

levelling is the process of removal of much of a tin/lead layer to leave behind a thin coating. These terms are often used incorrectly, and are even sometimes interchanged.

One of the main advantages of tin/lead protective coatings is that boards which have exceeded their shelf-life may be reheated, say, with a hot-air knife, to re-fuse the copper and tin/lead layers and renew solderability.

Manufacturing processes for circuit boards may include tin/lead plating of the copper track (see Chapter 2 regarding metallization). In such cases, it would appear that no secondary protective coating is required. However, the solderability of the original copper surface prior to tin/lead electroplating is important here. If the electroplated layer is applied to copper which is not solderable, on heating to ensure fusing the electroplated layer will become dewetted – the original copper surface *must* have acceptable solderability to prevent dewetting.

Soldering processes

There are a number of methods by which electronics assembly soldering processes may be categorized, the first, discussed here, is whether soldering is performed by hand or by machine.

Hand soldering

Hand soldering is usually performed either:

- During hand assembly. Components are assembled into or on to the circuit board individually, or in groups, then soldered. Following components are then assembled then soldered, and so on, until the board is completely assembled and soldered.

- After hand assembly. All components are assembled into or on to the circuit board, then soldered.

Hand soldering involves the use of purpose-built tools and specific operations, which depend primarily on the components being soldered. As a complete process, hand soldering is discussed later in this chapter.

Machine soldering

Machine soldering methods are, very simply, methods to solder components into or on to a board en masse. For this reason, they are called **mass soldering methods**. Primary aim of mass soldering methods is to speed up the manufacture of electronics assemblies.

Another method by which soldering processes may be categorized is by the mass soldering process used. There are two main categories of mass soldering processes:

- Those processes which rely on the insertion or onsertion of components *prior* to application of solder – from here called **component/solder** (CS) processes – sometimes, graphically, called **flow** soldering processes.
- Those processes which rely on the onsertion of components *after* the application of solder – from here called **solder/component** (SC) processes – sometimes, incorrectly, called **reflow** soldering processes.

Component/solder (CS) processes

There are three main CS soldering processes:

- Dip soldering.

Plate 5.1 *Research infra-red solder fusing machine (Astro Technology)*

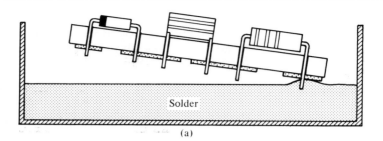

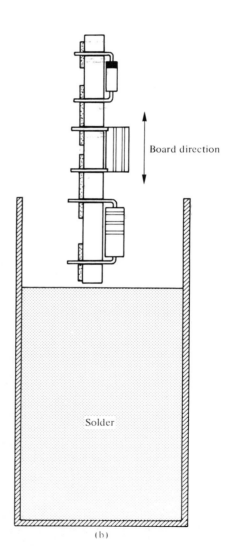

Figure 5.6 *Dip soldering. (a) Lowering and removing the board near-horizontally. (b) Dipping the board vertically*

- Drag soldering.
- Wave soldering.

Dip soldering

In dip soldering processes the assembled board is fluxed then lowered into a bath of molten solder. This can be in two ways. First, the board can be lowered into the solder bath near-horizontally, as shown in Figure 5.6(a). Once the lower edge of the board comes into contact with the solder, the board is dropped to a horizontal position on the solder. After a suitable period during which the solder achieves wetting over the whole of the areas to be soldered, one edge of the board is lifted (usually the edge which first came into contact with the solder), then the whole board is lifted clear of the bath. Second, the board can be lowered vertically into the bath (Figure 5.6(b)).

Dip soldering suffers from problems in that flux gases are easily trapped under the board and, as a consequence, contact times must be quite long (about 10 seconds) to ensure adequate wetting and solder temperature must be quite high.

Drag soldering

By dragging the assembled and fluxed board over the surface of molten solder (illustrated in Figure 5.7), the problems associated with dip soldering processes can be overcome. Consequent contact times are much shorter (about 5 seconds).

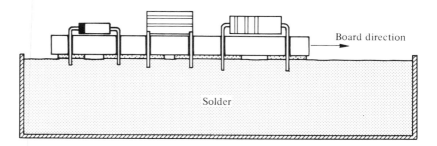

Board direction

Solder

Figure 5.7 *Drag soldering principle*

Wave soldering

Wave soldering processes use a pump to create a wave of solder over which the assembled and fluxed board is passed (illustrated in Figure 5.8). Contact times of only 1 to 2 seconds are usual, and required solder temperature is lowered.

Although dip and drag soldering processes are used, neither normally forms the preferred method. For mass CS soldering, wave soldering techniques are the norm, and will be discussed in the relevant section later in this chapter.

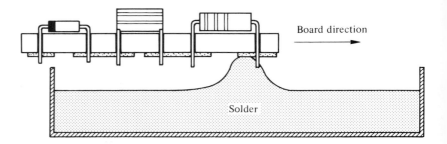

Board direction

Solder

Figure 5.8 *Wave soldering principle*

Solder/component (SC) processes – reflow soldering

SC soldering processes are used, primarily, in surface mounting assembly production, where solder and flux are applied as a paste followed by the placement of components and the application of heat (Figure 5.9). SC soldering processes are often termed reflow processes, known as such because the original idea uses a layer of previously applied solid solder which is reheated to cause it to melt, that is, flow again.

Under this light, the term *reflow* as it is *currently* used is obviously something of a misnomer, as solder and flux paste – now the normal method of applying solder before components are assembled – in no way can be thought of as solid solder.

There is a number of mass SC soldering techniques, categorized by the type and direction of applied heat, discussed in the relevant section later in this chapter.

Solder

As discussed earlier, most solders used in electronics assembly are alloys of tin and lead. Soldering, however, as a general process (more commonly called **soft soldering**) may be used to joint many more things than electric component leads and copper tracks of printed circuit boards. In effect, soft soldering is the basis of any process in which metallic parts are jointed by a molten alloy with a melting temperature less than 450°C.

Soft soldering is also an extremely old process. The Romans, for example, are known to have used a tin/lead alloy to joint lead water pipes. However, soft soldering using tin and lead may have but a limited life left – as an aside it is interesting to note that, at current production rates of tin, the world's resources of the metal will give less than fifty years' more use.

Tin/lead alloy properties

One of the most useful properties of tin/lead alloys as soft solders is the associated range of low melting temperatures. Table 5.1 lists melting temperatures of a selection of alloys, with proportions of the alloys shown as percentages. Note that over a central range of alloy proportions there is

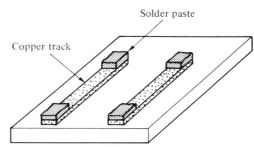

Stage 1: application of solder paste

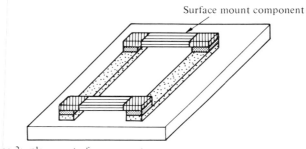

Stage 2: placement of component

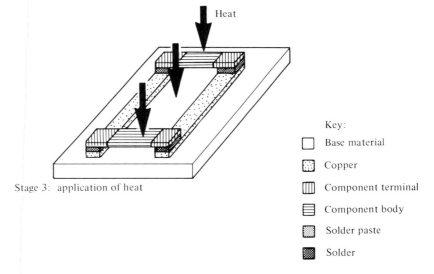

Stage 3: application of heat

Figure 5.9 *Illustrating the principle of SC soldering processes*

no particular melting-point, merely a range over which the alloy is neither molten nor solid – a pasty or plastic state. However, at one particular alloy proportion (62% tin/38% lead) the alloy melts at a single temperature (183°C) – also the lowest melting temperature of any tin/lead alloy. Figure 5.10 shows this graphically, in what is known as a **phase diagram**, where liquid, plastic and solid states of tin/lead alloys, together with the lowest melting temperature are shown.

Table 5.1   Melting temperatures of tin/lead alloys

Alloy as percentages of tin and lead	Melting temperature (°C)
100 lead	327
5 tin/95 lead	300
10 tin/90 lead	267
30 tin/70 lead	281
40 tin/60 lead	183 to 235
50 tin/50 lead	183 to 212
60 tin/40 lead	183 to 189
62 tin/38 lead	183
70 tin/30 lead	183 to 191
90 tin/10 lead	183 to 213
100 tin	232

A 62% tin/38% lead alloy composition is known as a **eutectic** composition, and the 183°C melting-point of this alloy is the **eutectic point**. All electronics assembly processes, with few exceptions, use solder with constituents around the eutectic proportions, owing to the guaranteed low melting-point.

As an aside, there appears to be some confusion over the exact eutectic proportions and melting-point of solders. Most authors refer to the eutectic composition as 63% tin/37% lead, but more recent studies (Klein Wassink) have noted a eutectic composition of 61.9% tin/38.1%, which sounds

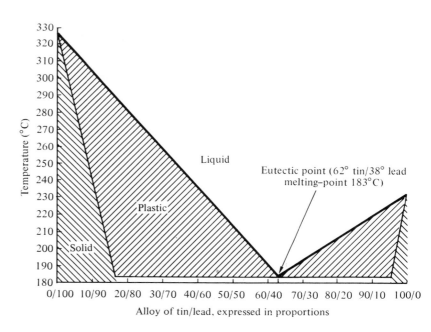

Figure 5.10 *Phase diagram of tin/lead alloys*

altogether more impressive. In the absence of first-hand proof (which I am sure most, if not all, other authors are similarly without) I shall comply with the more up-to-date findings. For practical purposes, at least, there is little difference, anyway.

Tin is an expensive metal, and so a reduction in the amount used in solder will make a cheaper solder, so a 60% tin/40 lead solder alloy is commonly used in electronics assembly. It exhibits a melting temperature range of around 6°C, rather than a defined melting-point, so this means a corresponding slightly higher process temperature is required; but this generally does not affect the soldering process significantly. Apart from precision soldering requirements of, say, multi-layer printed circuit boards and surface mounting of components, the cheaper 60% tin/40% lead alloy is perfectly acceptable.

Strength and stress resistance

Once made, the soldered joint must be strong and resist reasonable stresses. Figure 5.11 shows graphs of how tensile strength and shear strength of solder vary with tin/lead alloy proportions. Although not quite at the peak of either graph, eutectic tin/lead solder still affords reasonable strength for joints.

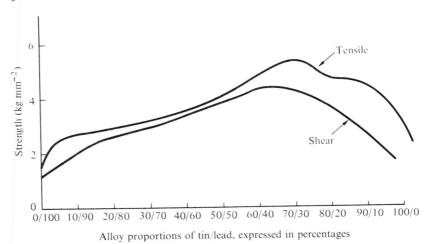

Figure 5.11 *Tensile strength and shear strength variations with tin/lead alloy proportions of solder*

Elasticity

Owing to the fact that tin/lead solders exhibit significant **creep**, elasticity of solder is difficult to ascertain, but its modulus lies somewhere in the region of 30,000 Nmm^{-2}.

Creep

Creep is a plastic deformation which occurs when a material is subjected to stress for a period. The closer the material is to its melting temperature the

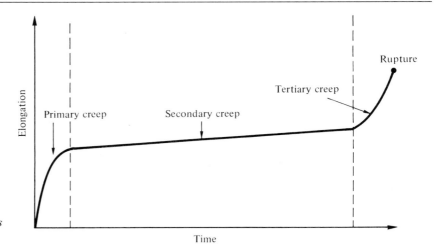

Figure 5.12 *Three distinct stages of creep*

more likely it is for creep to occur. It is thus of significance even at ambient temperatures for tin/lead solder, because an ambient temperature of, say, 25°C (298 K) is not too far from the melting-point of 183°C (461 K). Creep follows three distinct stages, illustrated in Figure 5.12:

- Primary creep, occurring rapidly when stress is first applied, but decreasing with time.
- Secondary creep, occurring at a constant rate for the greater part of the joint's lifetime.
- Tertiary creep, occurring after the joint has been subjected to sufficient secondary creep to cause its final demise. Tertiary creep occurs at an increasing rate, and ends with the joint's rupture.

This property is therefore a disadvantage in any choice of solder for electronic printed circuit board assemblies, but given that other solders will require a significantly higher soldering temperature which may damage the components being soldered, eutectic tin/lead solder is still preferable – a case of the advantage outweighing the disadvantage.

Surface tension

Generally speaking, the lower the surface tension of a fluid, the easier it will wet the surface to which it is applied. Molten lead has a much lower surface tension than molten tin, so it may be assumed that a higher content of lead than a eutectic solder would be appropriate. However, lead itself exhibits a significant interfacial tension with copper which prevents wetting, so eutectic tin/lead solder remains the best option.

Resistivity

Eutectic tin/lead solder has an electrical resistivity some ten times that of pure copper, but it is still only around $0.17\,\mu\Omega m^{-1}$ at ambient temperatures, and given the much larger area of a soldered joint compared with a copper printed circuit conductor the difference is not really a significant problem at all.

Thermal conductivity

Thermal conductivity of tin/lead solder is about $50\,Jm^{-1}s^{-1}K^{-1}$ at ambient temperatures; some eighth that of copper. If significant lengths of solder were used on a printed circuit board to make connections this could pose some problems, but the generally short distances filled by solder within soldered joints should cause few problems here.

Impurities

There are three categories of impurities which may occur in the tin/lead solder alloy:

- Those impossible to remove from the base tin and lead metals in the refinement processes.
- Those added by the solder manufacturer or the user, to improve the solder's performance.
- Those entering the alloy during the normal course of use.

Generally speaking, those in the first category are not significant and do not usually affect the performance of the solder. A number of impurities may, however, be added by the manufacturer with the aim of *improving* solder performance. For example, the addition of small quantities of antimony and copper can reduce solder creep. Table 5.2 lists a selection of tin/lead soft solder alloys. Associated temperatures and approximate proportions of tin, lead and antimony are shown.

Table 5.2 Selection of soft solder alloys, showing approximate proportions of tin, lead, and antimony

Grade	Tin (%)	Lead (%)	Antimony (%)	Solid at (°C)	Liquid at (°C)
A	63	36	0.6	183	185
B	49	48	2.5	185	204
C	40	58	2.0	185	227
D	30	68	1.7	185	248
F	50	50	0.5	183	212
G	40	60	0.4	183	234
H	34	65	0.3	183	244
J	30	70	0.3	183	255
K	60	40	0.5	183	188
M	44	52	2.5	185	215
R	44	56	0.4	183	224

Antimony can be also used to allow a reduction in the amount of tin required in the solder – tin is an expensive metal and so the lower the percentage of tin in solder, the cheaper the solder. An alloy of 52% tin/45% lead/3% antimony, for example, exhibits a slightly raised melting temperature and is, in fact, stronger compared with eutectic or near-eutectic tin/lead solder.

Standards

UK	USA	European
BS 441	QQ S571	DIN 1707
BS 3338		DIN 8516

Flux

Fluxes vary in their chemical **activity**. Type of flux used depends on the cleanliness of the surfaces to be soldered. If perfectly clean, so that only a thin oxide layer is present, a flux with only a low activity is required. On the other hand, unclean surfaces will require more highly active fluxes.

There is a price to be paid, however, when active fluxes are used – flux activity is closely allied with the corrosivity of the residues remaining after soldering has taken place. A highly active flux will leave corrosive residues which will corrode the solder itself. There are only two solutions to this problem: clean the metals to be soldered prior to soldering and use a low-activity flux; use a high-activity flux and clean the assembly after soldering. The former is the best solution.

Types of flux

In electronic applications, there are two main types of flux:

- Organically soluble fluxes.
- Water soluble residue fluxes.

It is important to note with this categorization, however, that the term *water soluble* refers purely to the residues left after soldering, and has nothing to do with whether the flux itself is soluble in water.

Organically soluble fluxes

These are, historically, often based on the use of gum **rosin**, obtained from pine tree sap. The sap, after distillation produces solid rosin, also called **colophony**. To clear up another potentially confusing point, it is sometimes common to hear the terms *resin* and *rosin* incorrectly interchanged. Rosin is, in fact, the solid residue obtained from the distillation of oil of turpentine from crude turpentine – this, by chance alone, happens to include the residue distilled from pine tree sap and used in solder fluxes. On the other hand, resin is an adhesive inflammable substance secreted by most plants and exuding naturally from fir and pine – that is, sap. So, rosin is distilled from a resin, but that does not mean all resins are rosin.

Where rosin is used as a flux, it is generally dissolved in some organic solvent. It has two excellent properties which make its use as an electronics solder flux preferable to many others. First, as a liquid at soldering temperature it is active, being a mild organic acid, and so exhibits good wetting capabilities on tarnished metal such as copper and gold. Second, as a solid it is basically non-reactive, so does not corrode the completed joint, and is a good insulator.

Where rosin itself does not provide sufficient wetting, that is, where the metals are too tarnished, rosin-based flux with added **activators**, known as **activated fluxes**, may be used. These increase the flux's cleaning activity at the soldering temperature, so improving wetting. Needless to say, such a flux will leave corrosive residues, however. Fluxes without activators, incidentally, are sometimes known as **non-activated fluxes**.

Activators include:

- Certain organic salts such as dimethylammonium chloride (abbreviation; DMA HCl) and diethylammonium chloride (DEA HCl).
- Organic mono-basic acids such as formic acid, acetic acid, propionic acid.
- Organic di-basic acids such as oxalic acid, malonic acid, sebacic acid.

Activating agents are selected according to their activity and corrosion properties, ease of cleaning, as well as their (or their vapour's) effects on humans.

Rosin production, as it is a natural substance, depends on adequate harvesting from a currently decreasing source. As such, it has fixed properties and, in future, may not be economic to produce. Synthetic substitutes could have superior properties and may be cheaper. Some have already been produced; at least one well-known solder manufacturer produces solder which is cored with such a synthetic flux. More will presumably follow.

Water soluble residue fluxes

These fluxes are usually produced to be highly active – taking over where organically soluble rosin-based fluxes cannot cope. So, their residues are highly corrosive and must be removed after soldering. However, as the residues are water soluble, this eases cleaning.

Formulation is based around use of an activator for surface cleaning of the metal to be soldered, and a solvent to ease application. Often, other substances to aid wetting may also be added. Activators include:

- Organic salts such as dimethylammonium chloride (DMA HCl).
- Organic acids such as lactic acid.
- Organic amines such as urea.
- Inorganic salts such as zinc chloride.
- Inorganic acids such as hydrochloric acid.

Table 5.3 Common flux abbreviations, meanings, and flux types

Abbreviation	Meaning	Flux type
OA	Organic acid.	Addition of organic acid activator.
R	Rosin.	Purest grade of rosin, no activator added.
RA	Activated rosin.	Rosin, with addition of activators.
RMA	Mildly activated rosin.	Rosin, with addition of mild activators.
SA	Synthetic activated.	Rosin, with addition of synthetic activators.
SRA	Superactivated rosin.	Rosin, with addition of very strong activators.
WW	Water white.	Purest grade of rosin.

Solvents typically include water or isopropanol although water is not preferred, as it has a tendency to spatter on rapid application of heat.

Often, flux types are quoted as an abbreviation; the abbreviations deriving from various specifications and standards, and usually referring to the type of activator added. Table 5.3 lists common flux abbreviations, abbreviation meanings, and subsequent types of flux.

Standards

UK	USA	European
BS 5625	EIA402	DIN 8511
Def Stan 34–4	Mil F14256	DIN 8516
DTD599		

Types of joints

Mechanical strength is an important criterion when designing soldered joints. Obviously the joint should be strong – strong enough to withstand all the possible stresses which it may experience: tensile, shear and compressive.

There are a few important types of joints associated with electronics assemblies. These fall into one of two categories:

- Through-hole joints.
- Surface mounted joints.

Performance of a joint is such that typical tensile strengths of around $5\,kg\,mm^{-2}$ and shear strengths of around $3\,kg\,mm^{-2}$ are obtainable when soldering two pieces of copper. To put this in perspective, peel strengths of typical printed circuit boards are such that the copper track will peel from

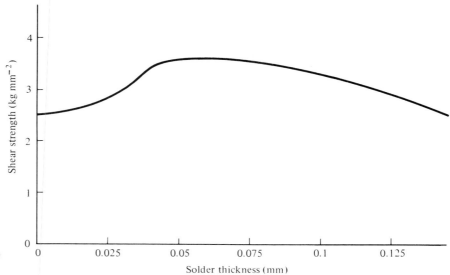

Figure 5.13 *Variation of shear strength for thickness of solder between two layers of copper in a lap joint*

the circuit board if a force of just a small fraction of this possible solder joint tensile strength is applied over the few square millimetres of a soldered joint. In effect, the materials surrounding a perfectly made joint usually form a limit to a solder joint – not the joint itself.

Joint strength depends to a great extent on solder thickness, too. Figure 5.13 shows a graph of the variation in shear strength which may be expected for differing thicknesses of solder between two layers of copper in a lap joint. A lap joint is shown in Figure 5.14.

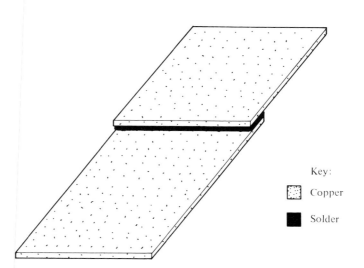

Key:

▨ Copper

■ Solder

Figure 5.14 *Basic lap joint*

Through-hole joints

Through-hole joints rely on the single fact that a wire lead is inserted through a hole in the board, then soldered to bond to a metal track. However, certain factors may differ and affect the exact type of joint, such that four different types of through-hole joint have been specified by previous authors:

- Non-plated-through hole, straight lead.
- Non-plated-through hole, clinched lead.
- Plated-through hole, straight lead.
- Plated-through hole, clinched lead.

In the following discussion, it is assumed that all joints are perfect, with good, continuous, wetting all round the area.

Non-plated-through hole, straight lead

Figure 5.15 shows the joint obtained when a straight component lead is soldered in a non-plated-through hole, such as would be obtained in a single-sided circuit board. This is the easiest joint to manufacture, as few processes, apart from insertion and soldering, are called for. It is, correspondingly, the weakest through-hole joint, however.

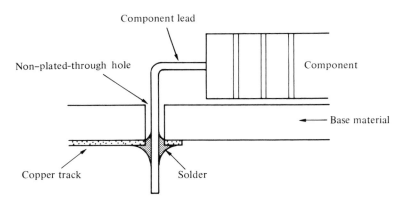

Figure 5.15 *Joint of a straight-leaded component in a non-plated-through hole*

Non-plated-through hole, clinched lead

This joint configuration is shown in Figure 5.16, for a lead clinched at the nominally preferred 45° angle to the horizontal (see Chapter 2). Now, part of the joint is the same as the non-plated-through hole, straight lead soldered joint, but the remaining part of the joint is a lap joint (between the lead and the board). This lap joint greatly increases overall joint strength.

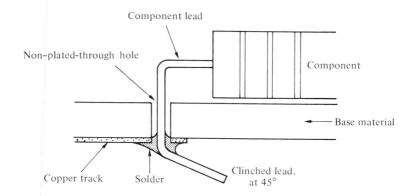

Figure 5.16 *Joint of a clinched component lead through a non-plated-through hole*

Plated-through hole, straight lead

This joint is shown in Figure 5.17. The effects of the metallized plated-through hole are to allow solder to be drawn up into the barrel of the hole, around the lead. This has the effects of increasing strength and decreasing the joint's electrical resistance, compared with the non-plated-through hole, straight lead joint of Figure 5.15. Where solder is drawn up through the barrel sufficiently, the joint may have a top fillet, as shown in Figure 5.1. In turn this will again increase joint strength and lower resistance, but is by no means essential.

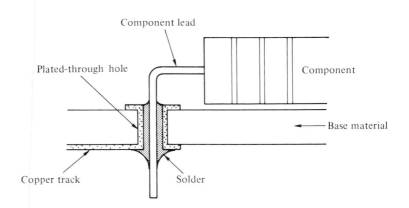

Figure 5.17 *Joint of a straight-leaded component in a plated-through hole*

Plated-through hole, clinched lead

By far the strongest, this joint is shown in Figure 5.18. It includes the strength of the lap joint between clinched lead and board and the soldered barrel of the hole, together with the lower joint resistance of the soldered barrel.

An important consideration in all joints is the hole-to-lead size ratio,

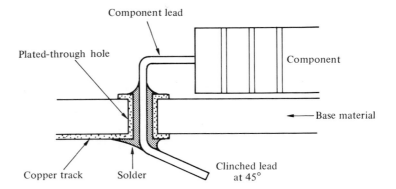

Figure 5.18 *Joint of a clinched component lead through a plated-through hole*

which has a large effect on the joint strength and ease of assembly. Generally, the closer the lead diameter is to the hole diameter, the stronger is the joint, while the opposite is true for ease of assembly. Table 5.4 lists typical joint strengths as percentages of maximum possible joint strength for clearances between leads and hole, against ease of insertion, for straight leads. Figure 5.19, on the other hand, shows how joint strength can be expected to decrease for increasing clearance between lead and hole diameters. A reasonable hole-to-lead ratio can be determined to be one where approximately 0.6 mm clearance between lead and hole diameters is involved. If joint strength at this clearance is insufficient, it is advisable not to decrease hole diameter (thereby decreasing lead-to-hole clearance and making insertion more difficult), but to clinch the lead instead, prior to soldering.

Surface mounted joints

Where joint strength in through-hole joints is, in reality, quite large (far larger, in fact, than the strength of the circuit materials surrounding the joint), the type of joint possible when soldering surface mounted compo-

Table 5.4   Joint strengths as percentages of maximum possible joint strength for clearances between leads and hole, against ease of insertion

Clearance between hole and lead (mm)	Tensile strength (%age of maximum)	Ease of insertion
0	100	Impossible
0.1	95	Impractical
0.2	87	Difficult
0.3	82	Difficult
0.4	76	Possible
0.5	70	Easy
0.6	60	Easy

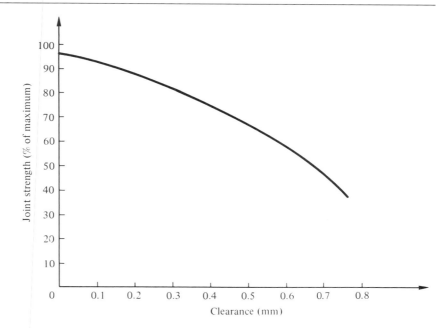

Figure 5.19 *Variation of joint strength with lead and hole diameters*

nents severely limits the joint strength. Even if a through-hole joint is not 100% perfect, the considerable joint area and volume of solder usually maintain adequate operation. Where surface mounted components are concerned, with their consequent small joint area and solder volume, however, joint performance is more critical. For this reason, it is in the study of the soldering of surface mounted components that soldering technology is being improved.

Two main types of soldered joint concerning surface mounted assemblies have been identified: lap joints and butt joints (Manko), although minor variations occur according to type of component being soldered.

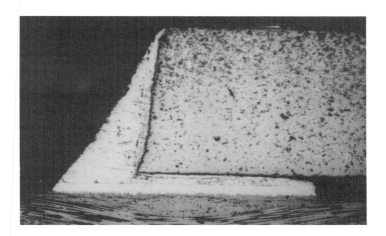

Plate 5.2 *Close-up and cross-sectional view of a surface mounted lap joint between a terminal of a small outline transistor and printed circuit board (RJ)*

Plate 5.3 *Close-up and cross-sectional view of a surface mounted lap joint between a chip component and printed circuit board (RJ)*

Surface mounted lap joints

Figure 5.20 shows a surface mounted component (a chip, two-terminal device) mounted and soldered to a circuit board. It is fairly rigid, there being no greatly flexible parts to the arrangement. This rigidity is the reason why components of up to only about 6 mm in length can be soldered to epoxy resin-bonded, fibre glass reinforced circuit boards; for the difference in the thermal coefficients of expansion between component and base material mean that on cooling after soldering, the component and circuit board decrease by different amounts. If the difference is great enough, shear stresses are set up which will fracture either the joint, the copper track, or the component. The 6 mm limit for length of components, is a simple rule-of-thumb which, if followed, will ensure fracturing will not occur. Many surface mounted components are within this size limit so remain unaffected by thermal coefficient of expansion mismatch.

Many other surface mounted components, on the other hand, are larger than 6 mm. Such rigid lap jointing of the components to epoxy resin-bonded, glass fibre reinforced circuit board is not, therefore, possible. Leadless chip carriers form the main group of larger surface mounted components which feature rigid lap joints.

There are, presently, two solutions to the problem of being able to use larger surface mounted components:

- Use a circuit board base material with a thermal coefficient of

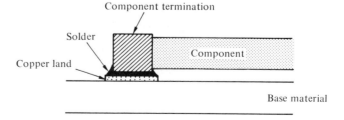

Figure 5.20 *Two-terminal surface mount component, soldered to a circuit board with rigid lap joints*

expansion matching that of the components (for example, ceramic, metal-bonded. See Chapter 2).

• Design the components to mount on the board with a compliant joint.

Figure 5.21 shows a component, lap jointed to a circuit board, in a formation which is compliant, owing to the addition of small terminating leads on to the component. (As surface mounted components are known for their advantage of being *leadless*, this is something of a backward step, not to mention a misnomer, but does form a short-term solution to a tricky problem.) Small outline diodes (SODs), small outline transistors (SOTs), small outline integrated circuits (SOICs), very small outline integrated circuits (VSOICs), tape automated bonded integrated circuits (TABs), and so on are all components having such compliant terminations.

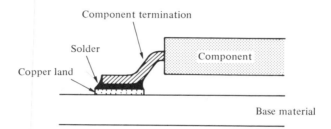

Figure 5.21 *Compliant lap joints, with certain types of surface mount components*

Surface mounted butt joints

Similarly, compliant butt jointing of components is obtained with such components as plastic leaded chip carriers (PLCCs), where terminations are formed by J-shaped leads (Figure 5.22). The resultant solder joint from such a termination is poor compared with the lap joint, however, but its small width remains very attractive for high termination-count integrated circuits.

Calculated typical land parameters of the three types of surface mounted component joints: rigid lap, compliant lap, and compliant butt, together with those of a non-plated-through hole joint are listed in Table 5.5, using the typical tensile and shear strengths suggested earlier to compare the

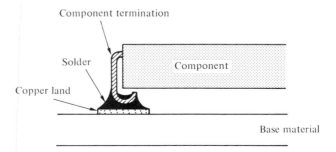

Figure 5.22 *PLCCs allow compliant butt joints*

Table 5.5 Comparison of typical non-plated-through, straight lead joint with typical surface mounted component joints

Land parameter (typical)	Rigid lap	Compliant lap	Compliant butt	Through-hole
Length (mm)	1.25	0.5	0.5	2 diameter
Width (mm)	0.5	0.6	0.4	
Area (mm²)	0.625	0.3	0.2	3
Tensile strength at 5 kg mm^{-2} (kg)	3.1	1.5	1	15
Shear strength at 3 kg mm^{-2} (kg)	1.9	0.9	0.6	9

various joint strengths. The large differences in tensile strength and shear strength between the through-hole joint and the surface mounted component joints are easily seen, particularly for the compliant butt joint (that is, the joint of the plastic leaded chip carrier). Study of the soldered joint, in the context of through-hole and surface mounted components, in this manner is forcing a re-appraisal of the use of solder in electronics assembly. The comparatively low strength of the surface mounted joint appears to be of only minor concern.

In effect, compliant lap and butt joints illustrate a successful short-term method of enabling surface mounted components, in quasi-leaded form, to be used with cheaply produced circuit board materials. In the long-term, though, the only solution to enable *pure* leadless surface mounted assembly must be to develop cheap and easy manufacture of thermally matched circuit boards, or to develop newer bonding processes with significantly improved shear strengths.

Solder resists

It is sometimes necessary to ensure that some areas of an assembly be kept free of solder. In such cases **solder resists**, sometimes called **solder masks**, can be used. Fairly obviously, a solder resist must provide two functions. First, it must be heat resistant, to prevent the heat of the soldering process from breaking it down. Second, it must be non-wettable.

Solder resists can be temporary, in that they are removed after the soldering process, or permanent. In general, temporary solder resists are used to protect particular areas of a PCB during mass soldering methods such as dip, drag and wave soldering. They are typically used to keep small areas such as plated-through holes, gold-plated contacts and so on, clear of solder for later purposes. After soldering, they are removed. Although usually of a liquid form, applied to the surface of the PCB, then left to dry before soldering, mechanical resists such as plastic or wooden plugs or inserts, and even adhesive tape are not unknown.

Permanent solder resists are often used to eliminate the risk of solder bridges between closely-spaced adjacent tracks. This means that PCB designers can reduce gap sizes and have extra freedom in track layouts. Secondary advantages include: physical protection of tracks, particularly those of a fine-line nature; reduced drainage of solder from joints which may otherwise cause the joints to be poorly soldered; reduced consumption of solder overall, coupled with reduced contamination of the solder in the bath; a known dielectric present between tracks; improved visual inspection of solder joints owing to the fact that resist will reflect light less than joints; good appearance.

Permanent solder resists are applied using conventional screen-printing techniques or, where high accuracy is important such as in the production of fine-line boards, they are photoprinted following screen-printed liquid or dry-film application. Application of solder resists is covered as a manufacturing process in Chapter 2.

Three main types of permanent solder resist are used:

- Epoxy-based.
- Rubber-based.
- Acrylate-based.

Hand soldering

Hand soldering is a process in which components are mounted on a circuit board, then individually soldered, joint by joint, until the assembly is completed. Where through-hole assemblies are being soldered (that is, with components mounted using component leads inserted through holes in the board), joints are of an easily-produced reasonable size and are of strong construction. Components themselves are large and easily handled, as are the tools used. A typical assembly and soldering process by hand is shown in Figure 5.23, where components are inserted then the assembly is held with foam padding and inverted, while soldering is undertaken.

Joint areas, defined primarily by land sizes, have typical values of around 5 mm^2. This ensures that assemblers can easily see the area to be soldered, and can manipulate the soldering iron and solder with no difficulty. Hand soldering of through-hole components into circuit boards is a well-established and well-defined process.

Hand soldering of surface mounted assemblies, on the other hand, is much more difficult owing to the small size of components, and their corresponding small joint areas. Land areas of much less than 1 mm^2 mean that considerable strain is placed on the assembler, to solder joints and, even, to see what is to be soldered. Hand soldering of surface mounted components is not, therefore, normally a process undertaken in any volume production of circuit boards.

On the other hand, where boards are to be reworked, say, for repair after manufacture, hand soldering (and desoldering) may be desirable. So hand tools and aids are available.

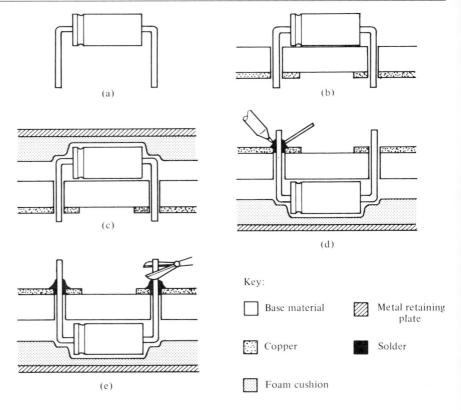

Key:

☐ Base material ▨ Metal retaining plate

▨ Copper ■ Solder

▨ Foam cushion

Figure 5.23 *Typical hand assembly and soldering process*

Tools

The soldering iron

Soldering irons for through-hole components are readily available. Tips are available in a large range of shapes and sizes, some are shown in Figure 5.24. Usually, a medium-sized general-purpose tip will be used to solder most types of through-hole components, although some specialized components may require smaller or larger tips.

Soldering irons specifically for surface mounted component soldering are becoming increasingly more common. Unlike soldering irons tips for through-hole components, tip shape and size for surface mounted components are more critical. Many are available with tips shaped to fit specific surface mounted components. Examples of two such tips, shaped to fit common surface mounted components, are shown in Figure 5.25. Many more are available. Where a number of types of components are to be mounted, generally, an equivalent number of soldering irons would be used, eliminating the requirement to change the tip with every new component type to be soldered.

Soldering iron tip temperature of some irons can vary considerably

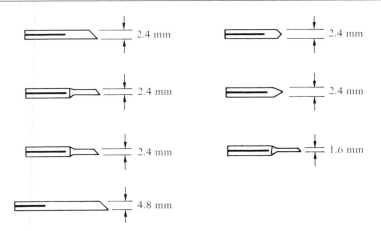

Figure 5.24 *Typical through-hole component soldering iron tips*

during use. When idling, that is, not being used to solder components but still turned on, to the situation where it is being used consistently to solder components, temperature may easily fall from, say, 420°C to around 300°C. So, an iron, after idling for a while, may be hot enough to damage temperature-sensitive components. Although less important when soldering through-hole components, this is not an ideal situation, so irons will usually be electronically controlled, to specific temperatures within the 240°C to 400°C temperature range, so that damage to temperature-sensitive components may be eliminated.

Portable gas irons are also available, running on a small, rechargeable, internal cylinder of gas lighter fuel.

Where surface mounted components are being soldered, electrically-heated hot plates may help to prevent damage owing to contraction. The circuit board is placed on the hot plate and heated before components are placed and soldered. In this way, the board and components are all at more or less the same temperature, before, during and after soldering.

Magnifying glasses, or simple microscope arrangements may be used, also, as sight aids when soldering surface mounted components.

Flux and flux-cored solder

Soldering of any component to a circuit board requires that flux be added prior to or at the same time as the molten solder (see page 149). This is

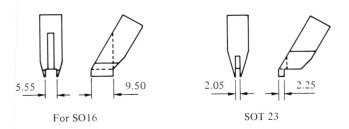

Figure 5.25 *Typical surface mount component soldering iron tips*

For SO16   SOT 23

always done, when hand soldering, with flux-cored solder wire; comprising a wire of solder containing cores along its length, filled with flux. Many solder alloys are available in this form, with many types of flux, and many wire diameters. For the hand soldering of electronic components the alloy is at or close to the eutectic composition of tin and lead (around 62% tin, see page 160), with four to six cores of rosin or synthetic flux (see page 164), with a typical diameter of around 1 mm.

Electrostatically sensitive devices

Certain electronic components are sensitive to electrostatic discharge (see Table 2.12). Where soldering such components it is important to use a soldering iron (the tip of which is earthed), using a resistor of a minimum value of around 100 kΩ. This will ensure that any part of the soldering iron tip will be at earth potential just a few milliseconds after coming into contact with a high electrostatic potential.

Desoldering

Occasionally, in rework or repair stages of an assembly's life, desoldering of components may be required. It is a tricky, time-consuming, operation requiring some extra tools.

First, the solder must be re-heated to be molten, then it must be removed, prior to component dismounting. Molten solder can be removed using implements to suck the solder away from a joint. Solder suckers can be separate tools, or form part of the soldering iron, comprising an air-bulb or plunger pump mechanism. Alternatively, woven copper wire can be made into a braid, called solder wick, impregnated with flux, which has the effect of drawing the molten solder up the braid, away from the joint.

Standards

UK	European
BS 441	DIN 8511
BS 5625	DIN 8516

Mass CS soldering – wave soldering

One of the first steps in the automation of PCB assembly is to upgrade a hand soldering production line to some form of mass soldering. Mass soldering falls into one of the two categories discussed earlier: component/solder (CS) processes; solder/component (SC) reflow processes. The usual mass CS soldering process is wave soldering; drag soldering machines are less common; dip soldering machines even less so. There are, however, a number of mass SC reflow soldering processes and they are discussed later.

A wave soldering machine may be included as part of a continuous electronics assembly production line, which is, no doubt, one of the biggest

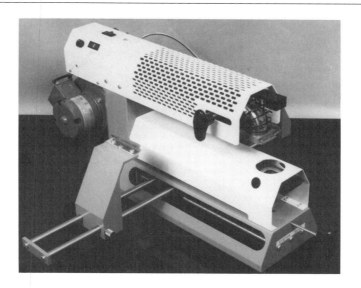

Plate 5.4 *System 1000 rework station, allows removal of through-hole components (Groatmoor)*

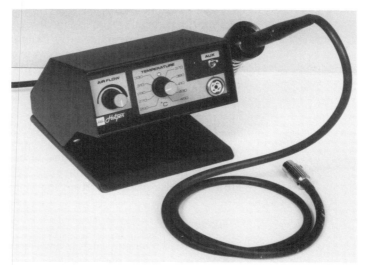

Plate 5.5 *SM10 hot air pencil for production and rework of surface mount assemblies (Groatmoor)*

advantages of the process. All types of plated-through hole assemblies and many surface mounted assemblies can be soldered using wave soldering, so it does hold promise for the future. Further, through-hole assemblies *cannot* be soldered by SC soldering processes, so for as long as through-hole components are used in assemblies wave soldering machines will be commonplace – only when assemblies are *totally* surface mounted and not of through-hole or mixed format, will wave soldering machines vanish from the electronics assembly production line.

Nevertheless, wave soldering does have drawbacks. It is a fairly complicated process, with some nine groups of variables (Klein Wassink),

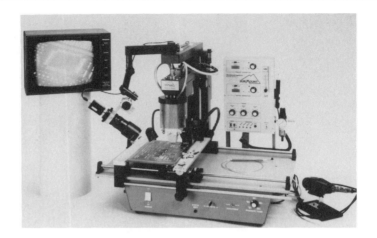

Plate 5.6 *Surmount surface mount assembly rework station (Dage)*

requiring regular maintenance both during and between operations by experienced staff. Also, running costs are high. Other minor considerations are the peculiarities of the soldering process which affect circuit board design for successful soldering – more so than any SC soldering process does wave soldering affect early design stages.

A typical wave soldering process is shown, in block diagram form, in Figure 5.26. There are three main parts, sometimes called **stations**, to the process:

- Fluxing.
- Preheating.
- Soldering.

Other relatively minor stations, although still necessary, are loading of boards into the wave soldering machine, cooling of boards after soldering, and unloading of boards from the machine.

Fluxing

The flux used to coat boards in a wave soldering machine is in liquid form. Some consideration must be placed on the type of electronics assembly to be fluxed, because not all methods generate a sufficiently high head of flux to successfully flux through-hole boards with long component leads. Fluxing in a wave soldering machine is accomplished using one of three main methods:

- Foam fluxing (shown in Figure 5.27), where air is forced through an aerator, into the flux, generating a foam of flux over which the board is

Figure 5.26 *Block diagram of a typical wave soldering machine process*

Boards → Load → Flux → Preheat → Solder by wave → Cool and unload →

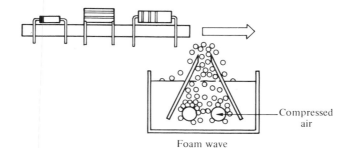

Figure 5.27 *Foam fluxing of printed circuit boards, prior to wave soldering*

Compressed air

Foam wave

conveyed. Aerators may be porous stone tubes, or air nozzles. Foam heights are usually only around 10 mm or so, so there are restrictions on component lead lengths. Where leads have not been cut prior to wave soldering, foam fluxing is not usually possible.

- Spray fluxing (shown in Figure 5.28). The first method is a finely-holed drum rotating in flux, while air is forced into the drum. The second method uses a rotary brush, the bristles of which strike a squeegee edge, catapulting the flux. The resultant spray of flux coats boards passing over the spray.
- Wave fluxing (shown in Figure 5.29), using a liquid wave applicator, similar, in principle, to the solder wave itself.

Preheating

The preheating stage prepares the assembly, recently fluxed, for the soldering stage. Its function is to:

- Dry the flux. Evaporating away solvents in the flux, reducing spattering of the flux in the solder wave. A secondary advantage of this function is a consequent speeding up of the soldering process itself: because the

Plate 5.7 *Ultra 2000 wave soldering machine, capable of soldering through-hole and surface mount assemblies (Electrovert)*

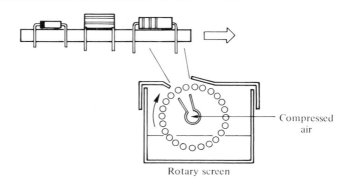

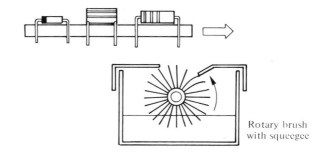

Figure 5.28 *Spray fluxing of printed circuit boards, prior to wave soldering*

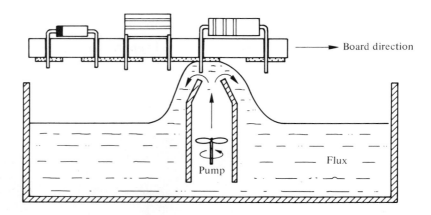

Figure 5.29 *Wave fluxing of printed circuit boards, prior to wave soldering*

solvents do not have to be evaporated by the solder wave, which would cool the solder wave and cause longer soldering times to be required.
- Activate the flux. Raising flux temperature to its activated state.
- Reduce thermal shock. By slowly (comparatively) raising the board and components' temperatures (both top and bottom) to between 80 and 130°C, thermal shock when the solder wave is applied is greatly reduced. Thermal shock does not, as its name would suggest, result in *damage* to components or board but may produce considerable

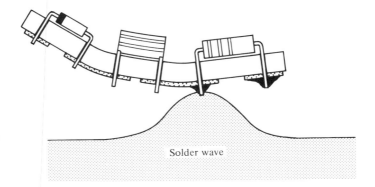

Figure 5.30 *Warpage caused by the heat of wave soldering, can be prevented by adequate preheating*

Solder wave

warpage of the board as it passes over the wave. Warpage is due to the different temperatures on the top and on the bottom of the board producing different thermal expansions, hence bending the board (Figure 5.30).

Preheating of different types of boards requires different preheat temperatures and times. Multi-layer boards, particularly many-layered ones, will require preheat temperatures at the upper end of the aforementioned range and longer times, so that flux in plated-through holes is adequately dried and heated.

Preheating is accomplished, typically, by convection heating, radiation heating, or a combination of both. Whatever heat system is used, maintenance is of importance, as flux dripping from the board will accumulate, and so must be easily removable. Often linings of aluminium foil are used as heat reflectors, which have the dual purpose of allowing easy removal and replacement for this reason.

Soldering

Once the assembly has been preheated, it is ready for soldering. In principle at least, the board is simply moved over a wave of molten solder, such that the heat of the solder performs a number of functions. It:

- Raises the area to be soldered to soldering temperature.
- Completes the activation of the flux (started in the preheating stage).
- Causes the component lands to be wetted by the solder.

The wave is produced by pumping the molten solder up through an ejection chamber, and out through a nozzle, as illustrated in Figure 5.31. After reaching a wave crest, the solder falls back into the bath down one or both sides of the chamber.

Wave shape

To perform all of the previous functions for every type of board, and for as many types of components as possible, requires that the board and component variations be taken into account. Thus, different wave

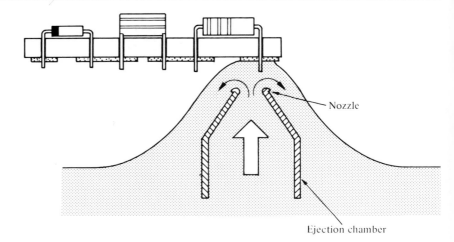

Figure 5.31 *Principle of wave soldering*

soldering machines are available for different applications, varying essentially in waveshape. The different waveshapes are, broadly:

- Single-sided wave (Figure 5.32(a)).
- Double-sided wave (Figure 5.32(b)).
- Extended wave (Figure 5.32(c)).

They are accomplished simply by changing the shape of the ejection chamber and nozzle. Further, some important changes can be made to the configuration to extend the use of the wave solder principle: notably addition of a second wave (creating the double-wave machine – Figure 5.33), and addition of a hot-air knife (Figure 5.34).

Of these types of wave soldering machine, all are basically suitable for through-hole component assemblies. However, where surface mounted or mixed assemblies are to be soldered consideration must be taken of the demands of the rather small, closely positioned, leadless components.

Initially, a fast-flowing turbulent wave is useful, to ensure that all components (however close to each other) are reached by the solder, and all terminations (however small) are adequately wetted. However, the very same turbulence tends to create solder bridges between the closely-spaced and small components terminations. Ideally, a second part of the wave would be calm, to clear any possible solder bridges.

This turbulent/calm wave situation can be accomplished with a single wave in double-sided wave machines or, better still, extended wave machines, where the nozzle is shaped to create a turbulent wave-entry, and a calm departure. However, a more appropriate solution would appear in double-wave soldering machines, where the first wave is turbulent and the second is calm.

An alternative solution is the hot-air knife, blowing a fine stream of extremely hot air over the circuit board after wave soldering to remove excess solder – eliminating solder bridges. Even surface mounted integrated circuits with quite finely pitched terminations, such as very small outline

Figure 5.32 *Typical waveshapes.
(a) Single-sided wave. (b)
Double-sided wave. (c)
Extended wave*

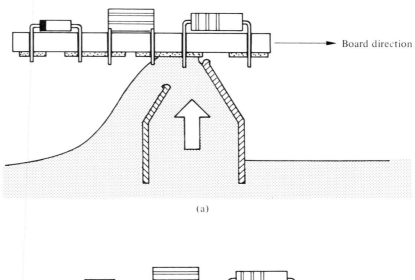

Board direction

(a)

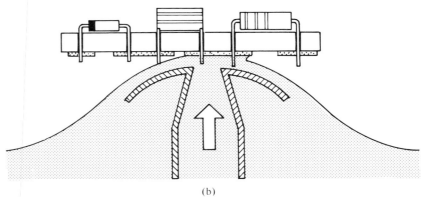

(b)

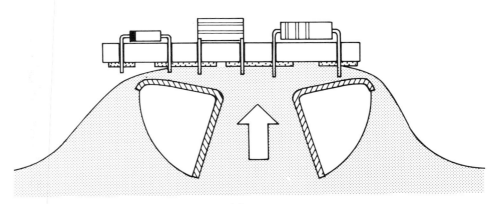

(c)

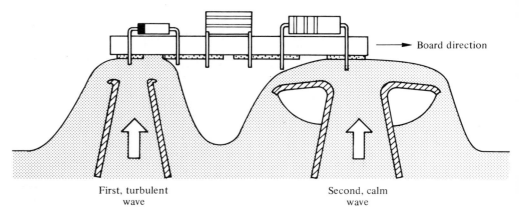

First, turbulent
wave

Second, calm
wave

Board direction

Figure 5.33 *Double-wave soldering principle*

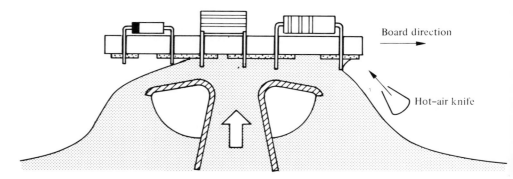

Board direction

Hot–air knife

Figure 5.34 *Use of a hot-air knife in the wave soldering process*

devices and leaded chip carriers, have been reported to be wave soldered with the hot-air knife as a backup to eliminate solder bridges.

The hot-air knife appears to have additional advantages, too, where it is reported that any dewetting of joints which may cause later problems become immediately and visibly apparent. Without the hot-air knife, such dewetting will cause later joint failure.

Standard

USA
Mil Std2000

Mass SC reflow soldering

In SC soldering processes, the component is applied at a later stage from the solder and flux. At a later stage still, heat is applied. In a nutshell, then, SC soldering processes involve three stages:

Plate 5.8 *Double-wave soldering of printed circuit boards. First turbulent wave, followed by second calm wave can be seen (Siemens)*

- Applying solder and flux, as a solder paste.
- Applying, that is, placing, components.
- Applying heat.

This separation of the application of solder from the application of heat (both go together in CS soldering processes – and cannot be split because the molten solder in a CS process itself supplies the heat) effectively means that the application of solder, in practice, becomes an *assembly process*, as is the placement of components on to the board, rather than a conventionally understood soldering process. Readers are therefore referred to the relevant section in Chapter 3, for a discussion on methods of application of solder paste and placement of components.

It only remains in this section to discuss the various methods of applying heat to the solder pasted, component placed, assembly. There are, of course, three ways in which heat may be applied, and these broadly help us to categorize the various mass SC processes:

- Conduction: hot liquid, hot plate, molten metal.
- Convection: hot air, hot gas, hot vapour.
- Radiation: infra-red, laser.

Also, heat may be applied selectively in a large number of ways (by heated collet, heated element, inductive coil, or even soldering iron). Of the various processes, only two (infra-red radiation and hot vapour convection) are used to any great extent. Laser soldering is currently in late developmental stages, and shows great promise for the mass SC soldering of surface mounted components.

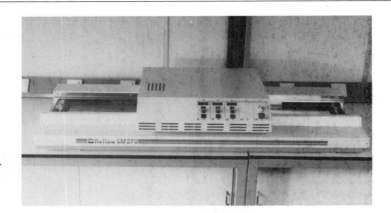

Plate 5.9 *Reddish SM270 infra-red soldering machine for SC soldering of surface mount assemblies (Groatmoor)*

Infra-red radiation soldering

Generally, infra-red (IR) soldering machines direct infra-red heat on to the board from above and below, as shown in Figure 5.35. Radiating elements have built-in thermocouples to allow temperature control.

Heat transferred and so the temperature of the joints to be soldered, however, depends on the materials and shapes of the board and components, as well as the wavelength of the infra-red radiation. For this reason, it is difficult to be sure that all joints, for any individual board, reach the same temperature. The effect of different joint temperatures is known as the **shadow effect**.

Wavelengths of between about 1 and 6.5 µm are generally used, with those in the range 1 to 2.5 µm classed (for soldering purposes) as short wave radiation, while those above 5 µm are classed as medium or long wave. (Infra-red wavelengths actually range from 0.73 to 100 µm.) Short wave infra-red radiating elements are, typically, tungsten lamps, while long wave elements are panel elements.

In operating terms, the shorter the wavelength of the infra-red element, the more likely is the machine, and hence boards soldered, to suffer from the shadow effect. On the other hand, more uniform heating of the solder paste is obtained with short wavelengths. The longer wavelength elements have an advantage, in that the air around them is heated.

Usually, therefore, boards are preheated by circulating the warmed air associated with long wave elements, to provide convection preheating, with the elements providing only final infra-red heating (around 40% of the

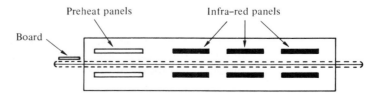

Figure 5.35 *Infra-red SC soldering process*

total) to raise joints to soldering temperatures. Other non-infra-red elements are sometimes used to aid preheating, too.

Preheating effectively minimizes the temperature differences which may occur between joints, while ensuring reasonably fast process times. An added advantage of preheating is that the solder paste itself may be cured in the single process – without preheating, the solder requires separate curing.

Infra-red machines are easily adapted to in-line processing of surface mounted assemblies.

Plate 5.10 *IR8 and IR16 long wave infra-red SC soldering machines for surface mount assemblies (Hollis Europe)*

Hot vapour soldering

Hot vapour soldering processes are sometimes called **saturated vapour**, **condensation**, or, most commonly, **vapour phase** (VPS) soldering processes. (The term vapour phase is rather loose, originating from the fact that the board is heated in a liquid which happens to be in its saturated vapour phase.)

Although classed here as a convection form of heating, heat transfer in a hot vapour soldering process takes place when a saturated vapour condenses on the board, and is thus a product of the liquid's latent heat of evaporation. If a liquid is selected with a boiling point of that required to convert the solder paste into molten solder (around 200°C to 230°C), then once that temperature has been reached, no further condensation can take place, and so no further temperature rise can occur. Temperature control in the process is therefore simply not required.

In turn the equipment, in principle, is extremely simple (Figure 5.36). An element heats the liquid to boiling point, while the assembly is positioned in the resultant vapour above the liquid. Times to reach soldering tempera-

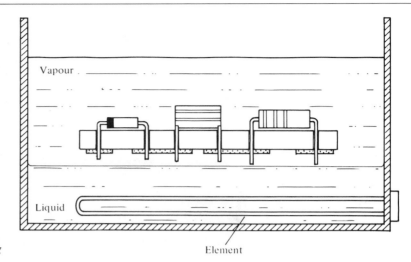

Figure 5.36 *Principle of hot vapour soldering, commonly known as vapour phase soldering*

ture range from as little as just 5 or 6 s for small assemblies, to around 50 s for large assemblies. The vapour also removes flux and flux residues after soldering has taken place, reducing the requirement for post-assembly cleaning.

In practice many problems arise, mainly owing to the liquid used, and the problems of its vapour escaping. First, to greatly reduce vapour loss, cooling coils must be positioned so that the local vapour immediately condenses and falls back into the liquid. Second, inlet and outlet extraction systems may be needed to totally eliminate any vapour still present after the cooling coils. Third, in batch machines, secondary vapours are required to form an effective blanket over the vapour to prevent loss. Fourth, there must be some method of filtering the liquid and cleaning the element, to enable flux and flux residue extraction. Fifth, to maintain fast heating rates, some rapid control over heating power must be included to ensure sufficient saturation of the vapour when large assemblies enter the vapour. An in-line version of a vapour phase soldering machine is shown in Figure 5.37.

Preheating of the assembly is also a good idea to reduce thermal shock, cure solder paste, and to help prevent vapour loss owing to increased circulation when a cold assembly enters the vapour.

To date, vapour phase soldering machines have proved themselves beyond doubt in the soldering of surface mounted assemblies. The fact that in-line systems are available ensures their use in automated electronics assembly production lines.

Nevertheless, vapour phase soldering processes do induce a few problems when soldering surface mounted components, including:

- **Misalignment**, where two-terminal components move during the soldering process owing to the different times that lands at opposite ends of the component reach soldering temperature (Figure 5.38(a)).

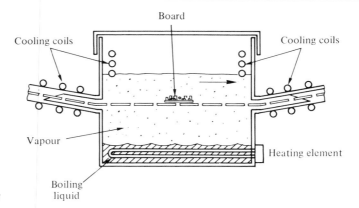

Board

Cooling coils   Cooling coils

Vapour

Heating element

Figure 5.37 *In-line version of a*   Boiling
hot vapour SC soldering machine   liquid

Different surface tensions may therefore be present at opposite component terminals resulting in a force which can move the component out of alignment (Figure 5.38(b)). In an infra-red process, on the other hand, lands are more likely to reach soldering temperature at the same time, and the exact opposite of misalignment can occur – the components actually align themselves more properly on the lands than they were originally placed (Figure 5.38(c)).

- **Solder wicking**, where the solder joint itself opens up, causing some solder to be drawn up the component lead, while the remainder stays on the land. Solder wicking occurs, generally, on the J-shaped leads of leaded chip carriers (Figure 5.39). It is owing to the fact that the component lead reaches soldering temperature some time before the land. In an infra-red soldering process, this difference in temperature is less likely to occur.
- **Tombstoning**, a more severe form of misalignment, where the different surface tensions at each end of a two-terminal component lift the component into a vertical position – resembling a tombstone (Figure 5.40).

Laser soldering

Mass laser soldering systems form the latest SC soldering process. Until recently, the possible advantages of a laser soldering process were known, but development had not reached a satisfactory conclusion.

Laser soldering has been used for a while to solder individual joints with great accuracy. Instant and fine control over the laser means that the smallest of joints can be soldered without damage, and the largest of joints can still be guaranteed sufficient heat.

More recently, process control has been developed such that many joints can now be soldered in a sequential fashion. With joint times in the region of 250 ms, however, multi-laser systems are essential to keep overall board soldering times (with possibly thousands of joints) to acceptable lengths.

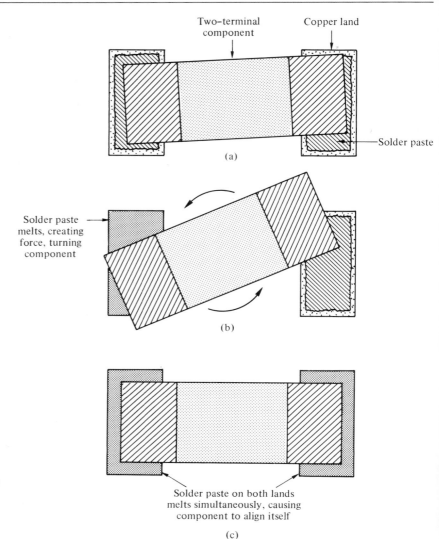

Two-terminal component

Copper land

Solder paste

(a)

Solder paste melts, creating force, turning component

(b)

Figure 5.38 *Misalignment of components when hot vapour soldering. Solder paste on lands at each end of two-terminal components may melt at different times (a) resulting in a force (b) which can move the component out of alignment. In an infra-red process the component is aligned (c)*

Solder paste on both lands melts simultaneously, causing component to align itself

(c)

Heated collet

One SC soldering process which is not a mass method, but should be described for completeness, is the **heated collet**, sometimes called a **thermode**, shown in Figure 5.41. Here an electrically-heated collet, the shape of the surface mounted component to be soldered, is positioned over the placed component, and heated so the solder paste under the component terminals melts. In effect, the method is a simple adaptation of a conventional hand-held soldering iron, designed to solder all terminals of a surface mounted component simultaneously, and allowing semi-automated or automated soldering on a small scale.

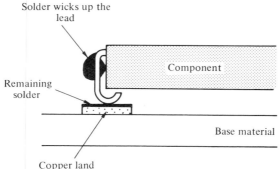

Figure 5.39 *Solder wicking when hot vapour soldering, caused by the component termination being at a higher temperature than the land*

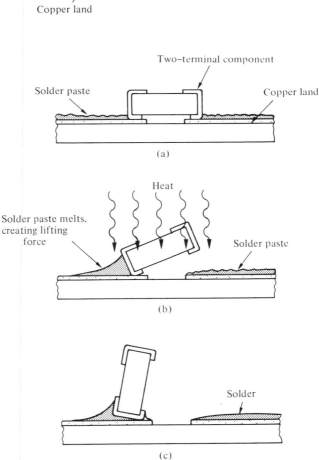

Figure 5.40 *Tombstoning, a severe form of misalignment*

In practice, the collet must be non-wettable. This allows the required temperature to melt the solder paste to be reached, after which the collet is allowed to cool (until the solder solidifies) before removal from the component's terminals. Fairly accurate control of temperature is needed to do this, so a thermocouple sensor is incorporated into or near to the collet.

A heated collet SC soldering process typically would be used where flat-pack or tape automated bonded integrated circuits are required to be mounted on a previously CS soldered assembly. As these components cannot be soldered by CS soldering processes, the heated collet method gives manufacturers who already have CS soldering equipment the option of using these multi-terminal surface mounted devices, without the expense of mass SC soldering equipment.

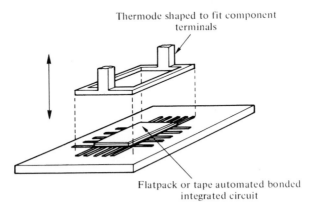

Figure 5.41 *Soldering by heated collet*

Comparison of soldering processes

Table 5.6 (adapted from Siemens) lists various components and compares the many soldering processes, summarizing the process suitabilities for component types, and possible production rates.

Standards

UK	USA
Def Stan 03–22	Mil Std2000

Cleaning of PCBs

Cleanliness in the electronics assembly industry has never been particularly sought after. Too often manufacturers have done as little as specifically requested by the customer, to produce clean assemblies. Although, externally, appliances may have appeared as bright as new pins, internally, they could be compared to rusty nails. Cleanliness costs money, after all.

However, as modern electronics assemblies increase in complexity and packing density, so do the requirements for cleanliness increase. One of the main areas where it is now essential that extremely high levels of cleanliness are maintained is directly after the soldering process.

Soldering, with its requirement for fluxes to aid the process, and the resultant flux residues, is a messy business. Flux and flux residues are

Table 5.6 Comparing soldering processes and component types (after Siemens)

Soldering process CS processes	Through-hole components	Two-terminal and SOT	SO VSO	PLCC	FP	TAB	Packing density	Production rate
Wave	+	+	0	–	0	–	Low	High
Dual-wave	+	+	+	–	0	–	Medium	High
Dual-wave with hot-air knife	+	+	+	0	0	–	Medium	High
SC processes								
Infra-red	–	+	+	+	+	+	High	High
Vapour phase	–	+[1]	+	+[2]	+	+	High	High
Laser	–	+	+	+	+	+	High	Medium
Heated collet	–	–	+	+	+	+	High	Low
Hot air	–	+	+	+	+	0	High	Medium

Notes:
[1] Risk of tombstoning.
[2] Risk of solder wicking.
+ Suitable.
0 Hardly suitable.
– Not suitable.

corrosive, to a greater or lesser extent, so if they remain on the assembly corrosion will occur. In the past, owing to low packing densities and large components, corrosion may not have had any effect, if any, for years in the appliance's life.

If corrosion, even just a little on the other hand, occurs where high packing densities, extremely thin copper tracks, fragile components and so on, are present; then rapid malfunction may occur. Of necessity, therefore, manufacturers are needing to clean their products.

Yet there are other advantages too, to cleaning, which manufacturers should see as useful. These are:

- To allow automatic test equipment access to test points.
- Easier visual inspection.
- To prepare the board for subsequent application of protective **conformal coatings**.
- To ease mechanical handling.

All these aspects help to improve quality and reliability of the product. All manufacturers, therefore, should view cleaning as part of the organization's defined quality assurance programme.

Conformal coatings are almost obligatory for fine-line boards, that is, with extremely thin and closely spaced tracks, where even small dust particles may cause circuit malfunctions. In turn, if a board must be conformally coated, it must first be suitably cleaned.

Depending on the assembly to be cleaned, and the flux used, either aqueous or solvent products are used to clean boards. These are applied in a number of ways, including:

- Brush.
- Immersion.
- Spray.
- Wave.
- Ultrasonic agitation.

Cleaning processes of all types are available in batch or in-line machines.

Often, residues and fluxes are classed as **polar** (sometimes called **ionic**), or **non-polar** (sometimes called **non-ionic**), referring to whether the materials' molecules are permanently polarized, and dissociate to form ions, in water or not. A general guideline is that where residues are polar; clean the assembly with a polar solution. Further, where the residues are non-polar; either convert them to polar form and clean with a polar solution, or clean with a non-polar solution.

Polar residues and fluxes pose the most serious problem, as any atmospheric moisture during operational life will cause them to dissolve, maybe forming chemical reactions and carrying electric currents. it is *essential* they are removed. Non-polar residues and fluxes, although not so important to remove for atmospheric moisture reasons, may prevent correct circuit operation by forming insulating films on connectors and the like. It is *preferable* they are removed, therefore, from most assemblies. In certain cases, customer specifications may call for their removal, too.

Plate 5.11 *Printed circuit board cleaning using solvent (ICI Solvents)*

Polar solutions are usually based on water, sometimes deionized, sometimes with the addition of alcohol or detergent. Non-polar solutions, on the other hand, are usually solvents of some form. Obviously, water-based cleaning methods are generally preferable, being easier to handle and less likely to damage the environment, but the chosen cleaning method depends primarily on the flux.

Figure 5.42 summarizes common cleaning methods, depending on the flux-type used in the soldering process. This shows the two flux types described earlier in this chapter, along with the three corresponding basic flux-removal methods. Two techniques are of note. First, the use of a biodegradable cleaner, say, an alkaline, to remove rosin-based flux by converting the rosin to a water-soluble, or at least water-washable, material called a **rosin soap**, then removing this with water. The reaction required to convert rosin to rosin soap is known as **saponification**. This method is becoming increasingly popular, owing to its environmentally friendly nature.

The second notable technique is the use of a household dishwasher to clean water soluble residue fluxes from assemblies. Generally, a dishwasher provides adequate heating and agitation to do the job, at a reasonable cost. Time for a cleaning programme, however, and batch operation prevents use in high-volume production lines.

Use of saponifying biodegradable cleaners is not restricted to organically soluble fluxes, and may benefit cleaning processes for water soluble fluxes, too. Similarly, dishwashers may also find applications in water cleaning of organically soluble fluxes.

Where water cleaning is undertaken, manufacturers must be aware of the

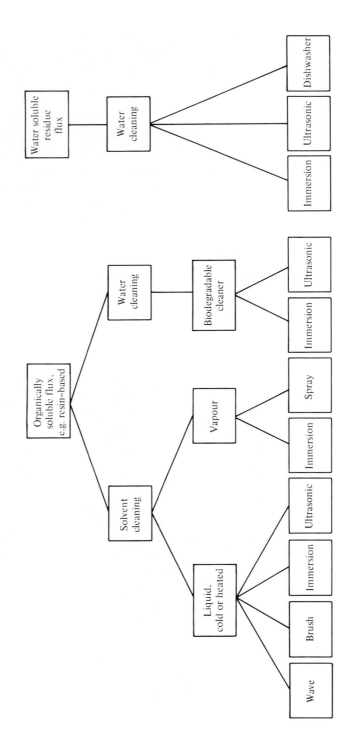

Figure 5.42 *Summary of common post-solder cleaning methods*

damage the water itself may do to assemblies. Salt in the water, even at extremely low concentrations such as found in tap water, will produce the very effects of ionic dissociation the cleaning was intended to remove. Further, water intake by capillary means may take these contaminants inside components. A final rinse in deionized water (which may not, incidentally, be capable of removing capillary-ingressed contaminants), followed by thorough drying is essential. Drying may take the form of hot-air knives to blow off excess water, followed by baking, and is a comparatively long operation, which may hold-up the production process.

On the other hand, where solvent cleaning is undertaken, manufacturers must be aware of the potential environmental and human damage which may occur in handling and disposal. Local, national, or international regulations may stipulate solvents which must not be used.

Standard

USA
IPC SC60
IPC AC62
Mil P28809

Plate 5.12 *Scanning electron microphotograph of tape automated bond integrated circuit joints on to a circuit board (RJ)*

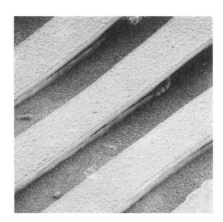

Plate 5.13 *As Plate 5.12, but in greater detail (RJ)*

Plate 5.14 *Scanning electron microphotograph of tape automated bond integrated circuit joints at the semiconductor die (RJ)*

Plate 5.15 *As Plate 5.14, but in greater detail (RJ)*

Plate 5.16 *Scanning electron microphotograph of defective tape automated bond integrated circuit joints (RJ)*

References

R.J. Klein Wassink, *Soldering in Electronics*, Scotland: Electrochemical Publications Ltd.

Howard H. Manko, *Soldering Handbook for Printed Circuits and Surface Mounting*, New York: Van Nostrand Reinhold.

Siemens, *Soldering in SMD Technology*, Munich: Siemens Aktiengesellschaft.

6 Testing for quality

The philosophy of quality

Qwertyuiop Electronics plc, is an established manufacturer of television receivers. Current sales are of around 20,000 sets a year, at an average price to the consumer of £500. Qertyuiop televisions are sold to the public through retail outlets around the country, and 30% of the retail price is profit for the outlets themselves.

A warranty period of one year is given with all televisions, and approximately 10% of televisions sold require some service work in that time. Retail outlets service the receivers, and bill Qwertyuiop Electronics for work carried out under warranty. Average service charge to the company is £30 per repair.

Service expenditure:

20,000 receivers, 10% require service, average cost £30
= £60,000

This is spent by the company, each year, to have television sets repaired.

The company installs test and inspection equipment to the tune of £100,000, which it intends to write off over a four year period, in an attempt to improve product reliability.

After the equipment is installed, an instant improvement is apparent, with only 3% of television sets requiring service work to be carried out during the warranty period. The service expenditure is now:

20,000 receivers, 3% require service, average cost £30
= £18,000

To demonstrate its improved product quality, Qwertyuiop Electronics decides to give customers a two year warranty period. During this time, a further 2% of receivers require service, so the service expenditure is now:

20,000 receivers, 5% require service, average cost £30
= £30,000 over two years
= £15,000 a year

Thus, a saving of £45,000 a year has been made on service expenditure. The test and inspection equipment cost can be written off in just over two years – not the original period allowed, of four years.

However, as Qwertyuiop televisions now have a two year warranty period, a price increase of, say, 2% is justified. Extra income, therefore, is:

20,000 receivers, at 70% of 2% of £500
= £140,000

This means the company is well into profit, simply because the test equipment was purchased.

Quality, goes the saying, is free. And, here, it gives a profit, too.

A strategy of costs

Now, this scenario is an extremely simple one, and will doubtless make many accountants wince, but it does show how the cost of testing and inspecting electronics assemblies may be offset, more than completely, by the advantages gained in the assembly's greater reliability.

The fact that defects have been reduced at an early stage in a product's life effectively eliminates the requirement for later repair of the defect (called **rework**). And rework is far more costly than early elimination. This principle is true at all stages of a product's life.

As a rough guideline, the cost of defect correction is considered to rise by a factor of ten with each production stage of an appliance's life. So, a defect which may cost 3p to correct at pre-assembly level (say, a faulty resistor), will cost 30p to correct at post-assembly level, £3 at packaged level, and £30 to repair in service. This factor of ten may rise, though, as assemblies become more and more complex.

Reliability

The term **reliability** is defined as a system's ability to perform its required function, under known conditions, for a certain period of time. In that, there is no defined connection between reliability and **quality**, which is the achievement of a system to conform to its specified performance. The two terms are often, not surprisingly, confused, as reliability and quality of a system are normally considered hand-in-hand. If a product is reliable, it is considered good quality: if it is a quality product, it is thought of as reliable. However, one term does not necessarily imply the other.

Failure and its causes

Any device or system may, at some time, break down or fail. **Failure** is the termination of a device or system's ability to perform its function. Failure may be owing to misuse; or it may be caused by an inherent weakness. It may be sudden; or it may be gradual. It may be partial; it may be complete.

Measuring failure

An important figure concerning failures and reliability, is the **failure rate**, given the symbol λ.

An important *measurement* of failure, on the other hand, is the average time between failures. This is measured as **mean time to failure** (MTTF), where:

$$MTTF = T/N = 1/\lambda$$

where T is the total operating time (in hours) and N is the number of times operation is interrupted. For example, if a system fails five times in 20,000 hours, the mean time to failure is 4000 hours.

Where the system is made up of a number of components, a failure in any one may cause system failure, so including individual components, the relationship can be adjusted to:

$$MTTF = nT/N$$

where n is the number of components. So, the failure rate per component is:

$$\lambda_c = N/nT = 1/MTTF$$

Another important time relating to failure, is the **mean time to repair** (MTTR), a measure of the system's **maintainability**. This is a basic measure of how long it takes the manufacturer's service engineer to get to the system, isolate the fault, and repair it.

The mean time to failure and the mean time to repair are related in a system, such that a measure of how often failure can be expected, the **mean time between failure** (MTBF), is:

$$MTBF = MTTF + MTTR$$

With a knowledge of a system's components, manufacturers are therefore able to specify these aspects.

Plotting failure

Reliability is often illustrated in a **bathtub curve**, called for its shape, where failure rate and time are plotted (Figure 6.1). Any device or system's bathtub curve will have the same general shape, there being three distinct parts to the curve:

- The **early period**.
- The **useful life period**.
- The **wear-out period**.

During the early period, failure rate is quite high. These **early failures** will be caused by substandard components or workmanship.

During the useful life period failure rate is constant; failures will occur at fairly predictable intervals, and will be caused by random faults. It is these random faults which basically define the system's mean time between failure.

Finally, during the wear-out period failure rate increases, as the system deteriorates through age.

For practical purposes the curve may be considered as made up from

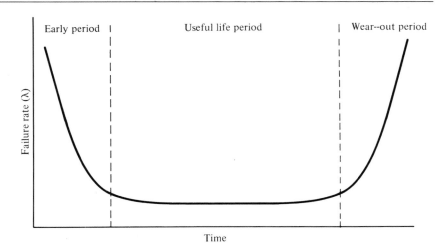

Figure 6.1 *The bathtub curve method of illustrating reliability*

three totally separate curves, shown in Figure 6.2: the early, useful, and wear-out curves. By improving (that is lowering) any of these curves the system's reliability is increased. The manufacturer's job is to separate the curves, isolate the causes of failure in each, and eliminate or at least reduce those causes. Generally, this is done by product testing.

Quality audits

One of the first questions any manufacturer must ask is: what should be tested?

In answering that, the manufacturer's effects on the assembly must be considered. In any assembly's life, there are only four stages in which the manufacturer has direct control over the assembly:

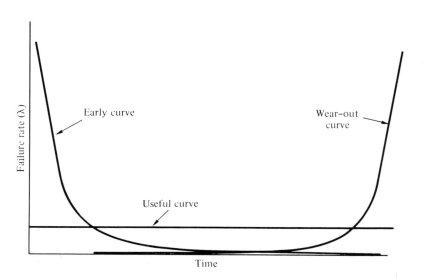

Figure 6.2 *Bathtub curve, broken up into three distinctly separate curves*

- When the assembly is being designed.
- As the component parts of the assembly enter the factory from suppliers, prior to production.
- During production.
- Immediately after production, prior to delivery of the assembly to customers.

Figure 6.3 shows an overall block diagram, illustrating how stages interrelate. As they *do* interrelate, any fault at any stage in the manufacturing process will affect other stages reducing overall product reliability, hence reducing quality. In a nutshell, tests must be built into all these stages so that quality is assured. Without those tests no such assurance can be stated.

Next question is: what tests are required? The ideal answer is: anything which the manufacturer has influence over should be tested. So, every part of the manufacturing process must come under scrutiny, including:

- Component parts as they arrive from the suppliers – resistors, capacitors, semiconductors, connectors, printed circuit boards and so on.
- Each production process – insertion, placement, soldering, post-assembly cleaning and so on.
- The unpackaged assembly.
- The packaged assembly.
- The design process itself.

In practical terms, this will not mean complete test and inspection procedures undertaken after each individual process and on each assembly – certain processes will need little or no testing, while others are more critical. Other tests may be performed occasionally, on samples.

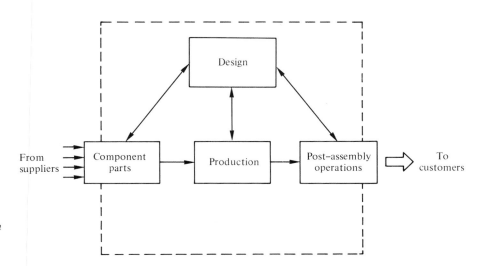

Figure 6.3 *Block diagram, illustrating interrelated stages in the manufacturing processes of an electronic assembly*

Standards

UK	IEC	USA	European
BS 54200	IEC 271	Mil Hdbk 217	DIN 40080
BS 5760	IEC300	Mil Hdbk338	DIN 55350
BS 6001	IEC319	Mil Std756	DIN VG95081
Def Stan 00–5	IEC362	Mil Std781	DIN VG95082
Def Stan 00–40	IEC409	Mil Std785	DIN VG95085
Def Stan 00–41	IEC812	Mil Std790	
Def Stan 00–970	IEC863	Mil Q9858	
Def Stan 05–21			
Def Stan 05–57			

Component parts testing

The testing of the electronic component parts which a manufacturer receives from its suppliers forms the first quality audit the manufacturer must make. In the ideal, all components should be purchased from vendors or distributors with BS 9000, CECC, or IECQ qualification approval or capability approval.

These are explained in detail in Chapter 9, but briefly, they are quality approval systems operated on national, regional and international specification systems, defining the quality of electronic components. BS 9000 is the British specification system. CECC operates in the UK and Europe, while IECQ operates in the UK and internationally. All components available through the systems are of defined quality.

The fact that component quality is defined, means that component vendors have themselves assessed their products to the defined level. Such **vendor assessment** alleviates the large requirement for electronics assemblers to test components as they enter the production area. Purchasing and contractual arrangements are made significantly easier with the systems, too, as lists of components which have approval – **qualified products lists** – are published, as well as an electronic database containing required information about all components listed.

Sometimes, though, components or materials which do not have qualifications or capability approval are required for assemblies. Where components or printed circuit boards are in this category then **purchasor assessment** remains the only viable methods of assuring quality.

Passive components

Components may vary in three basic ways:

- Value.
- Dimensions.
- Solderability.

Value and dimensions may be measured on delivery, with straightforward hand-operated, or automatic measuring equipment. Solderability, however, is more difficult to determine.

Solderability testing

A component's solderability is a measure of its suitability for soldering. Therefore, it is a property which concerns the surface of the component's terminations, that is, how wettable the surface is, under defined conditions of environment, temperature, and time (see Chapter 5).

Measurement of solderability may be done in quite a number of ways, and readers are referred to more specialized texts on the topic for accounts of these (Klein Wassink, Manko), as well as relevant standards. One of the most common methods, described here, is the **wetting balance** method.

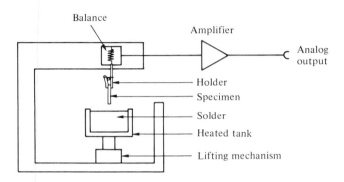

Figure 6.4 *Wetting balance method*

In the wetting balance method, the fluxed component is immersed, at a defined rate, in a bath of molten solder. After a defined dwell time it is then withdrawn from the bath, at the same rate. Various parts of the wetting balance method are shown in Figure 6.4, while the five stages of the procedure are illustrated in Figure 6.5. These stages are:

1. Just before immersion.
2. Just after the moment of immersion when the solder's surface meniscus is still curved down, resulting in an upward force.
3. When wetting has reached the point where the force of surface tension is zero; so the only force remaining on the component is that of buoyancy.
4. As the component is withdrawn when the meniscus curves upwards, resulting in a downward force from surface tension.
5. When the component is totally withdrawn.

A transducer allows a direct reading of the resultant of the vertical forces of buoyancy and surface tension acting on the component, such that it is

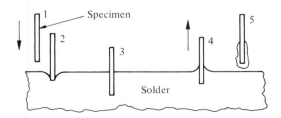

Figure 6.5 *Five stages of the wetting balance procedure for measuring solderability*

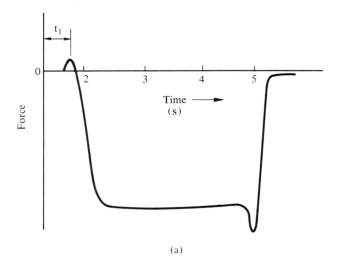

(a)

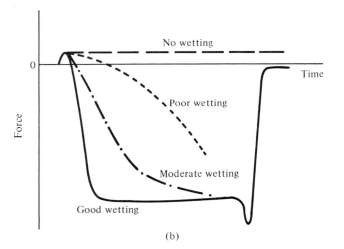

Figure 6.6 *Results of a wetting balance measurement of solderability. (a) Force-time diagram marked with the five stages of the process. (b) Several force-time diagrams showing various degrees of wetting*

(b)

possible to obtain a force-time diagram, using suitable test equipment, say, chart recorder or storage oscilloscope. Such a force-time diagram is shown in Figure 6.6(a), marked with various points corresponding to the five stages of the procedure.

Degrees of wetting will be visible on such a force-time diagram, where the degree corresponds to the rate at which the force changes after wetting commences, that is, during the third stages of the procedure. Figure 6.6(b) shows possible graphs representing those obtained at several degrees of wetting.

It is necessary to define conditions before a wetting balance measurement is made, such as:

- Type of solder (say, 62% tin/38% lead).
- The solder temperature (say, 215°C).
- The flux (say, pure resin, R or WW).
- Immersion rate (say, $25\,\mathrm{mm\,s^{-1}}$).
- Immersion depth (say, 5 mm).
- Preparation of the component (say, steam aging for a period of four hours).

It is then necessary to define a suitable standard of solderability, say, when not more than 5% of the terminals are dewetted, or non-wetted.

IC testing

Integrated circuits may be tested for functionality, that is, whether they perform the circuit function required of them, on delivery.

PCBs – bare board testing

Where printed circuit boards are tested prior to assembly, tests are often known as **bare-board tests**. Main procedures are to test the conductive track for:

- Continuity.
- Short circuits.
- Accuracy.
- Solderability.

Track continuity, short circuits, accuracy

Typical test methods include:

- Visual testing.
- Electrical testing.
- Automated optical testing.
- Destructive testing.

Simple boards may be checked visually, with the aid of a microscope, but visual testing of complex boards, particularly multi-layered and/or surface mounted assemblies, will be extremely difficult and time-consuming – if not impossible.

Electrical testing relies on probes touching the circuit board track at relevant points and taking resistance readings. A low resistance reading where it should be, indicates continuity. Low resistance where it should *not* be, on the other hand, indicates a short circuit. High resistance where it should not be indicates lack of continuity. Electrical testing is performed in one of two ways:

- On a bed-of-nails fixture.
- By moving probes.

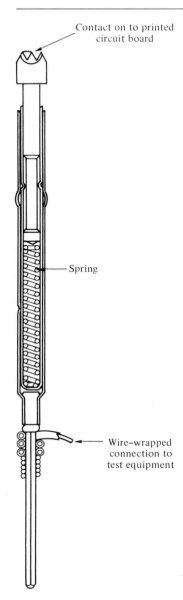

Contact on to printed
circuit board

Spring

Wire–wrapped
connection to
test equipment

Figure 6.7 *Typical spring-loaded test probe of a bed-of-nails test fixture*

A **bed-of-nails fixture** is an arrangement of pin-type test probes on a plate, which is pressed against the circuit board, such that probes touch the copper track of the board at relevant points. It is a useful method of access to circuit boards, used at post-assembly test stage also. One disadvantage, however, is that fixtures are specific to one type of circuit board – a new board-type requires a new fixture. Making of fixtures is a complex job; time-consuming and expensive, and positional accuracy of probes is limited. A typical spring-loaded test probe is shown in Figure 6.7, where the required wire-wrapped connection to the test equipment may be seen. It is this requirement of wire-wrapping or similar hard-wired connection which makes the job of making bed-of-nails fixtures very demanding in terms of time.

Many bed-of-nails fixtures are **universal**, allowing up to 50,000 test points, although individual fixtures will probably be bought with considerably fewer test probes. Often, at a later time, the equipment may be upgraded with additional test probes. This is possible because a standard grid is typically used (not always, though) where probes are located on 2.54 mm (that is, 0.1 in) centres. Use of smaller grids, say, on 1.27 mm (that is, 0.05 in) centres, is not usually recommended as the corresponding small diameter test probes are extremely fragile.

Other bed-of-nails fixtures are **dedicated**, following no particular grid, and are purpose-built according to the printed circuit board. Dedicated fixtures are correspondingly cheaper than universal ones, but cannot be adapted to printed circuit boards of other circuits.

Fixtures are forced against the circuit boards under test by either vacuum (effectively 'sucking' the fixture on to the circuit board) or pneumatic (pushing the fixture against the circuit board) means. Which method depends largely on the number of test probes. For example, a universal fixture with a full complement (that is, 50,000) of test probes, each requiring 80 g force to bed it down onto a test point, requires a total force of around 4000 kg: vacuum-operated fixtures cannot provide this. On the other hand, most dedicated fixtures *do* use a vacuum method, for simplicity.

The **moving probe** approach, on the other hand, has two robotic probes, which are positioned at points on the circuit board while the test relevant to those points is performed. The probes are then moved to the next two points, and so on. Positional accuracy of test probes is at least as good as that which bed-of-nails fixtures allow. Such sequential testing of complex circuit boards can take considerable time, though.

Design of printed circuit boards (specifically those for surface mounted assemblies) where the test probe testing is to be undertaken is covered in Chapter 3.

Electrical testing methods are sufficient for bare-board testing of many circuit boards. However, it may be that extremely complicated, multi-layered boards simply cannot be fully tested by their contact approach. In such cases, **automated optical inspection** systems may form a supplementary solution.

Main optical methods include cameras or scanning lasers to obtain images of the whole board, or its parts. In any automated optical inspection method, ideal characteristics must be previously defined; either as a perfect image, sometimes called the **golden** board, or as a complete set of rules determining each feature of the board.

In the first, images of the actual board are simply compared with the golden image to detect differences, which are treated as defects. In the second, inspected features which are not recognized, according to the rule set, are assumed to be defects.

Occasionally, destructive tests are required to assess features of bare printed circuit boards. Usually, such tests are only performed as a last resort, and used only to test features which cannot be tested by non-destructive means – destructive tests are, as may be expected, expensive and destroy the product. Typical destructive tests assess plated-through holes, etchback, multi-layer registration, and so on.

Solderability

Printed circuit board solderability may be measured using the wetting balance method described earlier.

Standards

UK	IEC	USA	European
BS 2011	IEC68	Mil Std202	DIN 40046
BS 4584	IEC160	Mil Std810	DIN group 1280
BS 5772	IEC721	Mil Std883	DIN group 1290
BS 6140		Mil F14256	DIN group 1420
BS 6221		QQ S571	
BS 6493			
Def Stan 00–13			
Def Stan 00–26			
Def Stan 00–52			
Def Stan 05–38			
Def Stan 07–55			
Def Stan 08–5			
Def Stan 59–41			
Def Stan 81–41			

Production processes

Any process through which a product is taken may affect the product's quality. However, in the case of electronics assemblies, a decision must be taken as to whether it is possible to split up the overall assembly process into its discrete parts, or whether this is impracticable. A typical electronics assembly process is shown as a block diagram in Figure 6.8. This is a process to manufacture a mixed assembly, on which some surface mounted components are placed then SC soldered, followed by insertion of leaded components and further placing of more surface mounted components,

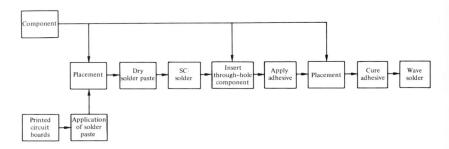

Figure 6.8 *Typical electronics assembly process*

followed finally by wave soldering. It represents a summary of the procedure shown in Figure 3.35, and described in Chapter 3.

Testing of the completed assembly after soldering may, of course, ascertain whether all production processes have been carried out correctly, but once soldered, it is difficult to correct any process which was *incorrect*. If, for example, an integrated circuit was placed the wrong way round, desoldering and re-soldering it the right way round will be very time-consuming and expensive.

To test assemblies immediately prior to soldering, though, is difficult. Electrical testing is virtually impossible, as it cannot be guaranteed that electrical connections occur between component terminations and the circuit board track. Visual testing could, however, be implemented, as could limited automated optical inspection.

Where testing of assemblies immediately after soldering takes places, on the other hand, prior testing may be considered unnecessary. This is especially true if the time between the soldering process and test is short, so that production defects have occurred in only a handful of assemblies before they may be resolved. Where the time between soldering and test is longer, many assemblies may have accumulated before the defect is isolated. Where the time between soldering and test is very long, or where little or no testing of soldered assemblies takes place, complete lots of assemblies may have defects, of course.

The unpackaged assembly

There are a number of tests which may be carried out on unpackaged assemblies (that is, boards, fully assembled and soldered, but not yet housed), including:

- Visual inspection.
- Destructive testing.
- In-circuit testing.
- Functional testing.

Another form of testing, reliability screening under stress conditions, is also sometimes performed on assembled boards. It is discussed later, as a packaged assembly test procedure.

Often terms such as **device under test** (DUT), **unit under test** (UUT), or **loaded board** are used to refer to the assembly being tested.

Visual inspection

Initial unaided visual inspections of assemblies can be made but may serve doubtful purposes, as many modern printed circuit boards are of such high component density, with such fine tracks and small components, that few faults may be noticed. An optical aid of at least 5 × magnification will usually be required, preferably higher for surface mounted assemblies. So-called **stereo microscopes**, offering three-dimensional inspection, with a range of up to around 250 × are available.

Human visual inspection of assemblies is comparatively simple; such things as missing components, incorrectly placed components and solder joints, are being looked for. For low volume production rates, it is often an acceptable test method. However, for medium or high volume production rates, it is very time-consuming and expensive. Whether low or high volume production, final quality depends on the people doing the inspection, too. Inspection criteria must be determined, and inspection personnel must be fully trained.

Visual examination of soldered joints entails looking at each joint in turn, to inspect its contours and appearance. From this, a number of things may be assessed, including:

- Degree of wetting at each joint.
- Dewetting.
- Thermal damage to surrounding materials.
- Amount of solder.
- Number of blow holes, cavities, inclusions or cracks.
- Solder balls.

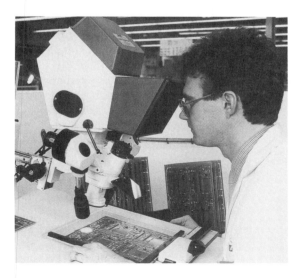

Plate 6.1 *Optical inspection of surface mount assemblies (Siemens)*

Plate 6.2 *Close-up of 5512 automated optical inspection head for printed circuit board assemblies (Universal)*

- Solder bridges.
- Concave shape to the fillet.
- Solder surface itself.

The solder surface depends on the soldering process. CS soldered joints are usually assessed by their shininess, whereas SC soldered joints typically have a finely-grained surface.

On the other hand, many **automated optical inspection** systems, similar to those for bare-board testing, are now available which alleviate the tasks of checking for incorrectly placed or missing components. Automatic inspection of soldered joints, however, is more difficult to perform. Various systems are used, including:

- Infra-red signature analysis.
- X-ray imaging.

In **infra-red signature analysis** systems, joints are heated by laser, then observed when cooling, by detecting infra-red emissions. The properties of the joint affect its cooling characteristics, so differences between good and poor joints may be detected.

In **X-ray imaging** inspection systems, the fact that X-rays pass more easily through components and board than through solder allows detection of solder bridges or joints with inadequate amounts of solder.

The same methods used in automated optical inspection of bare-boards, that is, where ideal characteristics of assemblies are previously defined (either as a perfect or **golden** board where inspected characteristics are simply compared to detect differences, or as a complete set of rules), are incorporated into inspection of assembled boards.

Destructive testing

Various mechanical tests can be performed to test assembly performance. Usually, they are based on destructively testing individual joints. For example, pulling a component lead from an assembly, and measuring the applied force when the joint breaks, qualifies as a destructive test. Similarly, a destructive test may be pulling a surface mounted component from a board, and measuring the force required. Vibrating the assembly until components and board part company, is another.

Destructive testing is expensive, slow and time-comsuming. Further, the results often require skilled interpretation. Usually, therefore, destructive tests are incorporated, if at all, only at design and development stages, then at selected stages during long production runs.

In-circuit testing

Usually the first electrical testing method applied to an assembly, **in-circuit testing** procedures access the assembly via nodal test points, allowing testing of individual components within the circuit, and their connections to the board's conducting track. By comparing the measured values with defined ideal values, in-circuit testing, therefore, may isolate short circuits, misplaced components, wrongly valued components, poor soldered joints and defective conductive tracks.

Such defects are known as **manufacturing defects**, that is, they have been caused by a problem somewhere in the manufacture of the assembly. In-circuit testing to isolate such defects is sometimes called **manufacturing defects analysis** for this reason. Another name for in-circuit isolation of manufacturing defects, often used, is **pre-screening**. Estimates have been made that 85 to 90% of all assembly defects are manufacturing defects, and so are of the sorts which can be easily detected by in-circuit testers. Thus, if results of all tests prove to be within defined limits of tolerances, it may be reasonable to assume the assembly will function correctly in use. Passing all tests is no guarantee of correct function, however.

In-circuit testing can go further than simple manufacturing defects analysis, however, by electrically testing individual components to see if they perform as they should. The in-circuit tester generates signals which are specific to the component under test, such that the component's operating characteristics may be measured and compared with the ideal. The test performed depends on the component to the extent that complex integrated circuits such as microprocessors require so many signals (bus, clock, power and so on) they are effectively undergoing a complete functional test (see the following section).

Access to each node in an assembly's circuit is through test points (which must be incorporated into the conductive track at design stage), located by test probes on a bed-of-nails fixture (see page 210). Tests are then performed automatically, one by one, on the assembly and its component parts.

In-circuit test equipment is computer-based, so is not specific to one assembly: a change of program allows another type of assembly to be tested. The bed-of-nails, on the other hand, *is* assembly-specific, and requires alteration with each new type of assembly tested. This is usually done by hand, hard-wiring the test probes to the equipment, although some in-circuit test equipment may involve pneumatic- or vacuum-actuated test probes. The number of test probes varies from just a few tens, to many hundreds.

Equipment typically contains a library of tests for components, the number of components and tests varying from equipment to equipment, up to around 5000.

The greatest advantage of in-circuit testing is its ability to detect and isolate many defects on a single assembly.

Functional testing

In **functional test equipment** the characteristics of the complete assembly, while operating, are tested. Access to the assembly is usually through the assembly's circuit board connectors, although bed-of-nails fixtures may be used instead. Test procedures involve applying power and test signal patterns, while monitoring assembly characteristics. In this way, a simulation is made of the assembly's normal function and operation, so that its performance is noted.

In operation, functional testing is much quicker than in-circuit testing. It gives a simple pass or fail indication (often called **go/no go** testing), which can be of particular benefit in high volume production lines. However, little

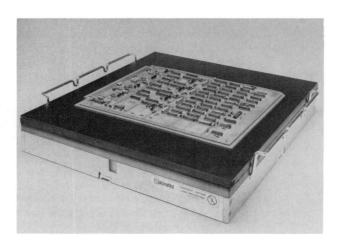

Plate 6.3 *Vacuum fixture for in-circuit testing of printed circuit board assemblies (Factron)*

(if any) indication of specific defects is given. Consequent finding of the defects may be time-consuming.

Combination testers are available, which perform both in-circuit and functional tests. Thus the in-circuit tester's inherent ability to perform functional tests on individual components complements the functional tester's ability for testing complete assemblies. This is, undoubtedly, the trend in modern electrical testing systems for unpackaged assemblies.

The packaged assembly

Assemblies which are fully housed are often subjected to stresses designed to simulate environmental conditions which the assembly may encounter in its normal life. Often the stresses assemblies are subjected to may be prolonged (for the length of the early period, see page 203), with the express purpose of forcing early failures to occur before the appliance is used by the customer. Sometimes, customer specifications, particularly military, call for such subjected stresses (sometimes called **certification tests**, or **qualification tests**) and specify details.

Of more potential, perhaps, are processes performed on the appliance where abnormal environmental conditions are simulated, with the purpose of accelerating the appliance's life cycle. Apart from inducing early failures, if interpreted properly, results of such processes may give manufacturers insight to appliance reliability over the *whole of the life cycle*, pointing the way to improvements.

Such **reliability screening**, sometimes called **environmental stress screening**, is accomplished by exposing the whole appliance batch to the stresses, forcing all possible failures to occur. It relies on a completely different philosophy to all other forms of testing, and indeed, may be seen not as a test at all – reliability screening is a production process, designed specifically to improve product quality. Conventional certification tests look for operation without failures as proof of reliability. Environmental stress screening acknowledges failures, relies on the fact that failures are unavoidable and, indeed, expects and desires them.

Quite a number of environmental stresses may be simulated in reliability screening including, in order of effectiveness (Institute of Environmental Sciences):

- Temperature cycling.
- Vibration.
- High temperature.
- Electrical stress.
- Thermal shock.
- Sine vibration, fixed frequency.
- Low temperature.
- Sine vibration, sweep frequency.
- Combined environment.
- Mechanical shock.
- Humidity.

- Acceleration.
- Altitude.

Reliability screening of unpackaged assemblies is often undertaken by manufacturers, too. This has benefits in that failures may be rectified before boards are housed, though packaging faults may then require a separate screen.

Generally, certification tests detailed by military specifications form the basis for reliability screening tests, using increased stresses. However, as yet, few national, regional, or international standards have been issued. Usually, therefore, screening tests are individually developed by the manufacturer.

Standards

UK	IEC	USA	European
BS 4200	IEC271	Mil Hdbk217	DIN 40080
BS 5760	IEC300	Mil Hdbk338	DIN 55350
BS 6001	IEC319	Mil Std756	DIN VG95081
Def Stan 00–5	IEC362	Mil Std785	DIN VG95082
Def Stan 00–40	IEC409	Mil Std790	DIN VG95085
Def Stan 00–41	IEC812	Mil Q9858	
Def Stan 05–21	IEC863		

References

Institute of Environmental Science, *ESSH (Environment Stress Screening of Electronic Hardware), Environmental Stress Screening Guidelines,* 1981

R.J. Klein Wassink, *Soldering in Electronics,* Scotland: Electrochemical Publications Ltd.

Manko, Howard H., *Soldering Handbook for Printed Circuits and Surface Mounting,* New York: Van Nostrand Reinhold.

7 Standardization of electronics manufacture: quality assurance

Standards

What are standards?

A question like 'What are standards?' taxes almost as much brain power as the question 'How long is a piece of string?'. Basically, a piece of string is about as long as you make it. Standards, likewise, are as you make them.

In definition, a **standard** is a:

> Technical specification or other document available to the public, drawn up with the cooperation and consensus or general approval of all interests affected by it, based on the consolidated results of science, technology and experience, aimed at the promotion of optimum community benefits and approved by a body recognized on the national, regional or international level.
>
> *(ISO Guide 2: 1980)*

Albeit coming from the International Organization for Standardization (ISO), the definition is still incomplete. To the three levels of body (national, regional and international) a fourth should be added: the company level. Although companies should follow national, regional and international standards wherever possible, internal standards applicable to the company must also be followed. In such instances, of course, the 'public' referred to in the ISO definition are company employees and sub-contractees.

The aims of standards and of standardization, stated in the British Standards Institution's guide to standards (BS 0: Part 1 1981), are simple. By providing technical criteria which are accepted by consensus, standards:

- Promote consistent quality.
- Promote economic production.
- Allow rationalization of processes and methods of operation.
- Help confidence in manufacturers and users alike.
- Provide a means of communication among interested parties.
- Promote economy in effort, materials and energy.
- Protect consumer interests.
- Promote the quality of life – safety, health and the environment.
- Promote trade.

Standards, however, are not legally binding regulations. There is no law which demands standards must be used. Compliance with standards is left to the individual, company or organization.

Why comply with standards?

Standardization, itself, is defined by BSI, as:

> The discipline of using the minimum number of parts for the maximum number of purposes, produced by the most economical manufacturing processes, of the appropriate quality to give reliable and acceptable performance at minimum (whole life) cost.
>
> (*PD6470: 1981*)

In short, standardization and the use of standards in product manufacture brings economies at the end of the day, while ensuring quality and reliability in the manufactured product.

Reference to standards

There are three ways in which standards are usually referred to:

- By exact identification. A strict reference to a standard and its date of issue (For example, BS 0: Part 1 1981). Thus, any updates of the standard is not to be incorporated as a matter of course.
- By undated reference. Referring to the standard, but not the date (for example, BS 0: Part 1). Thus any update of the standard *is* to be incorporated as a matter of course.
- General reference. Referring to a standard in non-specific terms (for example, as in BS 0).

Levels of standards

National standards

National standards can be, and often are, incorporated into standards of a higher level. A good example of this can be seen in the American standard EIA232 (often known as RS232) which defines, among other things, the signals of the interface between data circuit-terminating equipment such as computer and connecting cables. The *International Telegraph and Telephone Consultative Committee* (CCITT) recommendation V24 adopts that part of the EIA232 standard with little modification. Thus the EIA232 national standard has become, to all intents and purposes, the V24 international standard.

In the UK, the national standards organization is the British Standards Institution (BSI). It is, incidentally, the oldest national standards organization in the world, starting life in 1901. Now over eighty similar national standards organizations exist all over the world.

Regional standards

The European regional standards organization for general standards is the Comité Européen Normalisation (CEN), of which the European national standards organizations, like BSI, are a part. The electrotechnical counterpart of CEN is CENELEC. Together CEN and CENELEC form the Joint European Standards Institution.

International standards

Internationally, general standards are organized by ISO, while electrotechnical standards are organized by the International Electrotechnical Commission (IEC).

One of the best examples of the way in which national, regional and international standards interact can be seen in the series of standards, at all three levels, aimed at rationalizing quality assurance of electronic components (although dealt with briefly here, it is covered in detail later).

In the UK, the national series is known as the **BS 9000 series**. Standards numbered from BS 9000 through to BS 9999 refer to the UK national standard system for components of **assessed quality**. In Europe and the UK the regional series for assessed quality component is known as the **CECC** (Electronic Components Committee of CENELEC – the European Committee for Electrotechnical Standardization) series. Finally, in the UK and worldwide the equivalent international series is known as the International Electrotechnical Committee Quality Assessment System.

Standards organizations and bodies

Which standards to comply with?

Starting from the assumption that the product is some form of electronics assembly, the question of which standards to comply with really depends on where the product is to be sold, and who the customer is. In the UK, for example, four bodies must be considered. These, and the main types of standards relevant to electronics assembly are:

- BSI. The national organization for standards relevant to electrotechnical (and non-electrotechnical) industrial and commercial aspects. BSI represents UK viewpoints in regional and international organizations, too. The majority of UK standards are formed by the general *BS series*, and many relevant standards fall in this series. All aspects of component standards, from specification and manufacture, to distribution and test, make up the *BS 9000 series*. Many publications, referenced by prefix, are also produced by BSI, including harmonized series of component quality assessment (*BS CECC*), codes of practice (*CP*), published documents (*PD*) and handbooks. The work of BSI and some of the services it offers are detailed later in this chapter.
- CENELEC. The regional standards organization for Europe. To-

gether with CEN, as the Joint European Standards Institution, work is undertaken towards the harmonization of national standards into regional standards (see BS CECC, page 221), and the production of regional standards (the *CECC series*).

- IEC. The international, worldwide, standards organization, working towards the harmonization of regional standards into international standards. These international standards are to form the *CQ series* of standards in the International Electrotechnical Committee Quality Assessment System, for component quality assurance. More general work by the IEC is carried out by technical committees and their subcommittees, each responsible for a well-defined area in electrotechnical subjects. Four special committees also exist: the advisory committee on electronics and telecommunications (ACET); the advisory committee on safety (ACOS); the international special committee on radio interference (CISPR); and the information technology coordinating group (ITCG). With the exception of CISPR, committees produce standards with the general prefix *IEC*. International CISPR standards are prefixed *CISPR*.

- Ministry of Defence. Standards are produced for armed services purposes by the Ministry of Defence (MoD). These standards, generally with the prefix *Def Stan*, must be met by any manufacturer of components or assemblies proposing to sell to the MoD. Originally, defence standards were completely different from BSI standards although, increasingly, they now conform to the BS 9000 series or BS CECC series standards. Increasingly, therefore, manufacturers will follow normal standards, rather than pure defence standards. The main reason for this rationalized changeover is that, wherever possible in recent years, the MoD has offered draft defence standards to BSI to publish as UK standards. Only where absolutely necessary, in fact, does the MoD publish separate defence standards. The topic of selling components and assemblies to the MoD is covered in detail in Chapter 8.

Throughout Europe, member countries have their own national organizations, including:

- France: Association Française de Normalisation (AFNOR) which uses the main prefixes of *NF* or *UTE*.
- West Germany: Deutches Institut für Normung (DIN) which uses, among others, the *DIN* prefix.

In North America, things start to get complicated. The USA has no governmentally appointed national standards organization; instead many specific bodies have been formed, largely by concerned industrial groups to generate standards and other publications. Important bodies include:

- ANSI. American National Standards Institute (formerly the American Standards Association; before that, the American Engineering Standards Committee), was set up in 1918. Now comprising over 250 professional societies, trade associations, universities, utility organizations, government agencies and corporations, ANSI coordinates the production of the majority of American standards. Note that ANSI does not produce standards itself, instead acting as a national clearing house for standards produced by the other organizations. Around 4000 standards have been coordinated to date by ANSI. ANSI also forms the American representative in IEC production of international standards.

- EIA. The Electronic Industries Association, a national association of electronics manufacturers, issues many standards and publications helpful in promoting component interchangeability. Many of these, although not to national standard level, are issued and known as Joint Electron Device Engineering Council (JEDEC) publications.
- IEEE. The Institute of Electrical and Electronics Engineers only produces a few standards relevant to the manufacture of electronics assemblies.
- IPC. The Institute for Interconnecting and Packaging Electronic Circuits (formerly the Institute of Printed Circuits) was started in 1957. The IPC produces a wide range of relevant standards and other useful publications regarding the manufacture of electronics assemblies.
- ISA. The Instrument Society of America, although producing its own standards too, coordinates US governmental, Canadian and UK standards, relevant to instrumentation, some of which are relevant to manufacture of electronics assemblies.
- NEMA. The National Electrical Manufacturers Association produces standards for electrical and consumer products.

Products intended for sale to the US Department of Defense must comply with military standards and specifications although, since 1986 when a US presidential commission advised the Department of Defense to adopt ANSI standards wherever possible, a rationalization of defense standards (similar to the defence standards' rationalization in the UK) is currently underway. A number of military standardization groups which affect electronic products, exist. Groups, with their prefixing letters, include:

- DOD (Department of Defense). Where a standard is prefixed DOD, it indicates metric standardization. Thus new (and revised non-metric) military standards have the prefix.
- MS (military specifications). Developed by air force, army and navy departments to cover details of components used in electronic assemblies.
- Mil (military standards). Developed by air force, army and navy departments to cover details of circuits, codes, designations, drawing practices, procedures, test methods and so on relating to manufacture of electronic assemblies.
- Mil Std (military standard specifications). Developed by air force, army and navy departments to specify particular requirements.

Three national standards bodies exist in Canada:

- Canadian General Standards Board (CGSB).

- Canadian Standards Association (CSA).
- Underwriters' Laboratories of Canada (ULC).

Various worldwide organizations and bodies generating standards and relevant publications are listed in Table 7.1. These are given merely with the corresponding UK issuing organizations. Readers should note that Appendix 2 contains a listing of worldwide organizations and bodies generating standards and relevant publications, giving *actual* addresses.

The work of BSI

BSI is an independent profit-making standards organization, operating under a Royal Charter. In the large part, BSI makes its profit through sales of standards, although other income arises from members' subscriptions, and sales of services and facilities.

Its function is to help UK industry compete in world markets. To this end, it plays a great part in the overall rationalization of standards into internationally harmonized versions. By doing this, so that individual countries' standards are harmonized, exporting becomes easier and so a manufacturer's marketplace greatly increases.

Standards

This is not BSI's only role. For instance, it coordinates and issues around 700 new or revised standards each year; ensuring new materials, processes and technologies are covered by standards. Some 3000 committees carry out this work, coordinating consumers, government departments, manufacturers and research establishments. A total of over 10,000 standards are currently published.

BSI test centre

BSI provides confidential testing services at its test centre, which may be accessed by all industrial customers. Tests are performed to the customer's requirements; be they to internal, national, regional or international standards.

A technical advisory and consultation service is available through the BSI test centre, which can help on specialized aspects of electronics assembly manufacture.

Technical help to exporters

Another BSI advisory function is maintained through its Technical Help to Exporters (THE) service, which can give guidance to UK companies looking towards foreign markets. One of THE's functions is to identify any foreign technical requirements, regulations and standards which apply to the manufacturer's products; supplying the documents, translated if necessary. Advice is then available on the interpretation of details included.

Table 7.1 Issuing organizations in the UK, of worldwide standards, specifications and documents

Standard, specification or document code	Subject	Issuing organization and address
AFNOR (Association Française de Normalisation)	French standards organization	See BS
ANSI (American National Standards Institute)	US standards	See BS
ASTM (American Society for Testing and Materials)	Test method standards	See ANSI
AQAP (Allied Quality Assurance Publication)	NATO quality assurance	Directorate of Standardization Stan 2 Kentigern House 65 Brown Street Glasgow G2 8EX
BR (Book of Reference)	Handbook for various Service equipments and procedures	MoD(PE) CS(PS)3 Building 25A Royal Arsenal West Woolwich London SE18 6TJ
BS (British Standard)	UK standards organization	British Standards Institution Sales Office Linford Wood Milton Keynes MK14 6LE
BS CECC (British Standard CENELEC Electronic Components Committee)	Electronic components	See BS
BS CP (British Standard Code of Practice)	Various subjects	See BS
BS DD (British Standard Draft for Development	Various subjects	See BS
BSE (British Standard – European)	Harmonized system of quality assessment for electronic components	See BS
BS PD (British Standard Published Document)	Various subjects	See BS

Standard, specification or document code	Subject	Issuing organization and address
CECC (CENELEC Electronics Components Committee)	European Commission for Electrotechnical Standardization producing harmonizing documents with built-in quality assessment	See BS
DEF (Defence Specification, List and Guide)	Standard components, materials and processes for Service use	See HMSO
Def Con (Defence Condition)	Ministry of Defence contract conditions	Forms and Publications Branch PO Box 202 COD Donnington Telford Shropshire TF2 8QF
Def Stan (Defence Standard)	Standard components, materials and processes for Service use	Directorate of Standardization Stan 1 Kentigern House 65 Brown Street Glasgow G2 8EX
DG (Defence Guide)	Standard components, materials and processes for Service use	See HMSO
DIN (Deutsches Institut für Normung)	West German standards organization	See BS
DTD	Aircraft components, materials and processes	See HMSO
EIA (Electronic Industries Association)	Electronics standards	See ANSI
Home Office	Regulatory instructions, various subjects	See HMSO
HMSO (her Majesty's Stationery Office)	Various subjects	HMSO Publications Centre PO Box 276 London SW8 5DT
HS(G) (Health and Safety Guidance)	Guidance booklets	See HMSO
HS(R) (Health and Safety Regulation)	Regulation booklets	See HMSO
HSW	Booklets	See HMSO

Standard, specification or document code	Subject	Issuing organization and address
(Health and Safety at Work)		
IEC (International Electrotechnical Commission)	Electrical and electronics standards	See BS
IEEE (Institute of Electrical and Electronic Engineers)	American electrical and electronics standards	See ANSI
IPC (Institute for Interconnecting and Packaging Electronic Circuits) (formerly Institute of Printed Circuits)	American standards relating to printed circuit boards and assemblies	See ANSI
ISA (Instrument Society of America)	American standards relating to instrumentation	See ANSI
Mil	American military standards, specifications and booklets	MoD Library Services St Christopher House Southwark Street London SE1 0TD
NASA (National Aeronautics and Space Administration)	American research and development	British Library (Lending Division) Boston Spa Wetherby West Yorkshire LS23 MBQ
NES (Naval Engineering Standard)	Warships and equipment standards	MoD(N) ME 242 G Block Foxhill Bath BA1 5AB
NWS (Naval Weapon Specification)	Design requirements for Naval weapons and armaments	MoD CS(PS) 3 Building 25A Royal Arsenal West Woolwich London SE18 6TJ
RAE (Royal Aircraft Establishment)	Airborne communications equipment	Royal Aircraft Establishment MoD(PE) Farnborough Hants GU14 6TD

Standard, specification or document code	Subject	Issuing organization and address
SC (Standard Conditions)	UK Government contractual stipulations	See Def Con
SI (Statutory instrument)	UK Government regulations	See HMSO
STANAG (NATO standardization agreement)	Defence equipment specifications	see AQAP
WDP (Weapons Department Publication)	Weapons equipment management procedures	MoD(N) ME 242 G Block Foxhill Bath BA1 5AB

Following manufacturers' production of the goods, THE will finally inspect prior to shipment, if required. THE is sponsored by the British Overseas Trade Board (BOTB), and is available to all UK industry, whether members of BSI or not.

Information

BSI's information department comprises enquiry, library and database services. General enquiries can normally be handled over the telephone, although letter, fax or telex enquiries can be taken, too.

BSI's library currently holds around half a million international and foreign codes of practices, regulations, standards and technical requirements, available on loan to UK members. Publications can also be purchased through BSI: regularly purchased standards are usually held in stock for this purpose, and BSI prides itself in the fact that members will obtain standards faster by purchasing through BSI, than purchasing from the originating organization.

The Worldwide Standards Information Service is a monthly listing, produced by BSI, of all documents received by the BSI library. Similarly, the Overseas Standards Updating Service may be used to monitor customers' selected documents, resulting in a monthly update on changes or new editions.

Computer information services include online access to worldwide standards databases, and BSI's Standardline. Details of all UK standards (full and draft) are held on Standardline, which is a bibliographic database which may be accessed online by members.

BITS

BSI's Information Technology Services issues a monthly newsletter, comprising details of the latest standards developments.

BSS

The British Standards Society is an association of individuals concerned with standards and standardization. BSS promotes standards and standardization through its conferences, courses and publications.

Quality assurance

One of BSI's most important roles is fulfilled by its quality assurance division, which maintains all of BSI's assessment, certification and inspection facilities. Through this division, UK manufacturers are assessed for capability in manufacture and, following successful assessment, are certified and registered as firms of assessed capability. Registration through this scheme (BS 5750) is considered in detail on page 231.

As part of this work, the division also operates the BS9000 series of standards, ensuring quality assurance of individual components used in electronics assemblies. The BS 9000 scheme is considered in detail on page 231.

BSI publications

Major publications are, of course, UK standards. A catalogue listing all standards, publications and service is available. Standards are prefixed:

- A, B, C, CI, D, F, G, H, HC, HR, J, K, L, M, N, P, PL, R, S, SP, T, V, W, X: aerospace series.
- AMD: amendments.
- AU, BS AU: automobile series.
- BS: general-purpose standards.
- BS9xxx: the BS 9000 series of standards, for the quality assurance of components used in electronics assemblies.
- BS CECC: where BS 9000 series standards are harmonized with CECC regional standards.
- BS E; general-purpose standards.
- BS MA, MA: marine standards.

In addition, other publications are prefixed:

- BITS: BITS publications.
- CP: codes of practice.
- DD: standard drafts for development.
- PD: published documents or amendments.
- PP: education publications.
- TH: THE publications.

Assessed capability of companies

For a long time, large organizations which purchase components, assemblies, or services from outside suppliers have realized that there are only two routes to guaranteeing quality of their supplies. The first route merely tests and assesses all supplies as they are procured – altogether a time-consuming and expensive operation, which must be maintained full-time and for as long as the purchaser is in business.

The second route, on the other hand, simply assesses suppliers' capabilities to do the job. After all, if a supplier meets the purchaser's approval, the purchaser is assured of quality supplies.

The principle of assessing the supplier, rather than the supplies, forms the basis of the BS 5750 national system of assessed capability, in which UK companies are assessed by BSI for acceptable capability and, upon successful assessment, registered as being so.

A national system of assessing suppliers has a very great advantage in that purchasers no longer need to assess their suppliers personally. Further, the system *is* national, and hence unified, saving both purchasers' *and* suppliers' money.

On regional and international levels, BS 5750 has formed the basis of the EN29000 and ISO 9000 series of standards, for regional and international quality systems and management. The EN29000 series operates in the UK and Europe, while the ISO 9000 series operates in the UK, Europe and the rest of the world. These, in turn, help promote European and world trade.

Standards for quality assurance

BS 5750/EN29000/ISO 9000 are just that – standards which, by the very fact that companies are regularly assessed and registered, effectively guarantee assured quality of supplies. Benefits for purchasers of supplies are manifold, including:

- Easier purchasing. Buying of supplies becomes a simple matter of looking in BSI's buyers guide to locate registered suppliers.
- Greater confidence. Knowledge that the purchaser's manufactured product will comprise only quality component parts.
- Peace of mind. Quality supplies are the direct result.
- Savings in time and money. There is no need for the purchaser to assess its suppliers, and no need to test supplies on delivery.

Many benefits for suppliers are created by assessment to these standards, too. Benefits realized on assessment to BS 5750, for example, include:

- Inclusion in BSI's buyer guide. Every purchaser looking for suppliers who are certified and registered according to BS 5750 will consult this guide.
- Inclusion in the Department of Trade and Industry's register of quality assessed companies.
- Marketing tool. Certification and registration to BS 5750 is an effective marketing technique. Certification marks and symbols may be used on advertisements, company literature, letter headings, publicity documents, as well as product markings and packaging.
- Savings in time and money. Customers do not need to assess supplier quality; costs of management, rework, wastage and so on will be lower.
- Wide recognition. All major purchasers recognize BS 5750, and accept certification and registration as proof of quality and expertise.

Registering for assessed capability

BS 5750 comprises six parts. Parts 4 to 6 are intended merely as guides to parts 1 to 3. Part 1 is relevant to companies designing, as well as possibly manufacturing, testing and installing products. Part 2 is relevant to companies which manufacture, test and install products. Finally, Part 3 is relevant to companies which inspect and test products only.

Of necessity, BS 5750 is a general-purpose standard so, in addition, there may be a supplementary document known as a **quality assessment schedule** (QAS) which defines in more precise terms the requirements of a particular industry.

An application to be registered on to the BS 5750 scheme must, therefore, be initiated by complying with the relevant part of BS 5750, and any associated quality assessment schedule. A documented quality system in the form of a **quality manual** must be forwarded to BSI, along with a completed questionnaire, based on BS 5750 and the quality assessment schedule. BSI's **lead assessors** consider both, and notify the applicant of any deviations from the requirements for registration.

When the applicant's documented procedures are considered satisfactory, the lead assessor visits the applicant on a formal assessment basis. During the visit, the applicant is required to demonstrate practical applications of the documented quality system procedures. A company representative is allowed to accompany the lead assessor during the visit, after which the lead assessor reports verbally on the recommendations of the assessment. Subsequently the lead assessor produces a written recommendation which is presented to the company and BSI.

The recommendation is of three forms:

- Unqualified registration, where no discrepancies between the applicant's quality manual and practical procedures have been found. The applicant is certified and registered.
- Qualified registration, where some minor discrepancies between theoretical and practical procedures have been found. These, however, can be quickly rectified, so the applicant is certified (with an interim certificate which should be upgraded on a subsequent visit), and registered.
- Non-registration, where one or more large discrepancy is found, between theoretical and practical quality systems.

Initial assessment, certification and registration is followed by frequent unannounced assessment visits (around four each year) to ensure maintenance of quality.

Assessed quality of components

Where BS 5750 is a single standard for registration of manufacturing companies of assessed capability, the BS 9000 system comprises a group of standards relating to components which manufacturing companies must meet in order to specify that their components are of assessed quality.

The same principles of assessment of quality systems and certification used in BS 5750 are used in BS 9000. In fact, the BS 9000 system is considerably older than BS 5750 (BS 9000 originated in the late 1960s; BS 5750 originated in 1979).

BS 9000 is not the only quality assurance system for electronic components operating in the UK, however. As the BS 5750 quality systems standard has regional and international counterparts in the EN 29000 and ISO 9000 series of standards, so too does the BS 9000 series for quality assurance of electronic components. The CECC system operates in the UK and Europe; the IECQ system operates in the UK, Europe, and internationally. Also, like the supersession of BS 5750 by EN 29000 and, eventually, ISO 9000 the intention is for BS 9000, and eventually CECC, to be superseded by the worldwide IECQ. In this way, it is hoped international trade of electronic components can be increased.

Direct advantages for approved component manufacturers and purchasers are, of course, identical to those advantages listed previously for registered companies under BS 5750. Instead of company registration and listing in BSI's buyer guide, however, approved products are listed in frequently updated **qualified products lists** (QPLs).

All systems have similar arrangements for specification, inspection and approval of components of assessed quality. A **national supervising inspectorate** (NSI) assesses each applicant's quality system, conforming to a **national authorized institution** (NAI) if approval is obtained. In the UK the national supervising inspectorate is the Directorate General Defence Quality Assurance Technical Support (Components) (DGDQA/ TS(components). The UK national authorized institution is formed by the British Electrotechnical Committee and the Electrotechnical Council of BSI.

BS 9000 and the regional CECC and international IECQ, are comprehensive systems for component quality assurance. Unfortunately, they are difficult to get to grips with owing to the, largely unnecessary, abbreviation, jargon and defence-orientated idiom. This is probably the result of use of a wing of the MoD as the UK national supervising inspectorate (see Chapter 8). On the bright side, once the initial skirmish of understanding is over, approval of manufacturers' components into the system appears simple in comparison. Also, in the near future, it is planned the BSI itself, through the BS 5750 system for registration of manufacturing companies of assessed capability, will take over the inspectorate role.

Approval of components

For the purposes of BS 9000/CECC/IECQ, components are split into several groups. These groups (called **generic groups**) are:

- Active, including monolithic integrated circuits.
- Electromagnetic.
- Electromechanical.
- Electro-optical.
- Hybrid integrated circuits.
- Passive.

A manufacturing company must first obtain **manufacturer's approval** against the groups it seeks component approval for. To do this, the company must appoint a **chief inspector** or **quality manager** (if one does not already exist), acceptable to the national supervising inspectorate, who is responsible for the company's quality system.

Gaining manufacturer's approval to BS 9000/CECC/IECQ is somewhat like gaining certification and registration to BS 5750. A quality manual describing the company's quality system must be prepared. The company then applies to the national supervising inspectorate and an assessment visit is arranged.

On assessment, a **quality assurance representative** (QAR) from the national supervising inspectorate visits the company, checking that the theoretical quality system of the quality manual occurs in practice. If assessment is satisfactory, the national supervising inspectorate recommends to the national authorized institution that manufacturer's approval be granted. Like the BS 5750 quality system, frequent unannounced assessment visits may be made to the company.

Once the manufacturer's approval is obtained, the company must then obtain component approval before components may be supplied. There are two types of component approval:

- **Capability approval** (CA), where components are designed, as well as manufactured, by a company. This allows manufacture of custom-built, as well as standard components.
- **Qualification approval** (QA), where components are manufactured according to a specification.

Although there are procedural differences between the two types of approval, gaining approval is a basic matter of demonstrating to the national supervising inspectorate an ability to manufacture components according to agreed details.

For capability approval the manufacturer must first produce details in the form of a **capability manual**, acceptable to the national supervising inspectorate. For qualification approval, on the other hand, the details are in the form of a component specification, which may be taken directly from an existing national standard specification or be produced by the manufacturer. In either approval method, details must comprise tests, procedures, quality systems and so on, for acceptable component manufacture.

Once this manufacturing ability has been demonstrated to the national supervising inspectorate, the national authorization institution will award relevant approval for those components. After approval the national supervising inspectorate carries out component tests at frequent intervals, to ensure manufacturers maintain the standard shown on approval.

Setting up company standards

It is hoped that this chapter has adequately described the standards required to ensure quality assurance, as quality control of a company's product or services, or as quality assessment of electronic components.

Quality assurance is not a magical substance which can be bought, and applied to parts of a company. Quality assurance is more a philosophy which encompasses *the whole company*. The philosophy is one of standardization: as a by-product of which money can be saved, components can be compatible, products can be made more reliable, and customers can be satisfied.

Such a whole-company philosophy, on the other hand, can only be generated and maintained if the company makes a conscious decision to enforce the required standards. Generally, the only way this can be ensured is by setting up a department within the company which has sufficient status to allow it to specify those chosen standards to be followed. Conversely, this means that no other department within the company must have the power of veto over the standards department when the question of standards enforcement is raised. Although this last point may seem trivial and obvious, lack of standards departments' status to ensure a standard's acceptance wastes considerable time and expense within industry, and must be avoided for the system to work effectively. All too often, what standards are used by a company are held in a corner of the drawing office, poorly maintained and poorly enforced.

When setting up a standards department, or when upgrading an existing drawing office corner, it is essential to have some idea of what work the department should be undertaking. An estimation can be made by looking at the *types* of standards to be drawn up and maintained, as well as the *areas* within the company to which the standards must apply.

Types of standards are, in decreasing order of priority:

- International.
- Regional.
- National.
- Internally generated within the company.

In addition, depending on the work carried out by the company, defence standards and specifications, or industrial specifications, may need to be maintained.

Areas of standards involvement depend largely on company activities, but at most will involve four areas:

- Raw materials.
- Purchased components or parts.
- Manufactured parts, or services.
- Plant and equipment.

Thus, in the smallest of companies, a single standards engineer with some clerical support will satisfactorily maintain the department. In the largest of companies, on the other hand, a standards manager together with an engineer for each type of standard and area of company activity, with clerical, secretarial, and library support will be required. In the main, a standards department between these two extremes is typical. Whatever the size of the department, the standards manager should be either responsible, immediately, to director level or, better still, be a director.

Publishing standards

A main function of the standards department is to publish those documents which are deemed necessary by the company to ensure proper operation. Although varying in name, these documents will probably include:

- A company standards manual.
- A catalogue of preferred components, materials or parts.
- A catalogue of preferred manufacturers, service providers or subcontractors.
- Workmanship manuals for administration, design, packaging and production.
- Codes of practice for important company procedures.
- Specifications, conditions or standards, at company, regional, national or international levels, relating to the company's work.

Many of these documents will be generated by the department itself, yet must be accepted by the company as a whole, so a recognized sequence of stages should be followed when generating such documents. These stages are:

- Collection of data.
- Arrangement of the data logically.
- Elimination of inconsistencies and unnecessary variation.
- Publication.
- Promotion.
- Updating.

As BSI itself states of the first draft of a company standard:

A subject is first nominated for consideration, after which appropriate data such as relevant regulations, standards procedures, suppliers and prices are collected. In addition, national and trade standards are sought, suppliers' catalogues collected and examined and existing applications noted, as are stores inventories and rates of turnover.

If this investigation shows that the subject is worth pursuing, a first draft of the standard is prepared for discussion. Some of the many points to be decided at this stage are outlined below.

(a) *Proposed range.* Does it comply with established standards (international, national, company)? Is it adequate for possible future development? Are there too many sizes? Do the sizes follow a logical progression?

(b) *Application.* For what applications is the range suitable or unsuitable? Is the new standard to be applied retrospectively to existing designs or is it only for new designs?

(c) *Quality.* Are the articles specified in sufficient detail to ensure reasonable uniformity and interchangeability with one another?

(d) *Availability.* Can the articles specified be obtained at the right price, in the required quantities and at the right time?

The advantages of complying with British Standards and/or

international standards should not be overlooked. From such considerations, the final form of the standard will emerge to be published and distributed to all who may have occasion to use it.

(*PD3542: 1988*)

An agreed house style (that is, general appearance, layout, specialized terms and so on) is preferred in the publication of company standards. Where documents are generated by the standards department itself, little or no editing to this style will usually be necessary, as the style will usually have been generated by the department in the first place.

Where documents have been generated outside the department, on the other hand, significant editing in style, layout and, sometimes, use of English may be required.

References

British Standards Institution, *The Management of Design for Economic Production – PD 6470 1981*, Milton Keynes: BSI.

British Standards Institution, *The Operation of Standards in a Company – PD 3542 1988*, Milton Keynes: BSI.

International Organization for Standarization, *ISO Guide 2: 1980*, Geneva: ISO.

8 Selling to the Ministry of Defence

Defence organizations are traditionally difficult to sell to, at least for the smaller companies. In many respects this is understandable: defence organizations tend to be large, complex, and security-conscious. Many of their procurement contracts specify high standards – further, many of these standards are produced by the defence organizations themselves and are written in defence idiom; complex, jargon-ridden, and with many difficult-to-fathom titles and corresponding abbreviations. Often even publicity literature, produced by defence organizations specifically to assist companies wishing to sell to them, is equally so.

In the UK, the defence organization is the Ministry of Defence (MoD). Recently a move has taken place within the ministry at least, to make selling to the MoD an easier job. New creations within the MoD are the **small firms advice division**, and the **new suppliers service**, where advice is relatively easy to obtain: often a telephone call is enough to get information which may have been almost unlocatable before.

A change, too, possibly aided by these new services, is underway in the amounts and values of contracts with small firms. A growing proportion of the UK defence budget (last figures were some 12.5%) now goes to companies of less than 200 people. Interestingly, as much as 70% of all UK electronics work is reckoned to be devoted to defence, although MoD figures appear to contradict this.

Whatever, knowing the exact figures does not really help when getting down to the brass tacks of selling to the MoD.

MoD organization

The first thing of real value is to understand the MoD's internal organization. A number of self-published booklets are available, including:

- *Selling to the Ministry of Defence.*
- *The Procurement Executive – Ministry of Defence.*
- *Defence Quality Assurance.*

Even these booklets are difficult to fathom, however, as they are typically hampered by job descriptions of leading personnel within individual branches of the MoD, rather than giving decent explanations of the branches themselves. A summary of the Ministry of Defence is illustrated

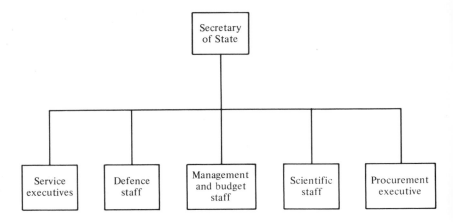

Secretary of State

Service executives Defence staff Management and budget staff Scientific staff Procurement executive

Figure 8.1 *Overall summary of the Ministry of Defence*

in Figure 8.1. The *Secretary of State for Defence* heads the ministry, politically directing the five main branches:

- Service executives, the three service departments: air force, army, navy.
- Defence staff.
- Management and budget staff.
- Scientific staff.
- Procurement executive.

Generally, it is the **procurement executive** (PE) which is responsible for central purchases of research, equipment, other goods and services ranging from nuclear submarines, aircraft and tanks through to batteries, hubcaps, and jerry cans.

Procurement executive

The PE is, in fact, UK industry's largest single customer, with some 40,000 contracts placed annually. Some 350,000 jobs are reckoned to be sustained because of this. Heading the PE is the *Chief of Defence Procurement* (CDP), who directly controls the four main branches illustrated in Figure 8.2. These branches, together with their main responsibilities, are:

- Central divisions. General procurement policy, including industrial aspects, purchasing, contracts, quality assurance.
- Service systems. Procurement of equipment for air force, army and navy.
- Research. The buildings and programmes to maintain required research.
- Export. Help to UK companies regarding export of defence equipment.

Central divisions

A summary of the central divisions of the PE is illustrated in Figure 8.3, where its five branches are shown under the direction of the *Deputy Under*

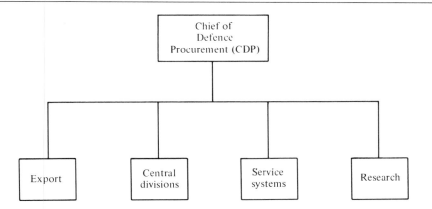

Figure 8.2 *Procurement executive of the Ministry of Defence*

Secretary for Defence Procurment (DUS(DP)). Three branches of the central divisions monitor and control procurement policy and finance. These are the *procurement policy*, the *procurement policy (studies)*, and the *procurement finance* branches.

Of greater relevance to companies wishing to sell to the MoD, though, are the remaining two branches. Quality assurance branch is responsible for ensuring that equipment bought by the MoD is of an adequate quality. To this end, required quality is specified initially, and monitored thereafter by staff within this branch. Project managers from this branch are deployed within the project management teams of companies involved in defence work. Quality assurance is headed by the *Director General Defence Quality Assurance* (DGDQA), and is detailed later in this chapter.

The contracts branch is headed by the *Director General of Defence Contracts* (DGDC). It is responsible for guidance on policy and procedures in the placing, pricing and administration of conracts. Its aim is to use purchasing practices which achieve best value for money for the MoD and, as such, overall contracts policy is changed by this part from time to time. Departments within the contracts branch deal with accountancy, technical costing and patents.

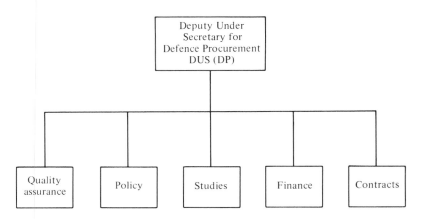

Figure 8.3 *Central divisions of the procurement executive*

Also, a contractors' list (the *defence contractors list*) is maintained by the contracts branch of PE central divisions, so for many companies wishing to sell to the MoD it is a main point of entry.

Procurement policy in the form of contracts and the requirements for quality assurance are discussed later.

Service systems – the systems controllerates

Procurement for the three services is organized by the three *systems controllerates*. The work of the *air systems controllerate* is illustrated in Figure 8.4. It is headed by the *Controller Aircraft* (CA), and is responsible for seven areas:

- In-service aircraft.
- Aircraft engines and helicopters.
- Air weapons and electronic systems.
- Strategic electronic systems.
- Future aircraft and associated systems.
- Air contracts.
- Saudi air force projects.

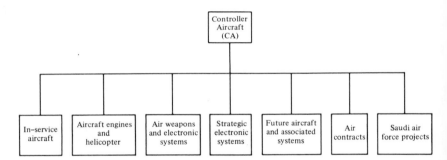

Figure 8.4 *Air systems controllerate*

The *land systems controllerate*, the work of which is illustrated in Figure 8.5, is headed by the *Master General of the Ordnance*, and is responsible for five areas:

- Proof and experimental establishments.
- Fighting vehicles and engineer equipment.
- Weapons.
- Guided weapons and electronics.
- Ordnance contracts.

    Work of the last of the service systems controllerates (alphabetically, that is), the *sea systems controllerate*, is illustrated in Figure 8.6. It is headed by the *Controller of the Navy* (CN), and is responsible for five areas:

- Warships.
- Warship equipment.

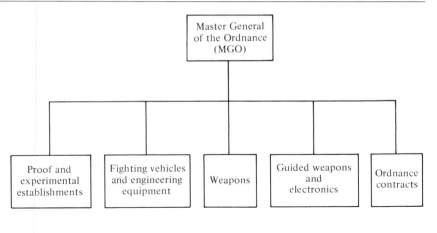

Figure 8.5 *Land systems controllerate*

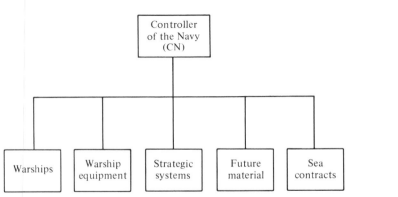

Figure 8.6 *Sea systems controllerate*

- Strategic systems.
- Future material.
- Sea contracts.

Research – Controllerate Establishments, Research and Nuclear

Currently, there are seven defence research establishments, headed by the *Controller of Establishments, Research and Nuclear* (CERN). These are illustrated in Figure 8.7 and are, together with their responsibilities:

- The Admiralty research establishment – naval ships and weapons.
- The Royal Armament research and development establishment – fighting vehicles and land armaments.
- The Royal Aircraft establishment – aircraft and airframes.
- The Royal Signals and Radar establishment – radar, communications, electronics and computing.
- The chemical defence establishment – defence against chemical and microbiological attack.
- The atomic weapons establishment – atomic weapons.

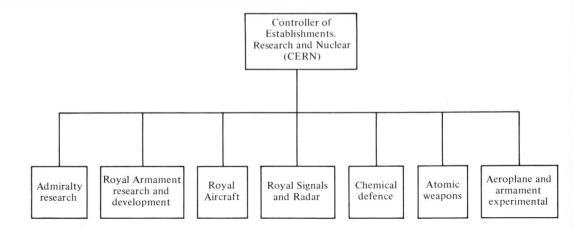

Figure 8.7 *Ministry of Defence defence research establishments*

- The aeroplane and armament experimental establishment – aeroplane and armament test, evaluation and delivery.

However, at the time of writing, the Admiralty research, Royal Armament research and development, Royal Aircraft, and Royal Signals and Radar establishments will shortly be taken out of the procurement executive branch of the MoD. Instead, in 1991, they will be combined in a single government-owned agency which is to run its research facilities on reasonably commercial lines. The agency will be required to break even in monetary terms, although a profit will not be a prerequisite. It will, however, be forced to compete for MoD research work with other, non-governmental, research organizations.

Export – Defence Export Services Organization

The *Defence Export Services Organization* (DESO) is headed by the *Head of Defence Export Services* (HDES). Its function is to help UK companies to market and sell their defence products and services to non-UK buyers. As such, it ensures that the MoD's procurements process takes note of non-UK sales potential.

DESO also handles the sale of surplus Army and Navy equipment.

Procurement executive policy and procedures

Initially, there are two main types of purchases made by MoD:

- Small purchases, by *local purchase officers* at service units and establishments throughout the world.
- Large purchases, through main contracts branches.

These *direct* purchases may be supplemented by *indirect* purchases through companies, subcontracted by main contractors.

Generally, all purchases follow the main policy and procedures outlined here, although some small local purchases may be sufficiently simple to avoid the total requirements.

The PE is committed to achieving the overall best value for money. Key principles in its equipment procurement policy, therefore, are that competition must be encouraged wherever reasonable and practicable, and that the policy itself must be commercially astute.

Contracts

As part of this procurement policy, the advantages of the use of standards and standardization are positively stressed. Where available, UK national standards published by BSI must be applied to all equipment and services sold to the MoD. Where no standards are available for any particular product or service, defence standards (see Chapter 7 and Appendix 1) should be applied. Where no defence standards are available, standards and publications from other MoD departments, other government department, other standards organizations and so on, should be applied. The preferred order of standard selection is:

- UK national standards, with the prefix *BS*.
- Defence standards, with the prefix *Def Stan*.
- Defence specifications, lists or guides.
- MoD department standards or specifications.
- Other government department standards.
- Recognized industry standards.

In any MoD contract the standards and specifications which are to be met will be specified. Further advice regarding specified standards and any other standards for that matter, is available from the *Directorate of Standardization* which is part of the quality assurance section of the PE central divisions (see page 238).

A number of *standard conditions* and *defence conditions* (Def Cons) may be specified in contracts. Standard conditions are summarized in Table 8.1, defence conditions are summarized in Table 8.2, while a list of guides to defence conditions is given in Table 8.3.

Project development

Any new project considered by the MoD goes through a number of steps, coordinated, generally, by the *operational requirements* (OR) department of the MoD defence staff. These steps, with descriptions, are:

- Staff target. A formal document expressing in broad terms the desired function and performance of equipment, usually involving relevant MoD research establishments and industry, and circulated to all interested parties inside and outside the MoD.
- Staff requirement. A formal document stating the aims of the project, which provides the basis of technical and cost criteria required – a sort of feasibility study.

Table 8.1 UK defence standard conditions

Standard condition	Content
SC1	Definitions and interpretations of terms
SC2	Specifications, drawings
SC3	Alteration of specifications, plans, drawings, patterns and samples
SC4	Inspection
SC5	Acceptance marks
SC6	Packages
SC7	Delivery
SC8	Rendering of bills
SC9	Recovery of sums due
SC10	Progress reports
SC11	Issue of Government property, rights of ownership, use, maintenance, loss and damage
SC12	Loss of or damage to articles prior to delivery
SC13	Value added tax
SC14	Default
SC15	Bankruptcy
SC16	Racial discrimination
SC18	Transfer and subletting, forbidding the unauthorized transfer of a contract from a contractor to any other party
SC19	Customs duty
SC20	Corrupt gifts and payments of commission
SC21	Official secrets act
SC24	Rejection and the right to reject any articles found not to conform with the contract
SC25	Acceptance
SC29	English law governing the contract
SC29a	Scottish law governing the contract
SC30	English law arbitration
SC30a	Scottish law arbitration
SC31	Defining the correct use of documents and information
SC32a	Authorization for use of patented inventions or designs, without the need to pay royalties
SC32b	Requires the contractor to inform the MoD of any agreement which restricts use of, or requires payment for, technical information
SC36	Labour conditions in textiles companies
SC41	Delivery under warrants or orders
SC42	Materials requirements
SC43	Price fixing
SC44	Variation of prices due to wages
SC45	Variation of prices due to materials
SC46	Variation of prices due to subcontracts
SC47	Variation of price due to general provisions
SC48	Availability of information in record form for a minimum period after completion of a non-competitive contract
SC49	Vesting, in respect of advance payments
SC50	Questions arising under the contract
SC51	Questions arising in relation to subcontracts
SC52	Questions arising in relation to work placed with subsidiaries
SC53	Pricing when a fixed price is not possible at the outset of work
SC56	Right to termination of contract
SC59	Security measures to safeguard the secret content of the work
SC60	Tests

Table 8.2   UK defence conditions (Def Cons)

Defence condition	Content
Def Con 5	Advice and inspection note
Def Con 14	Inventions and designs; Crown rights and ownership of patents and registered designs
Def Con 14a	Ownership of patents and registered designs
Def Con 15/15a	Design rights – ownership of the design remains the contractor's, but the MoD has free use of the design, through the original or any other contractor
Def Con 21	Drawings, specifications, and manufacturing data
Def Con 23	Special jigs, tools, and so on, allowing the contractor use of tools and jigs for commercial use, for which a charge is made
Def Con 47	MoD's invitation to tender
Def Con 52	Local purchase order form
Def Con 53	Small value order form
Def Con 76	General conditions of contract applicable to work performed by contractor's personnel at Government establishments
Def Con 90	Requiring that copyright must remain with the contractor, allowing the MoD to use copyright material for any Government purpose
Def Con 112 et seq.	Contract conditions applicable to specified products or services
Def Con 123	General conditions defining responsibilities, issue of Government property, transportation, packaging and so on
Def Con 126	Allowing the MoD to copy and issue information for international collaboration purposes
Def Con 127	Price fixing condition for contracts of lesser value than SC43
Def Con 129	Packaging responsibilities and instructions
Def Con 176	Requirements for competition in subcontract work

Table 8.3   UK defence condition guides

Def Con guide	Content
Def Con guide 1	Planning and cost management of major development contracts
Def Con guide 2	Planning and monitoring of minor development contracts
Def Con guide 3	Working guidelines for the pricing of non-competitive risk contracts
Def Con guide 4	Cost management of unpriced production contracts
Def Con guide 5	Incentive (target cost) contracting
Def Con guide 7	Issue of MoD owned equipment
Def Con guide 8	Code of practice for competitive subcontracting
Def Con guide 9	Financing terms for defence contracts
Def Con guide 10	Guidelines for competitive tendering

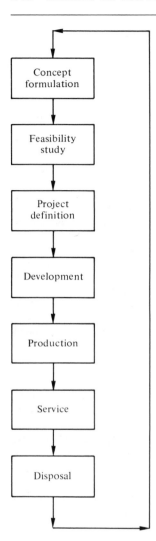

Figure 8.8 *Seven-stage cycle of Ministry of Defence procurement*

- Financial provision. Once the cost estimation has been completed, the MoD must decide if it can be afforded.
- Equipment policy committee. The *equipment policy committee* (EPC) or one of its subcommittees (EPSCs) has the responsibility of advising Government Ministers on projects. With ministerial approval, the project will be procured.

Procurement

Generally, procurement comprises seven stages in a cycle, as illustrated in Figure 8.8. The seven stages, listed with descriptions, are:

- Concept formulation. The project is first conceived, and a resultant staff target is generated.
- Feasibility study. Determining whether the project is feasible on technical and financial grounds, resulting in refinement of the staff target into a staff requirement.
- Project definition. A precise definition of the project, such that all previous technical unknowns may be specified and so costed. Firm plans for development, outline plans for production together with associated costs, together with a procurement strategy.
- Development. Starting with a development contract from the MoD, which specifies the project and its requirements, and ending with acceptance of the project in terms of performance and safety.
- Production. Manufacture of the project.
- Service. Use, maintenance, repair.
- Disposal. Making equipment obsolete.

Companies may, generally, be involved in any or all seven stages of the procurement cycle.

Quality assurance

The MoD's policy on quality is simple: responsibility lies with its direct contractors to ensure that quality is of the specified level. To this end, the MoD assesses each contractor, before and during the contracted period, to ensure quality control is at least to the level specified by a relevant *allied quality assurance publication* (AQAP), produced by NATO. Companies deemed to have adequate quality control according to an AQAP are registered in the direct contractors list, maintained by the contracts part of PE central divisions. Registration to an AQAP is for a maximum of three years. Table 8.4 lists the main AQAPs, although others may be specified, depending on the type of product or service procured by the MoD.

For certain purchases, national, regional or international standards of quality assurance (BS 5750/EN29000/ISO 9000) may be specified by MoD, instead of AQAPs. Chapter 7 introduces and describes assessed capability of companies to BS 5750/EN29000/150 9000 standards.

A subcontracted company's quality control, on the other hand, is not assessed by MoD. This remains the total responsibility of the direct

Table 8.4 Main NATO allied quality assurance publications (AQAPs)

Document	Title and content
AQAP1	NATO requirements for an industrial quality control system – the development and production cycle from the design stage onwards
AQAP2	Guide for the evaluation of a contractor's quality control system for compliance with AQAP1
AQAP4	NATO inspection system requirements for industry – for equipment requiring inspection throughout manufacture
AQAP5	Guide for the evaluation of a contractor's inspection system for compliance with AQAP4
AQAP6	NATO measurement and calibration system requirements for industry – AQAP1 and AQAP4 require compliance with this
AQAP7	Guide for the evaluation of a contractor's measurement and calibration system for compliance with AQAP6
AQAP9	NATO basic inspection requirements for industry – items which can be inspected after manufacture, but which must be ordered from suppliers with approved quality control systems.
AQAP13	NATO software quality control system requirements – where software, or equipment incorporating software, is required, this AQAP will be invoked as a supplement to AQAP1
AQAP14	Guide for the evaluation of a contractor's software quality control system for compliance with AQAP13

contractor, who may specify that the subcontractor maintains quality control to the level of a relevant AQAP or, more likely, is assessed to BS 5750/EN29000/ISO 9000 quality systems.

In addition to specification of a quality control system, contracts placed with contractors may specify one or more standards or specifications of a national, defence or other nature, as noted earlier.

The quality assurance branch of the central divisions of the PE is illustrated in Figure 8.9. The branch is headed by the *Director General of Defence Quality Assurance* (DGDQA). Parts of the branch are listed with main responsibilities:

- Policy. External policy between MoD, industry and international organizations, coordinating internal policies, quality assurance documentation and procedures, quality assurance training.
- Project support. Provision of quality assurance engineers for work in project management teams, revision of staff requirements, advice to contracts relating to quality assurance.
- Industry. Contractor assessment, contract surveillance at defence contractors.
- Administration. Legislative, legal, financial and procurement business.
- Technical support. Engineering, scientific and technical support, currently the national supervising inspectorates for the BS 9000/CECC/IECQ quality systems for electronic components.
- Standardization, see over.

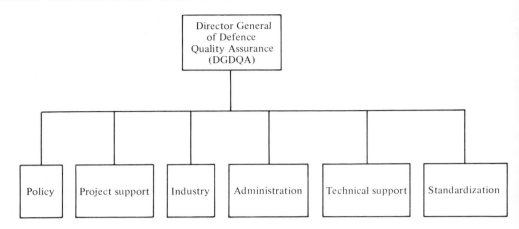

Figure 8.9 *Quality assurance branch of the central divisions of the procurement executive of the Ministry of Defence*

Standardization

The *Directorate of Standardization* produces all defence standards as well as maintaining MoD policy on standardization. It is headed by the *Director of Standardization* (D Stan). There are a number of branches to the directorate, illustrated hierarchically in Figure 8.10. These are, listed with responsibilities:

- *Policy*. Main standardization policy, followed by all other parts.
- *Stan 1 and administration*. Administration, library, printing, publications; focal point for all enquiries on defence standards.
- *Stan 2*. International defence standardization aspects such as NATO.
- *Stan 4*. Weapons, ammunition, vehicles and vehicle equipment.

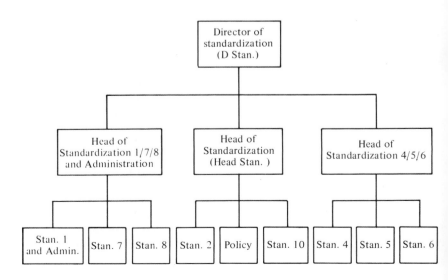

Figure 8.10 *Directorate of standardization*

- *Stan 5*. Chemicals and packaging.
- *Stan 6*. Hardware, technical procedures and general design data.
- *Stan 7*. Electrical and electronics components.
- *Stan 8*. Electrical and electronic equipment, computer-related subjects.
- *Stan 10*. Liason with BSI, MoD representation on BSI committees.

Glossary

Activated flux   Rosin-based flux, with one or more activators added.

Activator   Additive in a flux which aids the flux's cleaning ability.

Additive   Action of adding the track to a PCB base material.

Adherand   Material to be struck together by adhesive.

Automated optical inspection (AOI)   Text fixture method in which printed circuit boards are checked at bare-board, pre- or post-soldered stages of assembly by optical means.

Automatic component insertion (ACI)   Insertion of components into a through-hole board by automatic means.

Bare-board testing   Testing procedure in which printed circuit boards are tested prior to assembly of components.

Base   Insulating layer of a printed circuit board.

Bathtub curve   Graph plotting failure rate and time, over a system's life.

Bed-of-nails fixture   Arrangement of pin-type probes on a plate, which is pressed up against a printed circuit board, allowing electrical connections to be made for test purposes.

Blind via   A via on a multi-layer PCB which does not go completely through the board. *Syn:* Buried via.

Bumps   Inner terminations of a tape automated bond integrated circuit.

Buried via   *See* Blind via.

Capability approval   Component approval stage in BS 9000/CECC/IECQ systems, for components designed and manufactured by the manufacturer.

Capability manual   Documented manufacturing system required in the process of *capability approval* to BS 9000/CECC/IECQ systems.

Clinching   Act of bending component leads underneath the board, on insertion, to hold the component in position.

Colophony   *See* Rosin.

Combination test   Test procedure using both *in-circuit test* and *functional test* methods.

Conformal coating   Encapsulation process, comprising a thin coating over an assembly.

CS soldering process   Soldering process in which components are positioned on a printed circuit board, before application of solder and heat.

Defence conditions (Def Cons)   Contractual conditions stated by the Ministry of Defence.

Device under test (DUT)   Term used to describe a component, printed circuit board or assembly subjected to a test. *Syn:* Unit under test (UUT) and Loaded board.

Dewetting   Occurrence during soldering, where an initial bond is formed, followed by a withdrawal of solder from the joint.

Dip soldering   Mass CS soldering process in which assembled boards are dipped into a bath of molten solder.

Drag soldering   Mass CS soldering process in which assembled boards are dragged across the surface of a bath of molten solder.

Dry-film photoresist   Photoresist with thin surface layer of polyester, aiding handling.

Dummy track   Track underneath a surface mounted component, unused for electrical purposes, to aid component adhesion.

Electroless copper deposition   Process in which base laminate is coated with a layer of copper.

Electromagnetic compatibility (EMC)   Principle in which any electronic or electrical appliance should be able to operate without causing electromagnetic interference, and without being affected by electromagnetic interference.

Embedding   Encapsulation process, of thick protective material.

Encapsulation   Generic term for protection of assemblies, reducing the effects of environmental conditions.

Environmental stress screening (ESS)   Manufacturing stage in which all assemblies are subjected to abnormal stresses, with the aim of forcing all early failures to occur. *Syn:* Reliability screening.

Etchback   Process in PCB manufacture, in which holes are cleared of prepreg seepage, prior to metallization.

Etch resist   Chemical applied to PCB track surface to prevent subsequent etch.

Eutectic point of solder   Melting-point of solder with 62% tin and 38% lead alloy proportions.

Failure   The termination of a device or system's ability to perform its function.

Fiducials   Optically recognizable location marks on a circuit board.

Fillet   Solder between two metals in a joint.

Fine lines   General term to suggest accurate PCB production with very narrow track widths.

Finish   Protection of surface of cabinet.

Flexible PCB   A printed circuit board with a flexible base laminate.

Flexi-rigid PCB   A rigid PCB with a flexible tail.

Flux   Additive in the soldering process, which aids cleaning and wetting of the metal surfaces to be soldered.

Flux activity   A measure of the cleaning ability of a flux in the soldering process.

Functional test   Test procedure in which an assembly's overall operational characteristics are tested by simulating normal function. *Syn:* Go/no-go test.

Fusing   Heating an electroplated tin/lead layer to ensure an interfacing alloy bond occurs.

Gap   Spaces between adjacent PCB tracks.

Glob-top   Protective encapsulation over semiconductor die mounted directly on circuit board.

Golden board   Term to describe the ideal properties of a printed circuit board.

Go/no-go test *See* Functional test.

Heated collet Method of soldering surface mounted components, where an electrically-heated collet is positioned over the component terminals so that the solder under the terminals melts.

Heat management PCB design philosophy, ensuring adequate heat dissipation. *Syn:* Thermal design.

Hot vapour soldering SC soldering process using the latent heat of evaporation of a liquid, where the heat from the liquid's vapour heats the printed circuit board. *Syn:* Vapour phase soldering.

Hybrid assembly Electronics assembly in which thin- or thick-film passive components, and leadless components, are mounted on a substrate.

Image *See* Track.

Impregnation Encapsulation process, of protective material injected into all spaces or voids between components.

In-circuit test (ICT) Test procedure in which circuit nodes of an assembly are accessed by pin-type probes, to test individual components within the circuit. *Syn:* Manufacturing defects analysis and Pre-screening.

Infra-red signature analysis Test procedure in which soldered joints are heated by laser then optically monitored during cooling.

Infra-red soldering SC soldering process using infra-red radiating elements to create heat.

Inner lead bonding Process of bonding termination leads to a tape automated bond integrated circuit's bumps.

Intermetallic compound Compound of elements, having a fixed ratio of the elements in the compound.

Joint Metallic bonds between two or more component metal terminals, using solder as the bonding material.

Kiss pressure Initial pressure applied to layers to be bonded into multi-layer PCB, whereby the prepreg layers soften and flow to fill voids within the layers.

Land Part of PCB track, allocated to the connection of a component lead.

Layout Overall shape of conductive track on a PCB. *Syn:* Pattern; Image.

Leaded component A component with wire terminations.

Leadless component A component without wired terminations.

Levelling Process of removal of much of a thick tin/lead layer, to leave behind a thin, level, layer.

Loaded board *See* Device under test.

Loading Supplying an automatic component insertion head with components.

Manufacturer's approval First stage required in component approval through BS 9000/CECC/IECQ systems.

Manufacturing defects analysis *See* In-circuit test.

Mass soldering Process which solders many components to a printed circuit board simultaneously.

Mean time between failure (MTBF) A measure of how often failure can be expected.

Mean time to failure (MTTF) The average time between failures.

Mean time to repair (MTTR) A measure of how long it takes a service engineer to get to the failed system, locate and repair the fault.

Mesh size   Number of holes per linear measure in a screen printing material.

Metal-cored PCB   A printed circuit board, with an internal thermal plane.

Metallization   Processes involved in forming a conductive layer on a PCB base material, generally by electroless copper deposition, followed by subsequent copper and tin/lead plating.

Misalignment   Where two-terminal surface mounted components move during the soldering process, owing to the different times that lands at opposite ends of the component reach soldering temperature.

Mixed assembly   Electronics assembly in which leaded and leadless components are inserted and mounted. *Syn:* Mixprint.

Moulded circuit board (MCB)   *See* Moulded PCB.

Moulded PCB   A printed circuit board, comprising an injection-moulded base and plated track. *Syn:* Three-dimensional moulded circuit board; Moulded circuit board.

Moving probe   Test fixture method, in which two or more probes are robotically controlled to move around points on a printed circuit board.

Multi-layer PCB   A printed circuit board, comprising three or more layers of track, insulated and laminated together into one board.

Multi-wired PCB   A printed circuit board, comprising a conventional single- or double-sided board, with insulated wire tracks laid on to build up connections.

Non-activated flux   Rosin-based flux without activator.

Onsertion   Slang term for the placement of components on a PCB or surface mounting substrate.

Outer lead bonding   Process of bonding the terminations of a tape automated bond integrated circuit to a circuit board.

Panel plating   Processes in metallization of PCB track, in which tin/lead is selectively plated.

Pattern   *See* Track.

Pattern plating   Processes in metallization of PCB track, in which copper and tin/lead layers are plated selectively.

Photoprinting   Process of photographically applying a resist to the surface of a PCB.

Photoresist   Layer, laminated on to the surface of a PCB, as part of a photoprinting process.

Pick and place   Sequential placement of surface mounted components on to a circuit board.

Pickling   Process in metallization, where the base laminate is prepared for subsequent electroless copper deposition.

Placement centre   Area of an automatic component placement machine where the component is centred to an absolute position in the placement head.

Plated-through hole (PTH)   Method of connecting between track layers on a PCB, where drilled or punched holes are metallized.

Pre-screening   *See* In-circuit test.

Printed circuit board (PCB)   Assembly method using a base laminate of insulating material with selective tracks of conducting material to hold components and electrically connect between them. PCBs may be of *through-hole* or *surface mount* form.

Potting Encapsulation process, of embedding the assembly inside a container.

Preforming Act of shaping component leads prior to insertion into a PCB.

Prepping *See* Preforming.

Prepreg Bonding layer of fibre glass impregnated with epoxy resin, used in multi-layer and similar PCB manufacture.

Print and etch *See* Subtractive.

Protective coating Coating applied to a manufactured printed circuit board, prior to assembly with components.

Purchasor assessment Buying procedure in which parts must be assessed by the purchasor, prior to use.

Qualification approval Component approval stage in BS 9000/CECC/IECQ systems, for components simply manufactured (that is, not designed) by the manufacturer.

Qualified products list (QPL) List of components, whose manufacturers have been assessed as to their capability to manufacture.

Quality The achievement of a system to conform to its specified performance.

Quality assessment schedule (QAS) Supplementary document to BS 5750/EN 29000/ISO 9000 systems, defining in precise terms the quality requirements of an industry seeking capability assessment and registration under the standard.

Quality manual Documented quality system required for capability assessment and registration to BS 5750/EN 29000/ISO 9000 systems.

Reflow *See* SC soldering process.

Reliability A system's ability to perform its required function.

Reliability screening *See* Environmental stress screening.

Resin smear Prepreg between layers of a drilled multi-layer PCB which has softened and flowed to cover copper tracks within the structure.

Resist Chemical used to prevent part of a PCB from undergoing some action.

Rosin Constituent of many organically soluble fluxes, distilled from pine tree sap. *Syn:* Colophony.

Saponification Reaction converting rosin into rosin soap – process in post-soldering cleaning processes allowing water to be used as a cleaner, rather than solvent.

SC soldering process Soldering process in which solder is first applied to a printed circuit board, followed by components and heat.

Screen Grounded or earthed conductive enclosure, to prevent radiated electro-magnetic interference.

Screen printing Process to coat boards with resist, using a stretched material suspended above the board. A squeegee is used to force the resist through holes in the material and to push the material down to touch the board. *Syn:* Silk-screen printing.

Seeding Process in electroless copper deposition, where the sensitized board is dipped into an acidic solution of palladium chloride.

Semi-additive PCB manufacturing technique which uses both subtractive and additive processes.

Sensitize Process in electroless copper deposition, where the board is dipped into acidic stannous solution.

Sequential placement Placement of surface mounted components on to a circuit board one after the other.

Shadow effect Effect of different joint temperatures, in SC soldering processes.

Silk-screen printing *See* Screen printing.

Simultaneous placement Placement of more than one surface mounted component on to a circuit board at a time.

Solder Alloy of tin and lead, used to form mechanical joints between electronic components and printed circuit board copper lands.

Solderability The ability of a metal to be wet by solder.

Solder mask *See* Solder resist.

Solder resist Selective coating on a printed circuit board, to prevent wetting of solder over covered areas.

Solder thief Additional solder land, positioned to follow the last component mounting land of a surface mount assembly board through a mass CS process soldering machine, to prevent solder accumulation and bridging.

Solder wicking Where solder on the terminal of a surface mounted component soldered in an SC soldering process rises up from the printed circuit board land, leaving insufficient solder on the land to give a good joint.

Standard conditions Contractual conditions stated by Government purchasors.

Stripping Process of removal of resist.

Substrate Base of a thick-film hybrid, or surface mounted, assembly.

Subtractive Action of defining track on a PCB and removing excess conductor. *Syn:* Print and etch.

Surface mounted assembly (SMA) Electronics assembly in which leadless components are mounted directly on the board surface.

Tail A flexible circuit attached to a rigid PCB.

Tape automated bonded (TAB) Semiconductor die, in taped form, ready for surface mounted assembly (sometimes called milkropacks).

Thermal bridge Metal cover over components mounted on a PCB with a thermal plane. Specifically to aid heat dissipation.

Thermal design *See* Heat management.

Thermal mismatch Loose term describing the problems of different thermal coefficients of expansion of surface mounted components and circuit board base materials.

Thermal path analysis Thermal management design process.

Thermal plane A heatsink, bonded to the surface of a PCB before component insertion, or laminated within a PCB, to aid heat dissipation, specifically in closely packed PCBs.

Thermal via A via used specifically to aid heat dissipation from a component, thermally connecting the area around or underneath the component on a PCB to a larger area of copper.

Through-hole assembly Electronics assembly in which leaded component leads are inserted through holes in the board.

Tombstoning A severe form of *misalignment*, where the two-terminal component lifts into a vertical position.

Unit under test (UUT) *See* Device under test.

Vapour phase soldering (VPS) *See* Hot vapour soldering.

Vendor assessment Buying procedure in which the manufacturer of parts assesses the product, alleviating the necessity for the purchasor to do so, prior to use.

Vision Inclusion of some form of camera on an automatic component insertion or placement machine, to enable high accuracy of component positioning.

Wave soldering Mass CS soldering process in which assembled boards are dragged across the surface of a wave (or waves) of molten solder.

Wetting Action of initial flow of solder over a metal, under heat.

Wetting balance Method of assessing solderability of metals.

X-ray imaging Optical test procedure, using the ability of X-rays to pass through certain substances more easily than others.

Appendix 1 Worldwide standards

This appendix comprises two main parts:

- A listing of relevant worldwide standards and publications, by subject; where at least part of any specified standard covers the subject in question.
- Listing of relevant worldwide standards and publications, by reference number and title, for individual standards organizations.

So, an extremely useful guide to worldwide standards is the result. With care, a correlated cross-reference procedure may be followed, which will aid identification of individual standards. Initially, where standards or publications for a particular subject are sought, simply note the numbers of the standards or publications listed alongside the subject in the first part of the appendix (Table A1.1). Then, in the second part of the appendix (Tables A1.3 to A1.12), cross-refer the noted standard or publication number, to check the standard or publication really does cover your particular requirement.

Guide to relevant worldwide standards, by subject

Worldwide, there are obviously far too many standards and publications relevant to aspects of electronics assemblies to compile them *all* into a single table of this form. However, this part of the appendix (Table A1.1) comprises a listing of as many relevant standards and publications as possible, to form a good basic guide on worldwide standards.

Where standards for particular subcategories exist, they are not usually listed and readers are referred to standards catalogues available from the many standards organizations for further details. In this way, standards listed are for non-specific assembly purposes, that is, they are not listed for specific subcategories. So, for example, standards relating to individual types of components are not necessarily listed, but general component standards are. Exceptions to this generalization are some standards relating to common components such as capacitors and resistors.

Similarly, no mention of individual parts or sections of standards and publications can be included in a guide of this kind. Where possible, on the other hand, parts and sections *are* included in the listings of the second part of the appendix.

Table A1.1 International standards and publications, listed by subject

Description	BS	UK defence	IEC	ANSI	USA defense	DIN groups	Miscellaneous
Accelerated corrosion testing: electric contacts and connections	2011, 6917						
Accumulators: *see* Electric cells							
Adhesive:							
coated films: polymeric	4584	01–6				3310	
pressure sensitive tape	3924						
tapes test methods	5350		454				
Aerials: *see* Antennae							
Aluminium capacitors:							
fixed	9078	59–44	384				
fixed electrolytic	9070, 9930, C30300	59–44	384			2160, 2170, 2180	
Amperage: *see* Electric current							
Amplifiers:							
audio			268, 581				
bipolar transistors	5428, 5942, 415 E9372, E9373, E9377					2340	
differential comparator	9461						
integrated	9491						
Amplitude/frequency response: *see* Frequency response							
Analogue circuit:							
integrated	6493, 9491						
monolithic integrated	C90200						
symbols	3939		617				
Analogue–digital convertors:							
electronic DC	5704						
Symbols	3939						
Analysers (wave): *see* Spectrum analyzers							
AND gates: DTL AND gates	9402						
Anodes, for electroplating nickel							

silver 1561
tin 1468
Antennae:
  connectors for
    domestic receiving 5640 130,169
    mobile 489 EIA195
  radio and TV room
    aerials 5373
  Symbols 3939
Assembly of printed
  circuits *see* Production
Assessed quality:
  9000 series, CECC
    series, IECQ series QC001001, QC001002, QC001003, QC001005
  guide PD9004, C00200
  qualified products
    list PD9002, C00200
Attenuators 5817 574 IEEE474
Audiovisual equipment 6552 PH7
  connectors, for
    connection to TV
    receivers
Automatic PCB
  assembly:
  component lead taping 6062 286 EIA296, EIA467, EIA468
  tape automated
    bonding (TAB) 191
Avalanche diodes 9300 QC750001
Batteries: *see* Electric
  cells
Battery-powered 335
  appliances
Bipolar digital circuits 9440
Bipolar transistors 9300, E9372, E9373, E9374, E9377
  switching 9364
Bistable trigger circuits, 9420
  TTL
Board (paper) 5102
  phenolic resin bonded
    paper laminated
    sheet
Boards (printed): *see*
  Printed circuit boards
BSI organization, 0
  function

Description	BS	UK defence	IEC	ANSI	USA defense	DIN groups	Miscellaneous
Cabinets (electronic equipment)	771	59-46		UL65			
dimensions	5954						
Cable glands elastomer and plastics insulated cables	6121						
Cable terminations: see Connectors							
Cables (see also Standards catalogues for specific cables)		61-12				1600, 1610, 1630, 1640	
American and British sizes			228				
cable clamps	5772						
cable terminations	5372		228	EIA455			
classification			78, 96				
coaxial				IPCFC210, IPCFC213, IPCFC217 to IPCFC222		1610	
flat							
low-frequency			708				
Low-voltage			541				
radio frequency	2316, 9215		78, 92, 96				
telecommunications	4808			IPCFC213, ICEAS80		1640	
radiofrequency connector/cable assemblies	9215						
Capability approval of electronic components	9005						
Capacitance measurement	5772						
electromechanical components							
Capacitively coupled devices	9492						
digital integrated circuits							
Capacitor paper	5626						
electrolytic	5626				C25		
Capacitors (see Standards catalogues for specific detail)		59-44, 59-70	384			2110	
colour codes	5890		425				
custom-built, capability approval	9100						

Description	BS	UK defence	IEC	ANSI	USA defense	DIN groups	Miscellaneous
Combinational TTL gate circuits	9405						
Communication cables (see also Standards catalogues for specific details) coaxial	2316, 5425		78, 92, 96				
between video recorders and TV receivers	5819						
LF			189, 304, 344, 649				
polyethylene insulated and sheathed	4808, PD6455 3573						
Communication equipment, inductor and transformer cores	9925						
Comparator amplifiers: integrated, differential	9461						
Comparator circuits	C90302						
Computer terminals: connectors	6623						
Conformal coatings: see Printed circuits							
Connectors (see also Standards catalogues for specific details		59–3, 59–4, 59–5, 59–35, 59–40, 59–56		IEEE290, UL486		1850, 1880	
audio-visual equipment	5817		130, 268				
batteries			130				
cable terminations	5372						
circular	C75200				C5015 C3767		
crimped	G178, G204	59–49, 59–71					
coaxial	C22000		169, 313, 457	IEEE287	C3607, C3643, C3650, C3655		
corrosion tests	2011			EIA364			
DC, LF	9520						
DTE/DCE interface	6623						
DTE/DTE physical	6640						
electrical household appliances	4491, EN60320		320				
electronic equipment	5772					1850, 1880	
flat, quick-connect terminations	5057		760	EIA429, IPCFC217, IPCFC218, IPCFC219, IPCFC220, IPCFC221			

Term						
optical fibres and cables	9230	59–35	874, QC210000	EIA455		
peritelevision						
printed circuit board	6552					
radiofrequency	C75100 3041, 9210, C22000		130, 171, 603 169	EIA406	C3607, C3643, C3650, C3655	1870 1860
robustness testing	2011			EIA364		
snap-on	5057, 5630	59–49	760	EIA280		1780
solderless	6516		352			
sound system	5428, 6840					
symbols	3939		617			
Copper-clad printed circuit bases (*see also* Printed circuits)	4584		249	IPCL108, IPCL112, IPCL115, P13949, IPCL125, IPCAM361, UL746		
Counting circuits TTL	9442					
Coupled circuits: capacitively coupled digital	9492					
Couplers, opto	C20000	59–49, 59–71	875	IEEE290		
Crimped connectors copper, for aircraft	G178 G204					
Crimping tools, for wire terminations	5310					
Crystal filters dimensions	9600 5069					
Crystal oscillators	9620	59–1	679	EIA192		
Crystal resonators capability approval dimensions	9610 9618 5069					
Current-carrying capacity tests electromechanical components	5772					
Current noise, fixed resistors	4119					
Current-regulator diodes	6493					
Damp-heat tests	2011		68			
Dashboards: graphical symbols for controls, indicators	AU143					
passenger cars, location of controls etc.	AU199					
Data circuit-terminating equipment, connectors	6623			EIA232		

Description	BS	UK defence	IEC	ANSI	USA defense	DIN groups	Miscellaneous
interfaces, signal quality	6638			EIA404, EIA232			
Design of assemblies: see Production							
Detector diodes, microwave	9322						
Digital encoders, performance	5704						
Digital integrated circuits monolithic	6493, 9490 C90100						
Digital readouts, colour	4099						
Dimensions of components	5693		234, 294, 301, 451, 620, 717, 915				
Diode transistor logic circuits	9402						
invertor circuits	9404						
Diodes	C20000						
light emitting and infrared	9370						
semiconductor	9300		747	EIA531, NFPA513			
semiconductor, codes of practice	CP1016						
variable-capacitance voltage regulator and reference	E9376 E9375						
Direct-access storage, MOS	C90110, C90111						
Documentation	1219, 5261, 5775, 6868		27, 278		D1000, Std100, Std275	0020,0070, 5480	
Double electrical insulation	2754						
Dry-heat tests			68				
electrical components and equipment	2011						
DTL circuits: see Diode transistor logic							
Earth and earthing	2754	59–41		UL467, UL1053		2075, 2315	
Earth-leakage circuit breakers	842, 4293	61–16	129	UL943		1920	
Electric batteries: see Electric cells							
Electric cells			86			2250, 2260	
connectors for			130				

lead-acid	6745, 3031	61–9				2270	
nickel-cadmium	6260, 5932, 6115	61–9				2280	
primary		61–3				2250	
Electric conductors:							
copper sheet, strip and foil	4608		95,254	C18	EIA251		
flexible polymeric products, resistance	2050		285, 509, 622, 623	C18			
Electric power transmission: radio interference, measurement	5049					1180	
Electrical testing	5772, 4727					1280, 1290, 1420, 1660	
Electrolytic capacitors	5626, 9070, 9930, C30200, C30300, C30201001		261	EIA395	C62, C3965	2160, 2170, 2180	
Electromagnetic compatibility (see also Environmental design)	5941		CISPR11/16/19/ 20/21/22, 533, 801, 315	Std461, E6051	1250, 2310, 2315	CSAC108	108
Electromagnetic interference and radiation audio and TV equipment	G100, 613, 6667, 905		CISPR11/13/14, CISPR13	C63		2315	
glossary	4727						
household appliances	800		CISPR14 CISPR16 CISPR11/13/ 14/16/17/19 20/21/22/23, 106	C63 IEEE376			
instrumentation							
measurement				UL1283, EIA416			
passive radio interference filters	6299		CISPR17				
suppression units	613		CISPR17				
Electromechanical components testing	5775		50, 163, 512	C95			
Electronic assemblies, components and equipment (see also Components by individual names)	5772, C00009	58–95, 59–36, 59–59	512		Std242, Std454	1400, 1430, 1440	
assessed process average	C00014						
assessed quality, administrative guide	PD9004						
assessed quality series	900, CECC and	00–9, 05–14					

Description	BS	UK defence	IEC	ANSI	USA defense	DIN groups	Miscellaneous
auxiliary passive elements, sound system	IECQ 6840						
capacitors	5786, 5890, 5695, 6201, 6303	59-44, 59-70	60, 63, 70, 80, 143, 166, 324, 334, 358, 384, 415, 415, 418, 472, 499, 612, QC300000 to QC301300		C5, C20, C62, C81, C92, C3965, C10950, C11015, C11272, C11693	2110, 2120, 2140, 2150, 2160, 2170, 2180	
cleaning				IPCSC60, IPCAC62	P28809		
convertors, glossary	4727						
cylindrical, two axial leads	5692						
delivery							
design		00-10, 08-5, NES501, NWS100	321	EIA383 EIA213, IPCSM782, IPCD300, IPCD350, IPCD351, IPCD352, IPCDW425, IPCML910, IPCD949	Std275, Hdbk338	1400, 1430	
dimensions	5693		234, 294, 297, 301, 451, 620, 668, 717, 915				
electromechanical components, testing	5772					1420	
encapsulation	3815, 3816, 5664	59-47					
environmental testing	2011 729, 1706, 2569, 4921, 4950	07-55 03-3, 03-5, 03-7, 03-8, 03-9, 03-10, 03-13, 03-20, 03-26	68, 160, 721		Std810	1280, 1290, 1400, 3320	
finishes							
fire hazard testing	6458						
frequency characteristics, polar diagrams	6397			EIA325			
lead taping	6062		286	EIA296, EIA467, EIA468			
maintainability	6548	00-5, 00-13, 00-40, 00-41	706, 300	NFPA70			

packaging of assemblies		NES724, NWS1000					
packaging of components	6062	81-6	286	EIA296, EIA467, EIA468		1400, 1445	
panels and racks	5954	59-46, 59-48	297, 547	EIA310, UL65			
procurement		05-37					
qualified products lists	PD9002, C00200	59-59					
radiofrequency connectors	3041		QC01005				
reliability	4200, DD57	05-61, 05-62, 05-67			Hdbk338	1420, 1443	
resistors	5890, 5695, 6303	59-8, 59-30, 59-69	62, 63, 115, 190, 393, QC400000, QC400100 to QC400500		R11, R19, R22, R26, R93, R94, R10509	1970, 1980, 1995, 2000, 2010	
safety			65, 348, 536				
solderability	2011, 6516		68				
solderless connections				IPCS804, IPCS805			
symbols	3939	05-17	416, 417, 574, 617	IEEE315		1270, 3560, 3790, 7660	
tape automated bonding			191				
testing	2011			EIA162, EIA186	Std202, Std883	1400, 1420, 1442, 7680	NFC93, NFC96, UTEC20
Electrical engineering, drawing practice	308, 5070			Y14			
Electronic measuring equipment				C39			
documentation	4308		278	O-CD325		0070	
performance specification	4889		359				
safety	4743		348				
Electronic power supplies DC output stabilized	5654, 6688	61-5	443, 478, 686	UL1012			
Electroplating						2240, 3320, 5970	
gold	4292, 5658, 6670	03-17			G45204		
silver	1561	03-9					
tin-lead	6137	03-8			T10727, P38510		
Engineering drawings	308			Y1, Y14		7680	
diagrams	5070			Y14		1450	
graphic symbols	1553, 1646, 3238, 3939			IEEE315		0030, 1260, 1270, 7660	
Environmental design	6918	00-35, 00-3, 00-6, 721, 00-7, 00-10, 00-28, 00-29, 00-50, 00-970				3320	

Description	BS	UK defence	IEC	ANSI	USA defense	DIN groups	Miscellaneous
Environmental testing	2011, 6140	07–55, 08–4, 08–5, 59–41, 61–5, NES501, NES725, NWS1000 07–55, 08–5, 59–41, 81–41, NWS1000	68, 160, 721		Std810	1280, 1290, 1400	
adhesive-bonded joints	5350						
climatic tests	5772						
electrical components and equipment	2011						
electromechanical components and equipment	5772			EIA364			
enclosures	4864	81–41					
mechanical testing	5772						
semiconductor devices	6493						
EPROM	C90113						
Fibre optics cables	6558	60–1	693, 793 794	EIA472			
connectors	9230	59–35	874				
symbols	3939						
tests				EIA455			
Field-effect transistors (FET)	6493						
microwave	9352						
Filters			225	EIA197			
bandpass, octave and one third octave	2475						
passive radio interference suppression	9125						
piezoelectric			283, 368				
radio interference suppression filter	9120			EIA416			
Fire-resistant tests and characteristics, cables			331				
Fire tests			695				
electric cables	4066			IEEE634, NFPA262			
electrochemical products	6458						
Flow charts, data processing	4058			X3			

Description	BS	UK defence	IEC	ANSI	USA defense	DIN groups	Miscellaneous
electroplated coatings, test methods	4292, 5658, 6670	03–17					
Graphic symbols: *see* Symbols							
Grids, printed circuits	5830		97				
Ground and grounding: *see* Earth and earthing							
Gunn diodes	9325, 9326						
HCMOS circuits	C90100						
Heating tests	2011		68				
High-altitude tests	2011						
Humidity test	2011		68				
Hybrids (*see* Thick-film circuits and Thin-film circuits)							
I-cores, for tele-communications	4257						
Identification methods (*see also* Standards catalogues for specific methods)		61–7					
colours for	381, PD2379						
electric cable threads, Commonwealth		61–7					
electric cable and wire sleeves	3858, G198						
Index of standards and publications	BSI catalogue	00–00	IEC catalogue		DODISS	DIN catalogue	
Indicating instruments	5164, 5458						
Indicator lights		00–25					
colours	1376		73				
control switches	4794		73				
low-voltage, single-hole mounting	6517						
Inductive proximity switches, classification	6226						
Inductors	9720						
cores	9925, C25000		367, 401, 723				
dimensions	6600						
symbols	3939						
Information technology equipment functional standards development	PD6514						

Term							
radio interference characteristics	6527						
safety	DD138						
standardization	PP7315						
Infrared devices	4737, 6493, C20000		240, 335		1770		
Insulation displacement connectors							
flat, quick-connect terminations	5057		760	EIA429, IPCFC217, IPCF218, IPCFC219, IPCFC220, IPCFC221			
Instrumentation: *see* Electronic measuring equipment and Standards catalogues for specific details							
Insulating tape	6551	59–34	147, 747, QC700000			1440, 1443	NFC96
Integrated circuits (*also see* Standards catalogues for specific details							
analogue	9491, C90200 9450					1440	NFC96
assessed quality, capability approval							
assessed quality, qualification approval	9400, 9970						
digital	6493, 9490, C90100					1440	NFC96
dimensions	3934						
electrostatic sensitive, handling	5783						
film and hybrid	C63000				Std1772	1440	NFC96
fusible-link, programmable read-only memory	9494, C901005						
letter symbols, numbering, terminology	3363, 4727		148	EIA321, IEEE662			
memory	9443						
microprocessor	C90110						
monolithic	C90000						

Description	BS	UK defence	IEC	ANSI	USA defense	DIN groups	Miscellaneous
MOS memory	9490, C90112						
MOS read/write static memory	C90111						
tape automated bonding			191				
ultraviolet light erasable memory	C90113						
Interfaces (data processing)				X3, EIA232, IEEE855			
monolithic integrated circuits	C90300						
Interference suppression components and filter units	613						
passive radio interference filters	6299						
passive radio interference suppression	9125						
Intrinsically-safe electrical equipment	5501						
code of practice	5345						
Laminates (*see also* printed circuit bases)	3953, 5785, 5102, 6673						
Lead-acid batteries	6745						
Lead and alloys, tin/lead electroplated coatings	6137	03–8			T10727, P38510		
Light emitting diodes	6493						
capability approval	9370						
qualification approval	20001						
Line receivers, integrated	C90301						
Line transmitters, integrated	C90301						
Liquid crystal devices	C20000						
Logic analyzers	6653		776				
Logic devices, symbols	3939		617				
Logic gates:							
DTL circuits	9402						
TTL circuits	9401, 9405						
Long-life electronic components	9003						
Maintenance, electrotechnical	6548	00–5, 00–13, 00–40, 00–41,	300, 706, 863	NFPA70	Std470, Std471, M24365, M26512		

Description	BS	UK defence	IEC	ANSI	USA defense	DIN groups	Miscellaneous
Monolithic integrated circuits	C90000						
Multi-layer printed circuit boards	6221, 9761			IPCL108, IPCL109, IPCML910			
NAND gates:							
DTL circuits	9402						
TTL circuits	9401						
NOR gates, TTL	9401						
Operational amplifiers, integrated	9460, C90202						
Optical fibres	6558		693, 793				
cables			794				
connectors			874, 875, QC210000				
Optoelectronic devices	C20000						
Oscillators	9620						
quartz crystal microwave	9325 to 9328		122, 679	EIA192		2310, 2350, 2370	
Oscilloscopes	4739, 5788, 6647		351, 548				
Packaging, components automated handling	1133 6062		286	EIA296, EIA467, EIA468		1400	
tape automated bonding (TAB)			191				
Paper							
phenolic cellulose paper copper-clad sheet	4584					6390	
phenolic resin-bonded paper sheet	5102						
Paper capacitors	2131, 2136		80, 166	EIA401	C25	2140	
Passive filters, radio interference	6299						
Peritelevision connectors	6552						
Phenolic resins:							
bonded paper laminated sheet	5102						
cellulose paper copper-clad sheet	4584						
Photocouplers	6493, C2000						
Photodiodes	6493, C2000						
Photoelectric devices code of practice	CP1016					2515	

Description	BS	UK defence	IEC	ANSI	USA defense	DIN groups	Miscellaneous
Preferred values				Z17, EIA385			
capacitors and resistors	248B		63, 301				
Pressure-sensitive adhesive tape	1133, 3887, 3924		454				
Pressure testing	2011						
Primary batteries	397						
Printed circuit bases and substrates	4584, 3953, 5102, 5785, 6673	59–50	249	IPCL108, IPCL112, IPCL115, IPCL125, IPCAM361, IPCCF150, UL746	P13949	1430	NFC93, ULCC796
Printed circuits (see also Standards catalogues for specific details) acceptability	6221	58–95, 59–48	326	UL796, IPCFC240, IPCSD320	Std275, Std454, P28809, P55110	1430, 1443	NFC93
adhesion of track		59–48		IPCA600, IPCA610, EIA216			NFC93
artwork	6221			IPCD310	Std100		
assembly				IPCCM770			
assessed quality	9760 et seq	59–48		IPCAM372, IPCL112			NFC93
cladding	4584			IPCSC60, IPCAC62			
cleaning							
coatings	5917	59–47		IPCSM840	P28809 146058	1430	
components, cleaning solvents	2011			IPCSC60			
component mounting	5917	59–47		IPCCN770	Std2000 146058		
conformal coatings				IPCSM840			
connectors	9525, C75100		130,171, 603	EIA406 EIA208			
definition and registration							
design	6221		321	EIA213, IPCSM782, IPCD300, IPCD350, IPCD351, IPCD352, IPCDW425, IPCML910, IPCD949, IPCNC349	Std275, Hdbk338	1430	NFC93
drilling							

Description	BS	UK defence	IEC	ANSI	USA defense	DIN groups	Miscellaneous
basic rules							
rules of procedure							
Quality assurance, control, reliability	Handbooks 22/23/24, 4200, 5750, 5760	00–40, 00–41, 05–3, 05–21, 05–22, 05–61, AQAP10	QC001001 QC001002 271, 300, 319, 362, 409, 863	ASQCQ94	Hdbk217, Hdbk338, Std785, Q9858	1443, 5520	
acceptance				ASQCA2			
costs	6143						
glossary	4778		271			5520	
guide	4891	05–22, 05–62, 05–67	362				
inspection planning							
measurement and calibration systems	5781		605	ASQCE2	Std781		
sampling	600, 6000, 6001, 6002	05–58	410		Std105, Std414		
Quality assurance systems	5750, 9000, CECC 05–3, 05–33		IECQ	ASQCQ1 ASQCQ91		1400, 3355, 5520	
design/development, production, installation and serving							
final inspection and test				ASQCQ93		1443	
guidelines				ASQCQ90, ASQCQ94, ASQCQ92			
production and installation							
terminology				ASQCA3			
Quality control	Handbook 25				Q9858	1443	
Quartz crystal dimensions	5069	59–1	122, 444	EIA477, EIA512			
filters			283				
oscillators			679				
resonators	9610		642				
Racks	5954	59–46, 59–48	297, 547, 668	EIA310			
Radio antennae	5373, 5640						
Radio disturbances: see Electromagnetic interference and Radiation							
Radio equipment: glossary	4727			IEEE211			
mobile services	6160		489				
satellite earth stations			510				
symbols	3939						

Description	BS	UK defence	IEC	ANSI	USA defense	DIN groups	Miscellaneous
Semiconductor devices (*see also* under individual component name)		59–61	QC700000, 747			1400, 1440, 1442, 1445, 1660, 2370, 2375, 2380, 2390, 2400, 2410	
acceptance and reliability			147				
assessed quality	9300, 9970, C50000		QC750100				
code of practice	CP1016						
colour coding				EIA232			
dimensions	3934		191			2375	
electrostatic sensitive, handling	5783						JEP108
glossary	4727		148	IEEE662			
letter symbols, numbering, terminology	3363, 4727			EIA321, IEEE662			JESD99, JESD100, JESD1, JESD2, JESD11, JESD77, JEP69, JEP95, JEP104
optoelectronic	C20000		134, 147				
specification	6493						
symbols	3939		191				
tape automated bonding (**TAB**)							
Semiconductor diodes	6493, 9300, C50001	59–61	747, QC700000			2380	
code of practice	CP1016						
variable-capacitance	E9376						
voltage regulator and reference	E9375						
Semiconductor rectifiers	4417, 9300, C50000	59–61	119				
Semiconductor storage	9490, C90112						
Sensitive switches	9490, 9578	59–61		EIA437			
Shift registers, integrated	9444						
Shock tests	2011		68				
Signal diodes	6493, 9300, 9301		QC750100				
code of practice	CP1016						
Signal generators	6348		716				
Snap-on electric connectors	5057						
Sockets		59–4, 59–56					
chip carriers				EIA506			
electronic packages				EIA415			
integrated circuits				EIA415, EIA444, EIA5400000			

DescriptionBS	UK defence	IEC	ANSI	USA defense	DIN groups	Miscellaneous
AC switches, high voltage (specific types)						
voltage	5463		129, 265			
electromechanical	C96000			EIA448, EIA520		
lever, toggle	9561		131	EIA480, EIA520	S3950	
mechanical operating						
tests	5772					
microswitches	9578					
position	6518, 6520					
printed circuit board	9565					
mounting						
Switching circuits, integrated, analogue	9491, C90203					
Switching diodes	6493, 9300		QC750000			
PIN microwave diodes	9324					
Switching transistors	9364, E9374					
Symbols:						
audio-visual equipment	5817		574			0020
electrical engineering	3939	05–17	617	IEEE200, IEEE315	Std100	
electrical equipment	6217		416, 417			1260, 1270, 3560, 3790, 7660
engineering	5070					
function keys, keyboards	2481					
keytop and printed symbols	5478					
process control	1646					
semiconductor devices and logic	3363			IEEE91		
technical drawing	1553		113			0030
Tantalum capacitors	9073, 9930, C30200				C3965	2170
chip capacitors	C30800		384			
electrolytic	9070					2170
Technical documents	4308, 4884, PD6112	05–54	27,278	Z39	D1000	0020, 0070
Technical drawing, graphical symbols	1553	05–17	113	Y14		7660
engineering diagram drawing practice	5070	05–10, 05–53		Y14	Std100	1450, 7680
Television						
antennae, receiving	5640, 5373					2470
glossary	4727					
peritelevision connectors	6552			IEEE201		

Tests (see also Environmental testing)		00-13, 00-26, 00-52, 05-38					
assemblies	2011	00-13, 00-26, 00-52, 05-38				1280, 1290	
components			512		Std202, Std883	1420	JESD25, JEP65, JEP88, JEP96, JEP115, NFC96
printed circuit boards	4584, 6221		249, 326				
Thermal-cycling tests	2011						
Thermal-shock tests	2011						
Thermal testing	2011						
Thermistors	C43000		539, 696, 738, QC440000	EIA275, EIA337, EIA309		1990	
Thermocouples	4937		584	MC96		2290	
Thick-film circuits	C63000				Std1772	1440	
Thin-film circuits	C63000				Std1772	1440	
Thyristors	6493, C50000					2390	
code of practice	CP1016						
DC drives				IEEE597			
reverse-blocking triode	9300						
thyristors							
triacs	9343						
Transducers			184	ISAS37, S2		1220	
conversion of AC into DC	6253						
general purpose	6253		688	IEEE460, S2, ISAS37			
pressure	6174, 6447						
process control transmitters	4509						
temperature	6175						
vibration and shock	6955						
pick-ups, calibration							
Transformers (see also Standards catalogues for specific types)	3938, 3941, 9720, 9721		616	C93, C57, IEEC57, IEEE390, UL1411		1540, 1560	
cores	2857, 5336, 5347, 5938, 6554, 9925, C25000		QC250000/100/200/300, 329, 367, 401, 431, 723			1360, 1540, 1560	
dimensions	6600						
Transistors (see also Standards catalogues for specific types)	9300, 9364, C20003		747, 748			2400	
bipolar	E9372, E9374, E9377						

Description	BS	UK defense	IEC	ANSI	USA defense	DIN groups	Miscellaneous
code of practice	CP1016						
field-effect	C50012, 9352		747				
phototransistors	6493		747				
Transistor transistor logic (TTL) circuits	9401, 9403, 9405, 9420, 9442, 9443, C90101, C90102, C90103, C90106, C90107, C90108						
Ultraviolet erasable, MOS EPROM	C90113						
V24 interface				EIA232			
Varactors	6514, 6640						
Variable-capacitance diodes	9307, 9329, E9376 E9376						
Variable capacitors	5786, 5787, 6103, 9090		334, 415, 418, 472, 499, 612		C81, C92		
Variable inductors	9753						
Variable resistors: see Potentiometers							
Varistors	C42000			EIA349, EIA350			
Vibration testing	2011		68				
Voltage comparators, integrated	C90302						
Voltage-reference diodes	6493, 9300, 9305, E9375						
Voltage regulators, integrated	9430, C90201						
Voltmeters, digital electronicl, performance	5704		CISPR16				
Wafer switches, rotary	9563						
Wirebound resistors	9114, E9114				R19, R22, R26, R93		
Wrapped connections	6516		352	EIA280			

UK standards

UK standards and publications are simply prefixed *BS*. Following letters may be used to categorize further. Letters used in Table A1.1 include:

- *C*. Relating to CECC quality assurance standards (referred to in BSI literature as *BS CECC* standards.
- *CP*. Code of practice.
- *DD*. Draft for development.
- *E*. General-purpose standard.
- *EN*. European standard.
- *G*. Aerospace standard.
- *PD*. Published document.

UK defence standards

Defence standards published by the MoD are prefixed *Def Stan*. A number of other publications may be used by the MoD, however, to specify standard requirements. Other prefixes denoting these publications include:

- *AQAP*. Allied quality assurance publication; NATO quality assurance publication.
- *BR*. Book of reference; handbook for service equipment and procedures.
- *DEF*. Defence specification.
- *Def Con*. Defence conditions, specified in contracts.
- *Def Con guide*. Guides to defence conditions.
- *DTD*. Aircraft materials, components and processes publication.
- *NES*. Naval engineering standard.
- *NWS*. Naval weapon specification.
- *SC*. Standard conditions, specified in contracts.

A hierarchical system of preference is used by the MoD to select standards for defence use. The system currently follows the order:

- Relevant British standards (that is, with the prefix *BS*).
- Defence standards.
- Defence specifications, lists or guides.
- MoD department standards or specifications.
- Other government department standards.
- Recognized industry standards.

IEC standards

IEC standards and publications are usually prefixed *IEC*, unless otherwise specified. Other prefixes are:

- *CISPR*, referring to standards produced by CISPR committees.
- *QC*, referring to standards in the IECQ quality assurance system.

ANSI standards

ANSI is responsible for the publication of many standards (although not for production of the standards). A complicated prefixing arrangement is used for American standards which requires some explaining. For standards directly published by ANSI itself, prefixes are used for classification purposes: usually a single letter or pair of letters (for example PH7).

Other prefixes, denoting the standards publishing bodies or organizations within the ANSI banner, are:

- *ASQC*, American Society for Quality Control.
- *EIA*, Electronic Industries Association.
- *ICEA*, Insulated Cable Engineers Association.
- *IEEE*, Institute of Electrical and Electronic Engineers.
- *IPC*, Institute for Interconnecting and Packaging Electronic Circuits (formerly the Institute of Printed Circuits).
- *ISA*, Instrument Society of America.
- *NEMA*, National Electrical Manufacturers Association.
- *NFPA*, National Fire Protection Association.
- *UL*, Underwriters Laboratories.

So, standards are known by their ANSI prefix, followed by the initial letters of the individual standards organization, and the reference number (for example, ANSI/EIA208).

Sometimes, individual standards organizations choose to issue a further prefix, often the initial letter or letters of the standard's title (for example ANSI/IPCFC240). Generally, though not always, within each individual organization's standards, a numerical order systems operates, such that the standard may be located in the list simply by the standard number, thus making these further initial letter prefixes irelevant in any case.

USA defense standards

USA defense standards and publications are prefixed in one of two main ways:

- *DOD*, Department of Defense standards. Where a standard is prefixed DOD, metric standardization is indicated. Thus new (and revised nonmetric) military standards have this prefix.
- *Mil*, military standards.

USA defense standards will thus have either a *DOD* or a *Mil* prefix. Sometimes a further prefix, often the initial letter or letters of the title, is used, too. Standards and publications are in numerical order so, regardless of prefix, a standard may be located simply by the standard number.

DIN

Deutsches Institut für Normung, the main West German standards organization, produces standards and publications prefixed *DIN*. Other standards organizations produce standards which are incorporated and published by DIN, referenced with a further prefix. These further prefixes include:

- *IEC*, International Electrotechnical Commission.
- *ISO*, International Organization for Standardization.
- *LN*, Deutsches Luft und Raumfahrt Norm.
- *VDE*, Verband Deutscher Elektrotechniker.
- *VG*, Verteidigungsgeräte Norm.

Where DIN standards have been harmonized with CECC and ISO 9000 standards, DIN standards are usually given the same reference number, either directly or as a suffix.

In the DIN catalogue of standards, individual standards are organized into subject groups. This is a useful method of referencing standards, which has been used in the main listing of worldwide standards which follows. Some of the more relevant standards to be located within any particular group are shown listed in Table A1.11.

Many DIN standards are available translated into English – a separate *DIN catalogue* is available, totally in English, which lists those standards' titles.

Miscellaneous standards organizations

Other standards and publications listed include those of a number of organizations:

- AFNOR, the Association Française de Normalisation, the French standards organization. Two prefixes are used in this appendix relating to AFNOR standards, *NF* and *UTE*. Like DIN, AFNOR divides standards into subject groups, but two levels of group categories and subcategories are used, which makes standards identification extremely easy. First categorization (denoted by the letter immediately following the *NF* or *UTE* prefix) selects the main category, while second categorization (denoted by a two figure number) selects the subcategory. Thus, NFC93 is the subcategory relating to electronic components (93) in the electric category (C).
- CSA, Canadian Standards Association.
- JEDEC, the Joint Electron Device Engineering Council of EIA. JEDEC standards are prefixed *JESD*, while publications are prefixed *JEP*. JEDEC standards are *not* national American standards, however, they are recognized by most of the electronics assembly industry.
- US government, Federal specifications and standards.

Guide to relevant worldwide standards, by reference

The remainder of this appendix lists standards by reference number for relevant standards organizations. Generally, the index or catalogue of standards and publications is given first in each table.

Table A1.2 lists general British standards and publications, while Table A1.3 lists BS 9000 system standards and publications, and Table A1.4 lists those of the CECC system.

BS 9000 system

Standards BS 9000 to BS 9970 relate to specifications of individual components in the BS 9000 system of assessed component quality. Although individual standards should be located in the *BSI catalogue*, standards of particular note follow. These are mainly of generic data specifications for the component type, and include methods of test, together with rules and procedures for capability approval where necessary (see Chapter 8 for a description of the BS 9000 system). Immediately after any particular component standard reference (either having the same reference number or closely following it) will be found one or more of four further types of standard:

- A sectional specification for a component variety.
- Rules for the preparation of detail specification for the component.
- A blank detail specification for the component.
- A detail specification for the component and its varieties.

Table A1.2 General British Standards

Reference	Part	Content
Catalogue		BSI standards catalogue
0		Guide. A standard for standards
DD57		Methods of equipment reliability testing
88		Cartridge fuses for voltages up to and including 1000 V AC and 1500 D DC
	1	Specification of general requirements
	2	Specification for fuses for use by authorized persons
G100		Specification for general requirements for electrical equipment and indicating instruments for aircraft (multi-part)
DD138		Safety of information technology equipment including electrically operated business equipment
AU143		Specification for symbols for controls, indicators and tell-tales for road vehicles
G178		Specification for design requirements (including tests) for components and tools (multi-part)
G198		Sleeves for aircraft electric cables and equipment wires (multi-part)
AU199		Specification for location of hand controls, indicators and tell-tales in passenger cars
G204		Specification for copper terminal ends for crimping to electric cables with copper conductors
308	1	Engineering drawing practice: recommendations for general principles

Reference	Part	Content
	2	Engineering drawing practice: recommendations for dimensioning and tolerancing of size
	3	Engineering drawing practice: geometrical tolerancing
381C		Specification for colours for identification, coding and special purposes
397	1	Primary batteries: specification for general requirements
	2	Primary batteries: specification sheets
	3	Primary batteries: specification for batteries not included in Parts 1 and 2
415		Specification for safety requirements for mains-operated electronic and related apparatus for household and similar general use
441		Specification of purchasing requirements for flux-cored and solid soft-solder wire
558		Specifications for nickel anodes, anode nickel and nickel salts for electroplating
600		The application of statistical methods to industrial standardization and quality control
613		Specification for components and filter units for electromagnetic interference suppression
646		Specification: cartridge fuse-links (rated up to 5 A) for AC and DC service
729		Specification for hot dip galvanized coatings on iron and steel articles
771	1	Phenolic moulding materials: Specification for physical properties (excluding type L2 material)
	2	Phenolic moulding materials: Specification for physical properties of type L2 material
800		Specification for limits and methods of measurement of radio interference characteristics of household electrical appliances, portable tools and similar electrical apparatus
842		Specification for AC voltage-operated earth leakage circuit breakers
PP888		The safety and performance of domestic electrical appliances
905	1	Sound and television broadcast receivers and associated equipment – electromagnetic compatability: specification for limits of radio interference
	2	Sound and television broadcast receivers and associated equipment – electromagnetic compatibility: specification for limits of immunity
CP1016	1	Codes of practice for the use of semiconductor devices: general considerations
	2	Codes of practice for the use of semiconductor devices: particular considerations
1133		Packaging code (multi-part)
1219		Recommendations for preparation of mathematical copy and correction of mathematical proofs
1361		Specification for cartridge fuses for AC circuits in domestic and similar premises

Reference	Part	Content
1362		Specification for general-purpose fuse links for domestic and similar purposes (primarily for use in plugs)
1376		Specification for colours of light signals
1468		Specification for tin anodes and tin salts for electroplating
1523		Glossary of terms used in automatic controlling and regulating systems
1553		Specification for graphical symbols for general engineering (multi-part)
1561		Specification for silver anodes and silver salts for electroplating
1646		Symbolic representation for process measurement control functions and instrumentation (multi-part)
1650		Specification for capacitors for connection to power-frequency systems
1706		Specification for electroplated coatings of cadmium and zinc on iron and steel
1843		Colour code for twin compensating cables for thermocouples
1872		Specification for electroplated coatings of tin
2011		Basic environmental testing procedures (multi-part)
	1.1	General and guidance
	2.1	Tests

    A cold
    B dry heat
    C damp heat, steady state
    D damp heat, cyclic
    Ea shock
    Eb bump
    Ec drop and topple
    Ed free fall
    Ee bounce
    Fc vibration (sinusoidal)
    Fd random vibration (multi-part)
    Ga acceleration
    J mould growth
    Ka salt mist
    Kb salt mist cyclic
    Kc sulphur dioxide
    Kd hydrogen sulphide
    M low air pressure
    N change of temperature
    Pz flammability
    Q sealing
    R resistance to fluids
    Sa simulated solar radiation
    T soldering
    U robustness of terminations
    XA immersion in cleaning solvents
    Z/AD combined temperature/humidity cyclic
    Z/AFc combined cold/vibration
    Z/AM combined cold/low air pressure
    Z/AMD combined sequential cold, low air pressure and damp heat

Reference	Part	Content
		Z/ABDM climatic sequence primarily intended for components
		Z/BFc combined dry heat/vibration
		Z/BM combined dry heat/low air pressure
	2.2	Guidance on above tests (multi-part)
	3	Background information (multi-part)
	4	Miscellaneous (multi-part)
2050		Specification for electrical resistance of conducting and antistatic products made from flexible polymeric material
2131		Specification for fixed capacitors for direct current using impregnated paper or paper/plastics film dielectric
2136		Specification for fixed metallized-paper dielectric capacitors for DC
2316		Specification for radiofrequency cables (multi-part)
PD2379		Register of colours of manufacturers' identification threads for electric cables and cords
2475		Specification for octave and one-third octave bandpass filters
2481		Typewriters (multi-part)
2488		Schedule of preferred numbers for the resistance of resistors and the capacitance of capacitors for telecommunication equipment
2569	1	Specification for sprayed metal coatings: protection of iron and steel by aluminium and zinc against atmospheric corrosion
	2	Specification for sprayed metal coatings: protection of iron and steel against corrosion and oxidation at elevated temperatures
2692		Fuses for voltages exceeding 1000 V AC (multi-part)
2754		Construction of electrical equipment for protection against electric shock
2857		Method for determining the thermal classification of electrical insulation
2950		Cartridge fuselinks for telecommunication and light electrical apparatus
3031		Specification for sulphuric acid for use in lead-acid batteries
3036		Semi-enclosed electric fuses (up to 100 A and 240 V)
3041		Radiofrequency connectors (multi-part)
3192		Specification for safety requirements for radio transmitting equipment
3238		Graphical symbols for components of servo-mechanisms (multi-part)
3338		Method for the sampling and analysis of tin and tin alloys (multi-part)
3363		Specification for letter symbols for semiconductor devices and integrated microcircuits
3456		Specification for safety of household and similar electrical appliances (multi-part)
3535		Specification for safety isolating transformers for industrial and domestic purposes
PD3542		The operation of standards in a company
3573		Specification for polyethylene-insulated copper-conductor telecommunication distribution cables

Reference	Part	Content
3593		Recommendation on preferred frequencies for acoustical measurements
3779		Specification for glass and glass polyester fibre woven tapes for electrical purposes
3815		Specification for epoxide resin casting systems for electrical applications
3816		Specification for cast epoxide resin insulating material for electrical applications at power frequencies
3858		Specification for binding and identification sleeves for use on electric cables and wires
3887		Pressure sensitive adhesive closing and sealing tapes for packaging (multi-part)
3924		Specification for pressure sensitive adhesive tapes for electrical insulating purposes
3934		Specification for dimensions of semiconductor devices and integrated circuits (multi-addendums)
3938		Specification for current transformers
3939		Guide for graphical symbols for electrical power, telecommunications and electronics diagrams (multi-part)
3941		Specification for voltage transformers
3953		Specification for synthetic resin bonded woven glass fabric laminated sheet
4058		Specification for data processing flow chart symbols, rules and convention
4061		Dimensions of pot-cores made of magnetic oxides and associated parts (multi-part)
4066		Tests on electric cables under fire conditions (multi-part)
4099		Colours of indicator lights, push-buttons, annunciators and digital readouts
4119		Method of measurement of current noise generated in fixed resistors
4145		Specification for glass mica boards for electrical purposes
4200		Guide on the reliability of electronic equipment and parts used therein
	1	Introduction
	2	Terminology
	3	Presentation of reliability data on electronic components (or parts)
	4	The collection of reliability, availability and maintainability data from field performance of electronic items
	5	Reliability programme for equipment
	6	Feedback of reliability information on equipment
	7	The inclusion of reliability clauses into specifications for components for electronic equipment
	8	The screening (sorting) of electronic equipment and parts
4257		Specification for the dimensions of E-cores made of ferromagnetic oxides for use in telecommunication and allied electronic equipment
4265		Specification for cartridge fuse links for miniature fuses
4292		Specification for electroplated coatings of gold and gold alloys

Reference	Part	Content
4293		Specification for residual current-operated circuit breakers
4308		Specification for documentation to be supplied with electronic measuring equipment
4417		Specification for semiconductor rectifier equipments
4491		Specification for appliance couplers for household and similar general purposes
4509		Methods for evaluating the performance of transmitters for use in industrial process control systems
4584		Metal-clad base materials for printed wiring boards
	1	Methods of test
	2	Epoxide woven glass fabric copper clad laminated sheet, general-purpose grade: EP-GC-Cu-2
	3	Epoxide woven glass fabric copper clad laminated sheet, flame retardant grade: EP-GC-Cu-3
	5	Phenolic cellulose paper copper clad laminated sheet of medium electrical quality: PF-CP-Cu-5
	6	Phenolic cellulose paper copper clad laminated sheet of medium electrical quality, flame retardant grade: PF-CP-Cu-6
	8	Phenolic cellulose paper copper clad laminated sheet of high electrical quality, flame retardant grade: PF-CP-Cu-8
	9	Flexible copper clad polyester (PETP) film: PETP-F-Cu-9
	10	Flexible copper clad polyimide film: PI-F-Cu-10
	11	Bonding sheet material for use in the fabrication of multi-layer printed boards: EP-GC-11
	12	Thin epoxide woven glass fabric copper clad laminated sheet of defined flammability for use in the fabrication of multi-layer printed boards: EP-GC-Cu-12
	13	Silicone woven glass fabric copper clad laminated sheet: Si-GC-Cu-13
	15	Adhesive coated polymeric Film: PETP-F-15 and PI-F-15
	16	Epoxide glass reinforced copper clad laminated sheet of defined flammability: EP-GCA-Cu-16
4608		Specification for copper for electrical purposes; rolled sheet, strip and foil
4727		Glossary of electrotechnical, power, telecommunication, electronics, lighting and colour terms (multi-part)
4737		Intruder alarm systems (multi-part)
4739		Method for the expression of properties of cathode-ray oscilloscopes (multi-part)
4743		Specification for safety requirements for electronic measuring apparatus
4778		Quality vocabulary
	1	International terms
	2	National terms
4794		Specification for control switches (multi-part)
4801		Specification for varnish-bonded glass-braided copper conductors
4808		Specification for LF cables and wires with PVC insulation and PVC sheath for telecommunication (multi-part)
4864		Recommendations on the design and testing of enclosures for environmental testing

Reference	Part	Content
4884		Specification for technical manuals
	1	Content
	2	Presentation
4889		Method for specifying the performance of electronic measuring equipment ·
4891		A guide to quality assurance
4921		Specification for sherardized coatings on iron or steel
4937		International thermocouple reference tables (multi-part)
4950		Specification for sprayed and fused metal coatings for engineering purposes
5049		Methods for measurement of radio interference characteristics of overhead power lines and high voltage equipment
5057		Specification for flat quick-connect terminations
5069		Dimensions of piezoelectric devices
5070		Engineering diagram drawing practice
	1	Recommendations for general principles
	2	Recommendations for electrotechnology diagrams
	3	Recommendations for mechanical/fluid flow diagrams
5102		Specification for phenolic resin bonded paper laminated sheets for electrical applications
5164		Specification for indirect-acting electrical indicating and recording instruments and their accessories
5191		Glossary of production planning and control terms
5261		Copy preparation and proof correction
	1	Recommendations for preparation of typescript copy for printing
	2	Specification for typographic requirements, marks for copy preparation and proof correction, proofing procedure
5271		Specification for low-voltage switchgear for industrial use
5310		Hand crimping tools for the termination of electrical cables and wires for low frequency and radiofrequency applications
5336		Cores made of ferromagnetic oxides for use in high flux density transformers
5345		Code of practice for selection, installation and maintenance of electrical apparatus for use in potentially explosive atmospheres (multi-part)
5347		Specification for silicon-iron strip wound cores for use in transformers and inductors for telecommunications and electronic equipment
5350		Methods of test for adhesive (multi-part)
5372		Specification for cable terminations for electrical equipment
5373		Specification for electrical safety requirements for room aerials
5378		Safety signs and colours (multi-part)
5408		Glossary of documentation terms
5425		Coaxial cable for wideband distribution systems
5428		Methods for specifying and measuring the characteristics of sound system equipment
5458		Specification for safety requirements for indicating and recording electrical measuring instruments and their accessories
5463		Specification for AC switches for over 1000 V

Reference	Part	Content
5478		Calculators and adding machines (multi-part)
5501		Electrical apparatus for potentially explosive atmospheres (multi-part)
5529		Specification for low voltage switchgear
5564		Specification for high voltage fuses for the external protection of shunt power capacitors
5625		Specification of purchasing requirements and methods of test for fluxes for soft soldering
5626		Cellulosic papers for electrical purposes (multi-part)
5630		Specification for interface dimensions of snap-on connections for use with electrically controlled hydraulic equipment
5640		Aerials for the reception of sound and television broadcasting in the frequency range 30 MHz to 1 GHz (multi-part)
5648		Specification for screw cores made of magnetic oxides or iron powder
5654		Stabilized power supplies, DC output (multi-part)
5658		Specification for gold potassium cyanide for electroplating
5664		Solventless polymerizable resinous compounds used for electrical insulation (multi-part)
5683		Specification for low voltage switchgear
5684		Specification for low voltage switchgear
5692		Method for measurement of the dimensions of a cylindrical electronic component having two axial terminations
5693		Recommendations for preferred diameters of wire terminations of capacitors and resistors
5694		Method for measurement of non-linearity in resistors
5695		Recommendations for maximum case dimensions for capacitors and resistors
5704		Method for specifying the performance of digital DC voltmeters and DC electronic analogue-to-digital convertors
5750		Quality systems
	0	Principal concepts and applications
		0.1 guide to selection and use
		0.2 guide to quality management and quality system elements
	1	Specification for design/development, production, installation and servicing
	2	Specification for production and installation
	3	Specification for final inspection and test
	4	Guide to the use of BS 5750 Part 1
	5	Guide to the use of BS 5750 Part 2
	6	Guide to the use of BS 5750 Part 3
5760		Reliability of constructed or manufactured products, system, equipments and components
	0	Introductory guide to reliability
	1	Guide to reliability and maintainability programme management
	2	Guide to the assessment of reliability
	3	Guide to reliability practices: examples
	4	Guide to specification clauses relating to the achievement and development of reliability in new and existing items

Reference	Part	Content
5772		Basic testing procedures and measuring methods for electromechanical components for electronic equipment (multi-part)
5775		Specification for quantities, units and symbols (multi-part)
5781		Measurement and calibration systems (multi-part)
5783		Code of practice for handling of electrostatic sensitive devices
5785		Combined flexible materials for electrical insulation (multi-part)
5786		Variable capacitors
5787		Guide to the use of variable capacitors in electronic equipment
5817		Audio-visual, video and television equipment and systems (multi-part)
5819		Specification for interconnections between videotape recorders and television receivers for 50 Hz, 625 line systems
5830		Specification for grid system for printed circuits
5890		Guide for choice of colours to be used for the marking of capacitors and resistors
5917		Specification for conformal coating materials for use on printed circuit assemblies
5832		Specification for sealed nickel cadmium cylindrical rechargeable single cells
5938		Cores for inductors and transformers for telecommunications
5942		High fidelity audio equipment and systems; minimum performance requirements
5954		Specification for dimensions of panels and racks for electronic equipment
5958		Code of practice for control of undesirable static electricity
5961		Method for determination of coefficients of friction of plastic film and sheeting for use as electrical insulation
6000		Guide to the use of BS 6001
6001		Sampling procedures for inspection by attributes
	1	Specification for sampling plans indexed by acceptable quality level (AQL) for lot-by-lot inspection
	2	Specification for sampling plans indexed by limiting quality (LQ) for isolated lot inspection
	3	Specification for skip-lot procedures
6002		Specification for sampling procedures and charts for inspection by variables for per cent defective
6041		Method of sampling of electrodeposited metallic coatings and related finishes: procedures for inspection by attributes
6062		Packaging of electronic components for automatic handling
	1	Specification for tape packaging of components with axial leads on continuous tapes
	2	Specification for tape packaging of components with unidirectional leads on continuous tapes
	3	Specification for packaging of leadless components on continuous tapes
6096		Marking inks and solder resist coating materials for printed circuits
	1	Methods of test
	2	Specification for marking inks

Reference	Part	Content
	3	Specification for solder resist inks
	4	Specification for permanent polymer (dry film solder mask) material
6103		Specification for dimensions for the mounting of single-hole, bush-mounted spindle operated electronic components
PD6112		Guide to the preparation of specifications
6115		Specification for sealed nickel cadmium prismatic rechargeable single cells
6120		Specification for low voltage switchgear
6121		Mechanical cable glands
6122		Specification for low voltage switchgear
6123		Specification for low voltage switchgear
6137		Specification for electroplated coatings of tin/lead alloys
6138		Glossary of terms used in the adhesives industry
6140		Test equipment for generating vibration (multi-part)
6143		Guide to the determination and use of quality related costs
6160		Method of measurement for radio equipment used in the mobile services (multi-part)
6174		Specification for differential pressure transmitters with electrical outputs
6175		Specification for temperature transmitters with electrical outputs
6201		Fixed capacitors for use in electronic equipment (multi-part)
6217		Guide to graphical symbols for use on electrical equipment
6221		Printed wiring boards
	2	Methods of test
	3	Guide for the design and use of printed wiring boards
	4	Method for specifying single- and double-sided printed wiring boards with plain holes
	5	Method for specifying single- and double-sided printed wiring boards with plated-through holes
	6	Method for specifying multi-layer printed wiring boards
	7	Method for specifying single- and double-sided flexible printed wiring boards without through connections
	8	Method for specifying single- and double-sided flexible printed wiring boards with through connections
	20	Guide for the assembly of printed wiring boards
	21	Guide for the repair of printed wiring boards
6226		Specification for low voltage switchgear
6227		Specification for low voltage switchgear
6234		Specification for polyethylene insulation and sheath of electric cables
6236		Electrical insulating materials based on mica
6253		Electrical measuring transducers for converting AC electrical quantities into DC
6260		Specification for open nickel cadmium prismatic rechargeable single cells
6299		Methods of measurement of the suppression characteristics of passive radio interference filters and suppression components

Reference	Part	Content
6301		Specification for safety requirements for apparatus for connection to British Telecommunications networks
6303		Method for determination of the space required by capacitors and resistors with unidirectional terminations
6348		Method for the expression of the properties of signal generators
6397		Specification for scales and sizes for plotting frequency characteristics and polar diagrams
6447		Specification for absolute and gauge pressure transmitters with electrical outputs
PD6455		Metric dimensions for LF cables and wires for telecommunication
6458		Fire hazard testing for electrotechnical equipment (multi-part)
PD6470		The management of design for economic production. Standardization philosophy aimed at improving the performance of the electrical and mechanical manufacturing sectors
6491		Electro-sensitive safety systems for industrial machines (multi-part)
6493		Semiconductor devices
	1	1.1 discrete devices
		1.2 rectifier diodes
		1.3 signal and regulator diodes
		1.5 optoelectronic devices
		1.6 thyristors
		1.8 field effect transistors
	2	Integrated circuits
		2.1 general
		2.2 digital integrated circuits
		2.3 analogue integrated circuits
	3	Mechanical and climatic test methods
PD6495		IFAN (International Federation for the Application of Standards) Guide 1. Method for determining the advantages of (company) standardization projects
6514		Guide for implementation of V24 or RS232 as an asynchronous local interface
PD6514		Guide to basic references for the development of functional standards in the field of information technology equipment
PD6515		IFAN Guide 2. Company use of international standards
6516		Solderless wrapped connections
6517		Specification for low voltage switchgear
6518		Specification for low voltage switchgear
6519		Specification for low voltage switchgear
6520		Specification for low voltage switchgear
6527		Specification for limits and methods of measurement of radio interference characteristics of information technology equipment
6534		Method for quantitative determination of lead in tin coatings

Reference	Part	Content
6548		Maintainability of equipment
6551		Specification for polyester fibre woven tapes for electrical purposes
6552		Specification for domestic and similar electronic equipment interconnection: peritelevision connector
6553		Guide for selection of fuse links of high voltage fuses
6554		Laminations for transformers and inductors for use in telecommunication and electronic equipment
6558		Optical fibres and cables
6600		Outline dimensions of transformers and inductors for use in telecommunication and electronic equipment
6623		DTE/DCE interface connectors and pin assignments (multi-part)
6638		Guide to transmission signal quality at DTE/DCE interfaces
6640		Guide to arrangements for DTE to DTE physical connection
6647		Guide to oscilloscopes and peak voltmeters for impulse tests
6653		Method for expression of properties of logic analyzers
6667		Electromagnetic compatibility for industrial-process measurement and control equipment
	1	General introduction
	2	Method of evaluating susceptibility to electrostatic discharge
	3	Method of evaluating susceptibility to radiated electromagnetic energy
6670		Methods of test for electroplated gold and gold alloy coatings (multi-part)
6673		Specification for polyester glass mat sheets for electrical purposes
6688		Method for specifying requirements for low voltage power supplies, switching type, DC output
6745		Portable lead-acid cells and batteries
6811		Winding wires (multi-part)
6840		Sound system equipment (multi-part)
6868		Specification for standard generalized markup language (SGML) for text and office systems
6885		Specification for miniature cartridge fuse links for use on printed wiring boards
6893		Flexible insulating sleeving for electrical purposes (multi-part)
6917		Method for corrosion testing in artificial atmospheres
6918		Glossary of terms for corrosion of metals and alloys
6955		Calibration of vibration and shock pickups
PP7315		Standardization for information technology

Table A1.3 BS 9000 system standards and publications

Reference	Part/section	Content
9000		General requirements for a system for electronic components of assessed quality
	1	Specification of basic rules and procedures
	2	Specification for national implementation of CECC basic rules and rules of procedure
	3	Specification for national implementation of IECQ basic rules and rules of procedure
PD9002		BS 9000, BSCECC and IECQ qualified products lists
9003		Requirements for the manufacture of electronic components of assessed quality intended for long life applications
PD9004		BS 9000, CECC and IECQ UK administrative guide
9005		Specification for general procedures to be followed for the capability approval of electronic components covered by BS 9000 Part 1
9070		Specification for fixed capacitors
	1/2	Principles and procedures
	3	Tantalum electrolytic capacitors
	4	Polystyrene dielectric capacitors
	5	Ceramic dielectric capacitors
	6	Polycarbonate and polyethylene terephthalate dielectric capacitors
	7	Mica dielectric capacitors
	8	Aluminium electrolytic capacitors
	10	Tantalum electrolytic capacitors modules
9090		Specification for variable capacitors
9100		Specification for custom-built capacitors
9110		Specification for fixed resistors
9120		Specification for radio interference suppression filters
9125		Specification for passive radio interference suppression filter units
9130		Specification for potentiometers
9150		Specification for electrical relays
9200		Specification for reed contact units
9210		Specification for radiofrequency connectors
9215		Specification for custom-built radiofrequency connector/cable
9230		Specification for optical fibre and cable connectors
9300		Specification for semiconductor devices
9370		Specification for light emitting and infra-red diode arrays
9400		Specification for integrated electronic circuits and micro-assemblies
9450		Specification for capability approval of integrated electronic circuits and micro-assemblies
9500		Specification for sockets for electronic tubes and valves and plug-in devices
9520		Specification for electrical connectors for DC and low frequency applications

Reference	Part/section	Content
9521		Specification for removable contacts for electrical connectors
9530		Specification for cable fitting accessories for circular electrical connectors
9561		Specification for lever operated switches
9562		Specification for microswitches
9563		Specification for rotary (manual) switches
9564		Specification for push-button switches
9565		Specification for printed board mounted programming switches
9600		Specification for piezoelectric crystal filters
9610		Specification for quartz crystal units
9618		Specification for capability approval of quartz crystal units
9620		Specification for quartz crystal oscillators
9720		Specification for custom-built transformers and inductors
9750		Specification for fixed radiofrequency inductors
9760		Specification for printed circuits
9761		Sectional specification for capability approval of manufacturers of multi-layer rigid printed wiring boards of assessed quality with plated-through holes
9762		Sectional specification for capability approval of manufacturers of double-sided rigid printed wiring boards of assessed quality with plated-through holes
9763		Sectional specification for capability approval of manufacturers of single- and double-sided rigid printed wiring boards of assessed quality without plated-through holes
9764		Sectional specification for capability approval of manufacturers of single- or double-sided rigid printed wiring boards of assessed quality without through hole connections and with or without rigidizing component materials
9765		Sectional specification for capability approval of manufacturers of double-sided flexible printed wiring boards of assessed quality with through hole connections and with or without rigidizing component materials
9766		Sectional specification for multi-layer flexi-rigid printed circuits with through-hole connections
9800		Specification for capability approval of modular electronic networks
9925		Harmonized system of quality assessment for electronic components: inductor and transformer cores for telecommunications
9930		Harmonized system of quality assessment for electronic components: fixed capacitors
9940		Harmonized system of quality assessment for electronic components: fixed resistors

Reference	Part/section	Content
9970		Harmonized system of quality assessment for electronic components: semiconductor devices
Handbook 22		Quality assurance
Handbook 23		Quality management systems. General management
Handbook 24		Quality management systems. Quality control
Handbook 25		Quality management systems. Statistical interpretation of data

Table A1.4   CECC system standards and publication

Reference	Content
00007	Basic specification: sampling plans and procedures for inspection by attributes
00009	Basic specification: basic testing procedures and measuring methods for electromechanical components
00012	Basic specification: radiographic inspection of electronic components
00013	Basic specification: scanning electron microscope inspection of semiconductor dice
00014	Basic specification: CECC assessed processed average procedure
00200	Qualified products list
00800	Code of practice for the use of the ppm approach in association with the CECC system
11000	Generic specification: cathode ray tubes
12000	Generic specification: image converter and image intensifier tubes
13000	Generic specification: camera tubes
14000	Generic specification: photomultiplier tubes
16000	Generic specification: electromechanical all-or-nothing relays
17000	Generic specification: mercury wetted make contact units
18000	Generic specification: dry reed changeover contact units
19000	Generic specification: dry reed make contact units
20000	Generic specification: semiconductor optoelectronic and liquid crystal devices
22000	Generic specification: radiofrequency coaxial cables
25000	Generic specification: inductor and transformer cores for telecommunications
30000	Generic specification: fixed capacitors
30100	Sectional specification: polyethylene terephthalate film dielectric metal foil capacitors
30200	Sectional specification: tantalum capacitors
30300	Sectional specification: aluminium electrolytic capacitors
30400	Sectional specification: metallized polyethylene terephthalate film dielectric capacitors
30500	Sectional specification: metallized polycarbonate film dielectric capacitors

Reference	Content
30600	Sectional specification: class 1 ceramic capacitors
30700	Sectional specification: class 2 ceramic capacitors
30800	Sectional specification: tantalum chip capacitors
30900	Sectional specification: polystyrene film dielectric metal foil capacitors
31100	Sectional specification: ceramic dialectric capacitors
31200	Sectional specification: polypropylene dielectric capacitors with metallized electrodes
31300	Sectional specification: mica dielectric capacitors
31400	Sectional specification: ceramic dielectric (class 1) capacitors
31500	Sectional specification: ceramic dielectric (class 2) capacitors
31700	Sectional specification: polycarbonate dielectric capacitors with thin metal foil electrodes
31800	Sectional specification: polypropylene dielectric capacitors with thin metal foil electrodes
35000	Generic specification: travelling wave amplifer tubes
36000	Generic specification: magnetrons
40000	Generic specification: fixed resistors
40100	Sectional specification: low power non-wirewound resistors
40200	Sectional specification: power resistors
40300	Sectional specification: precision resistors
41000	Generic specification: potentiometers
41100	Sectional specification: lead screw actuated and rotary preset potentiometers
41200	Sectional specification: power potentiometers
41300	Sectional specification: low power single turn rotary potentiometers
41400	Sectional specification: rotary precision potentiometers
42000	Generic specification: varistors
43000	Generic specification: negative temperature coefficient thermistors
45000	Generic specification: space-charge controlled tubes
46000	Generic specification: cold cathode indicator tubes
50000	Generic specification: discrete semiconductor devices
51000	Generic specification: mercury wetted, magnetically biased, changeover contact unit
52000	Generic specification: mercury wetted, mechanically biased, changeover contact units
63000	Generic specification: film and hybrid integrated circuits
75100	Sectional specification: two-part and edge socket connectors for printed board applications
75200	Sectional specification: circular connectors
90000	Generic specification: monolithic integrated circuits
90100	Sectional specification: digital monolithic integrated circuits
90101	Family specification: TTL circuits
90102	Family specification: TTL SCHOTTKY circuits
90103	Family specification: TTL low power SCHOTTKY circuits
90104	Family specification: CMOS circuits
90105	Blank detail specification: fusible link programmable bipolar read only memories
90106	Family specification: TTL advanced low power SCHOTTKY circuits

Reference	Content
90107	Family specification: TTL FAST circuits
90108	Family specification: TTL advanced SCHOTTKY circuits
90109	Family specification: HCMOS circuits
90110	Blank detail specification: microprocessor circuits
90111	Blank detail specification: MOS read/write static memories
90112	Blank detail specification: MOS read/write dynamic memories
90113	Blank detail specification: MOS ultraviolet erasable electrically programmable read only memories
90200	Sectional specification: analog monolithic integrated circuits
90201	Blank detail specification: voltage regulators
90202	Blank detail specification: operational amplifiers
90203	Blank detail specification: analog switching circuits
90300	Sectional specification: interface monolithic integrated circuits
90301	Blank detail specification: line transmitters and receivers
90302	Blank detail specification: voltage comparators
96000	Generic specification: electromechanical switches

CECC publications

The intention of the CECC system is to form a harmonized quality system of components, to promote trade throughout Europe.

CECC standards are listed in Table A1.1 prefixed, for simplicity, by the letter *C*. Their actual prefix is *CECC*. Where they are harmonized as British standards, their prefix is usually *BS CECC*. Like BS 9000 system standards CECC system standards are formed by many types of standard specifications. Also like BS 9000 system standards component types and varieties are headed by a generic specification. This is then typically followed by one or more sectional specification. Sectional specifications are then followed by one or more detail, blank detail or family specification. Numbering of CECC standards is a bit more logical than BS 9000, however: generic specifications are numbered *xx000*; sectional specifications are numbered *xxy00*; while detail, blank detail or family specifications are numbered *xxyzz*.

UK defence standards and publications

Defence standards are given the prefix *Def Stan*, and are placed in groups based on the NATO supply classification system, in which subject groups are allotted group numbers varying from 10 to 99. Additionally the series 00 to 09 are used for subject groups not covered by the NATO classification. A full listing of group numbers and subjects is given in Table A1.5, while standards given in Table A1.1 are listed in Table A1.6.

IEC standards

Standards and publications of IEC, including CISPR publications, are listed in Table A1.7.

IEC QC standards of particular note, meanwhile, are listed in Table A1.8. The IECQ system is intended to form an internationally harmonized quality system for components, to promote worldwide trade. Organization and number of standards is similar to the CECC system, in that generic specifications are numbered *xxx000*; sectional specifications are numbered *xxxy00*; while detail and blank detail specifications are numbered *xxxyzz*.

USA standards

ANSI standards and publications, incorporating those of the ASQC, EIA, IEEE, IPC, UL and others are listed in Table A1.9. USA defense standards and publications are listed in Table A1.10.

Others

DIN standard groups, with selected standards, are listed in Table A1.11, while miscellaneous standards are listed in Table A1.12.

Table A1.5   UK Defence Standard subject groups

Group number	Subject
00	General data
01	Materials not covered by or related exclusively to a unique NATO group
03	Processes not related to a unique NATO group
05	Procedures not related to a unique NATO group
07	Standard where distribution is limited for reasons other than security (e.g. because they contain proprietary information)
08	Standards graded 'restricted'
09	Standards graded 'confidential' or above
10	Weapons
11	Nuclear ordnance
12	Fire control equipment
13	Ammunition and explosives
14	Guided missiles
15	Aircraft: airframe structural components
16	Aircraft components and accessories
17	Aircraft launching, landing and ground handling equipment
18	Space vehicles
19	Ships, small craft, pontoons and floating docks
20	Ship and marine equipment
22	Railway equipment
23	Motor vehicles, trailers and cycles
24	Tractors
25	Vehicular equipment components
26	Tyres and tubes
28	Engines, turbines and components
29	Engine accessories
30	Mechanical power transmission equipment
31	Bearings

Group number	Subject
32	Woodworking machinery and equipment
34	Metalworking machinery
35	Service and trade equipment
36	Special industry machinery
37	Agricultural machinery and equipment
38	Construction, mining, excavating and highway maintenance equipment
39	Materials handling equipment
40	Rope, cable, chain and fittings
41	Refrigeration and air conditioning equipment
42	Firefighting, rescue and safety equipment
43	Pumps and compressors
44	Furnace steam plant and drying equipment, also nuclear reactors
45	Plumbing, heating and sanitation equipment
46	Water purification and sewage treatment equipment
47	Pipe, tubing, hose and fittings
48	Valves
49	Maintenance and repair shop equipment
51	Hand tools
52	Measuring tools
53	Hardware and abrasives
54	Prefabricated structures and scaffolding
55	Lumber, millwork, plywood and veneer
56	Construction and building materials
58	Communication, detection and coherent radiation equipment
59	Electrical and electronic equipment components
60	Fibre optics materials, components, assemblies and accessories
61	Electric wire and power and distribution equipment
62	Lighting fixtures and lamps
63	Alarm and signal systems
65	Medical, dental and veterinary equipment and supplies
66	Instruments and laboratory equipment
67	Photographic equipment
68	Chemicals and chemical products
69	Training aids and devices
72	Household and commercial furnishing and appliances
74	Office machines, visible record equipment and data processing equipment
75	Office supplies and devices
79	Cleaning equipment and supplies
80	Brushes, paints, sealers and adhesives
81	Containers, packaging and packing supplies
83	Textiles, leather, furs, apparel and shoe findings, tents and flags
84	Clothing, individual equipment and insignia
85	Toiletries
89	Subsistence
91	Fuels, lubricants, oils and waxes
93	Non-metallic fabricated materials
95	Metal bars, sheets and shapes
96	Ores, minerals and their primary products
99	Miscellaneous

Table A1.6 UK Defence Standards

Reference	Part	Content
00–00	3	Index of standards
00–3		Design guidance for transportability of equipment
00–5	0	Requirements for achieving reliability and maintainability of MGO procured material
	1	Design criteria for reliability, maintainability and maintenance of land service material: general aspects
	2	Design criteria for reliability, maintainability and maintenance of land service material: mechanical aspects
	3	Design criteria for reliability, maintainability and maintenance of land service material: electrical and electronic aspects
	4	Design criteria for reliability, maintainability and maintenance of land service material: optical aspects
00–6		Fording and flotation requirements for mobile equipment
00–7		Immersion requirements for ground role service equipment
00–9		General requirements for qualification approval, capability approval and quality assurance of components for MoD use
00–10		General design and manufacturing requirements for service equipment
00–13		Guide to the achievement of testability in electronic and allied equipment
00–25	1	Human factors for designers of equipment: introduction
	2	Human factors for designers of equipment: body size
	3	Human factors for designers of equipment: body strength and stamina
	6	Human factors for designers of equipment: vision and lighting
	7	Human factors for designers of equipment: visual displays
00–26		Guide to the evaluation and expression of the uncertainties associated with the results of electrical measurements
00–28		Fire environmental conditions affection design criteria of military material
00–29		Fungal contamination affecting the design of military material
00–35	1	Environmental handbook for defence material: general requirements
	2	Environmental handbook for defence material: specification of service environments
	4	Environmental handbook for defence material: natural environments
00–40	1	Achievement of reliability and maintainability: reliability design philosophy
	2	Achievement of reliability and maintainability: general application guidance
00–41	1	MoD practices and procedures for reliability and maintainability: reliability design philosophy
	2	MoD practices and procedures for reliability and maintainability: reliability apportionment, modelling and calculation
	3	MoD practices and procedures for reliability and maintainability: reliability prediction
	4	MoD practices and procedures for reliability and maintainability: reliability engineering

Reference	Part	Content
	5	MoD practices and procedures for reliability and maintainability: reliability testing and screening
00–50		Guide to chemical environmental contaminants and corrosion affecting the design of military material
00–52		General requirements for test specifications and test schedules
00–970		Design requirements for service aircraft
01–6		Guide to the selection of adhesives and adhesive tapes for use on service material
03–3		Protection of aluminium alloys by sprayed metal coatings
03–5		Electroless nickel coating of metals
03–7		Painting of metal and wood
03–8		Electro-deposition of tin
03–9		Electro-deposition of silver
03–10		Electro-deposition of nickel and chromium
03–13		Guide for the prevention of corrosion of metal caused by vapour from organic materials
03–15		Electro-deposition of tin-lead alloy for soldering purposes
03–17		Electro-deposition of gold
03–20		Electro-deposition of zinc
03–22		Guide to soldering and brazing
03–26		Hard anodizing of aluminium and aluminium alloys
05–3		Mutual acceptance of Government quality assurance
05–10		Drawing procedure
05–14		Mutual acceptance of qualification approvals for electronic components within NATO countries
05–17		Electrotechnical terms and graphical symbols
05–21		Quality control system requirements for industry
05–22	1	Guide for the evaluation of a contractor's quality control system for compliance with Def Stan 05–21
	2	Guide for the evaluation of a contractor's quality control system for compliance with Def Stan 05–21
05–24		Inspection system requirements for industry
05–25		Guide for the evaluation of a contractor's inspection system for compliance with Def Stan 05–24
05–26		Measurements and calibration system requirements for industry
05–27		Guide for the evaluation of a contractor's measurement and calibration system for compliance with Def Stan 05–26
05–29		Basic inspection system requirements for industry
05–33		Allied quality assurance publications
05–37		Policy for procurement of electronic components
05–38		General principles of gauging
05–53		Identification of drawings for their retrieval
05–58		NATO guideline for the specification of technical publications
05–61	1	Quality assurance procedural requirements: concessions and production permits
	2	Quality assurance procedural requirements: Government surplus material
	3	Quality assurance procedural requirements: quality assurance of subcontract work

Reference	Part	Content
05–62		Guidance on quality assurance procedures: planning to achieve quality (multi-part)
05–67		Guide to quality assurance in design
07–55	1	Environmental testing of service material: general requirements
	2/1	Environmental testing of service material: mechanical tests
	2/2	Environmental testing of service material: climatic tests
	2/3	Environmental testing of service material: chemical and biological attack tests
	2/4	Environmental testing of service material: penetration and immersion tests
	2/5	Environmental testing of service material: radiation tests
	2/6	Environmental testing of service material: fire and explosion tests
08–4		Nuclear weapons explosions effects and hardening (multi-part)
08–5		Design requirements for weapon systems
34–4		Fluxes for soft soldering electrical and electronic assemblies
58–59	1	Electronic assemblies: general requirements
	2	Electronic assemblies: amplifier assemblies
	90	Electronic assemblies: detail
59–1	1	General requirements for quartz crystal units
59–3		Electrical terminals (multi-part)
59–4		Plugs and sockets (multi-part)
59–5		Clips (multi-part)
59–7		Relays (multi-part)
59–8		Resistors, variable and rheostats
59–11		Switches (multi-part)
59–30		Resistors, fixed, of assessed quality (multi-part)
59–34		Insulation tape, electrical
59–35		Connectors, electrical and optical fibre (multi-part)
59–36	1	Electronic components for defence purposes: role of defence standards in relation to BS 9000 series
	2	Electronic components for defence purposes: procedure for selection, specification and quality assurance of electronic components
59–40		Lugs, terminals and terminal strips (multi-part)
59–41	1	Electromagnetic compatibility: general requirements
	2	Electromagnetic compatibility: management and planning procedures
	3	Electromagnetic compatibility: technical requirements, test methods and limits
	4	Electromagnetic compatibility: open site testing
59–44		Capacitors, fixed, of assessed quality (multi-part)
59–46		Cases, equipment, rack mounting, and associated lids, panels, and shelves – suitable for use with 19 inch racks
59–47		Conformal coatings for panels, printed circuit and panels, electronic circuit
59–48		Printed circuits of assessed quality: general requirements for the procurement of rigid and flexible printed circuits
	4	Printed circuits of assessed quality: general requirements for

Reference	Part	Content
		printed wired boards with discreetly wired layers
59–49		Solderless wrapped electrical connections
59–50		Requirements for plastics sheet laminated copper clad, epoxide resin bonded, woven glass fabric base – fire retardant (metal clad base materials for printed circuits)
59–51		Relays, of assessed quality (multi-part)
59–56		Plugs and sockets, electrical
59–59		Electrical/electronic components for defence use. Services qualified products list including components of assessed quality
59–61		Semiconductor devices (multi-part)
59–69		Resistors, variable, of assessed quality (multi-part)
59–70		Capacitors, variable, of assessed quality (multi-part)
59–71		Crimped electrical connections for copper
59–75		Switches of assessed quality (multi-part)
59–96		Fuse links (multi-part)
59–100		Fuseholders (multi-part)
60–1		Fibre optics (multi-part)
61–3		Primary batteries (multi-part)
61–5		Electrical power supply systems below 650 volt (multi-part)
61–7		Identification of electrical and electronic systems, wiring and components (multi-part)
61–9		Secondary batteries (multi-part)
61–12		Wires, cords and cables, electrical (multi-part)
61–15		Precautions against electric shock (multi-part)
61–16		Differential current operated earth-leakage circuit breakers
81–6		Packaging of electronic valves, semiconductor devices and integrated circuits
81–31		Packaging of capacitors
81–33		Packaging of relays
81–36		Packaging of switches
81–37		Packaging of resistors
81–41	1	Packaging of defence material: general requirements
	2	Packaging of defence material: design
	3	Packaging of defence material: environmental testing
	4	Packaging of defence material: documentation
	5	Packaging of defence material: production processes
	6	Packaging of defence material: package markings
BR4601		Staff maintenance requirements
DTD599		Non-corrosive flux for soft soldering
NES501		General requirements for the design of electrotechnical equipment
NES724		Packaging
NES725		General environmental conditions for surface ships
NES784		Requirements for safety signs and colours
NWS1000		Equipment design – design requirements

Table A1.7 IEC standards and publications

Reference	Part	Content
27		Letters to be used in electrical technology
	1	General
	2	Telecommunications and electronics
	3	Logarithmic quantities and units
50		International electrotechnical vocabulary
	00	General index
	55	Telegraphy and telephony
	60	Radiocommunications
	101	Mathematics
	111	Physics and chemistry (multi-section)
	121	Electromagnetism (multi-section)
	151	Electrical and magnetic devices
	301	General terms on measurements in electricity
	302	Electrical measuring instruments
	303	Electronic measuring instruments
	446	Electrical relays
	521	Semiconductor devices and integrated circuits
	551	Power electronics
	581	Electromechanical components for electronics
	725	Space radiocommunications
	726	Transmission lines and waveguides
	902	Radio interference
62		Marking codes for resistors and capacitors
63		Preferred number series for resistors and capacitors
65		Safety requirements for mains operated electronic and related apparatus for household and general use
68		Basic environmental testing procedures
	1	General and guidance
	2	Tests
	2–1	A	cold
	2–2	B	dry heat
	2–3	Ca	damp heat, steady state
	2–5	Sa	simulated solar radiation
	2–6	Fc	vibration (sinusoidal)
	2–7	Ga	acceleration
	2–9		guidance for solar radiation testing
	2–10	J	mould growth
	2–11	Ka	salt mist
	2–13	M	low air pressure
	2–14	N	change of temperature
	2–17	Q	sealing
	2–20	T	soldering
	2–21	U	robustness of terminations
	2–27	Ea	shock
	2–28		guidance for damp heat tests
	2–29	Eb	bump
	2–30	Db	damp heat, cyclic
	2–31	Rc	drop and topple

Reference	Part	Content
	2–32	Ed	free fall
	2–33		guidance on change of temperature tests
	2–34	Fd	random vibration wideband – general requirements
	2–35	Fda	random vibration wideband – reproducibility high
	2–36	Fdb	random vibration wideband – reproducibility medium
	2–37	Fdc	random vibration wideband – reproducibility low
	2–38	Z/AD	combined temperature/humidity cyclic
	2–39	Z/AMD	combined sequential cold, low air pressure and damp heat
	2–40	Z/AM	combined cold/low air pressure
	2–41	Z/BM	combined dry heat/low air pressure
	2–42	Kc	sulphur dioxide
	2–43	Kd	hydrogen sulphide
	2–44		guidance on test T
	2–45	XA	immersion in cleaning solvents
	2–46		guidance to test Kd
	2–47		mounting of parts for tests Ea, Eb, Fc, Fd, Ga
	2–48		guidance on tests to simulate effects of storage
	2–49		guidance to test Kc
	2–50	Z/AFc	combined cold/vibration
	2–51	Z/BFc	combined dry heat/vibration
	2–52	Kb	salt mist cyclic
	2–53		guidance to tests Z/AFc and Z/BFc
	2–54	Ta	solderability
	2–55	Ee	bounce
	3		Background information (multi-part)
70			Power capacitors
73			Colours of indicator lights and push-buttons
78			Characteristic impedances and dimensions of radiofrequency coaxial cables
80			Fixed impregnated paper or paper/plastic film dielectric capacitors
86			Primary batteries (multi-part)
92			Electrical installations in ships (multi-part)
95			Lead-acid batteries (multi-part)
96			Radiofrequency cables (multi-part)
97			Grid system for printed circuits
106			Methods of measurement of radiated and conducted interference
113			Diagrams, charts, tables (multi-part)
115			Fixed resistors
	1		Generic specification
	2		Sectional specification: low power non-wirewound
	4		Sectional specification: power
	5		Sectional specification: precision
	6		Sectional specification: resistor networks with individually measurable resistors
	7		Sectional specification: resistor networks in which not all resistors are individually measurable

Reference	Part	Content
119		Polycrystalline semiconductor rectifier stacks and equipment
122		Quartz crystal units (multi-part
127		Cartridge fuse links for miniature fuses (multi-section)
129		Alternating current disconnectors and earthing switches
130		Connectors for frequencies below 3 MHz (multi-part)
131		Lever switches (multi-part)
132		Rotary wafer switches (multi-part)
133		Dimensions of pot cores made of magnetic oxides
134		Rating systems for electronic tubes and valves and analogous semiconductor devices
143		Series capacitors for power systems
147		Essential ratings and characteristics of semiconductor devices
	0	General and terminology (multi-section)
	1	Essential ratings and characteristics (multi-section)
	2	General principles of measuring methods (multi-section)
	3	Reference methods of measurement
	4	Acceptance and reliability
148		Letter symbols for semiconductor devices and integrated circuits
160		Standard atmospheric conditions for test purposes
163		Sensitive switches
166		Fixed metallized paper dielectric capacitors
169		Radiofrequency connectors (multi-part)
171		Fundamental parameters of connectors for printed wiring boards
173		Colours of the cores of flexible cables and cords
184		Methods for specifying the characteristics of electromechanical transducers for shock and vibration
189		Low frequency cables and wires with PVC insulation and sheath (multi-part)
190		Non-wirewound potentiometers
191		Mechanical standardization of semiconductor devices
	1	Preparation of drawings of semiconductor devices
	2	Dimensions
	3	General rules for the preparation of outline drawings of integrated circuits
	4	Coding system and classification into forms of package outlines for semiconductor devices
	5	Tape automated bonding (TAB) of integrated circuits
194		Terms and definitions for printed circuits
196		IEC standard frequencies
225		Octave, half-octave and third-octave band filters
228		Conductors of insulated cables
234		Dimensions of plate-type ceramic dielectric capacitors
240		Characteristics of electric infra-red emitters for heating purposes
241		Fuses for domestic and similar purposes
249		Base materials for printed circuits
	1	Test methods
	2–1	Phenolic cellulose paper copper-clad laminated sheet, high electrical quality

Reference	Part	Content
	2–2	Phenolic cellulose paper copper-clad laminated sheet, economic quality
	2–3	Epoxide cellulose paper copper-clad laminated sheet, defined flammability
	2–4	Epoxide woven glass fabric copper-clad laminated sheet, general purpose grade
	2–5	Epoxide woven glass fabric copper-clad laminated sheet, defined flammability
	2–6	Phenolic cellulose paper copper-clad laminated sheet, defined flammability
	2–7	Phenolic cellulose paper copper-clad laminated sheet, defined flammability
	2–8	Flexible copper-clad polyester (PETP) film
	2–9	Epoxide cellulose paper core, epoxide glass cloth surfaces copper-clad laminated sheet, defined flammability
	2–10	Epoxide non-woven/woven glass reinforced copper-clad laminated sheet, defined flammability
	2–11	Thin epoxide woven glass fabric copper-clad laminated sheet, for multi-layer printed boards
	2–12	Thin epoxide woven glass fabric copper-clad laminated sheet, defined flammability, for multi-layer printed boards
	2–13	Flexible copper-clad polyimide film
	2–15	Flexible copper-clad polyimide film, defined flammability
	3	Special materials
	3–1	Prepreg
	3A	Copper foil
255		Electrical relays (multi-part)
257		Fuse-holders for miniature cartridge fuse-links
263		Scales and sizes for plotting frequency characteristics and polar diagrams
265		High voltage switches
268		Sound system equipment (multi-part)
269		Low voltage fuses
271		List of basic terms, definitions and related mathematics for reliability
278		Documentation to be supplied with electronic measuring equipment
283		Methods for the measurement of frequency and equivalent resistance of unwanted resonances of filter crystal units
285		Sealed nickel-cadmium cylindrical rechargeable single cells
286		Packaging of components for automatic handling
	1	Tape packaging of axial components
	2	Tape packaging of components with unidirectional leads
	3	Tape packaging of leadless components
291		Fuse definitions
294		Measurement of the dimensions of a cylindrical component having two axial terminations
297		Dimensions of mechanical structures of the 482.6 mm (19 in) series
	1	Panels and racks

Reference	Part	Content
	2	Cabinets and pitches of rack structures
	3	Subracks and associated plug-in units
300		Reliability and maintainability management
301		Preferred diameters of wire terminations of capacitors and resistors
304		Standard colours for insulation for low frequency cables and wires
306		Measurement of photosensitive devices (multi-part)
313		Coaxial cable connectors used in nuclear instrumentation
314		Temperature control devices for quartz crystal units
315		Methods of measurement on radio receivers for various classes of emission (multi-part)
319		Presentation of reliability data on electronic components (or parts)
320		Appliance couplers for household and similar general purposes (multi-part)
321		Guidance for the design and use of components intended for mounting on boards with printed wiring and printed circuits
324		Ceramic dielectric capacitors
326		Printed boards
	1	General information for the specification writer
	2	Test methods
	3	Design and use of printed boards
	4	Specification for single- and double-sided printed boards with plain holes
	5	Specification for single- and double-sided printed boards with plated-through holes
	6	Specification for multi-layer printed boards
	7	Specification for single- and double-sided flexible printed boards without through connections
	8	Specification for single- and double-sided flexible printed boards with through connections
328		Switches for appliances
329		Strip-wound cut cores of grain-orientated silicon-iron alloy used for electronic and telecommunication equipment
331		Fire-resisting characteristics of electric cables
334		Air dielectric rotary variable capacitors
335		Safety of household and similar electrical appliances (multi-part)
337		Control switches (multi-part)
341		Push-button switches (multi-part)
344		Guide to the calculation of resistance of plain and coated copper conductors of low frequency cables and wires
348		Safety requirements for electronic measuring apparatus
351		Expression of the properties of cathode ray oscilloscopes
352		Solderless connection
	1	Solderless wrapped connections
358		Coupling capacitors and capacitor dividers
359		Expression of the performance of electrical and electronic measuring equipment

Reference	Part	Content
362		Guide for the collection of reliability, availability, and maintainability data from field performance of electronic items
367		Cores for inductors and transformers for telecommunications (multi-part)
368		Piezoelectric filters (multi-part)
371		Specification for insulating materials based on mica (multi-part)
375		Conventions concerning electric and magnetic circuits
384		Fixed capacitors
	1	Generic specification
	2	Metallized polyethylene terephthalate film dielectric capacitors
	3	Tantalum chip capacitors
	4	Aluminium electrolytic capacitors
	5	Mica dielectric capacitors
	6	Metallized polycarbonate film dielectric capacitors
	7	Polystyrene film dielectric capacitors
	8	Ceramic dielectric, class 1 capacitors
	9	Ceramic dielectric, class 2 capacitors
	10	Multi-layer ceramic chip capacitors
	11	Polyethylene terephthalate film dielectric metal foil capacitors
	12	Polycarbonate film dielectric metal foil capacitors
	13	Polypropylene film dielectric metal foil capacitors
	14	Radio interference suppressions
	15	Tantalum capacitors capacitors
	16	Metallized polypropylene film dielectric capacitors
	17	Metallized polypropylene film dielectric capacitors
393		Potentiometers
	1	Terms and methods of test
	2	Lead screw actuated preset potentiometers
	3	Single turn rotary precision potentiometers
	4	Single turn rotary power potentiometers
	5	Single turn rotary low power potentiometers
401		Information on ferrite material appearing in manufacturers' catalogues of transformer and inductor cores
409		Guide for the inclusion of reliability clauses into specifications for components or parts for electronic equipment
410		Sampling plans and procedures for inspection by attributes
415		Plastic film dielectric rotary variable tuning capacitors
416		General principles for the formulation of graphical symbols
417		Graphical symbols for use on equipment (multi-section)
418		Variable capacitors (multi-part)
425		Guide for the choice of colours to be used for the marking of capacitors
431		Dimensions of square cores (RM cores) made of magnetic oxides
440		Method of measurement of non-linearity in resistors

Reference	Part	Content
443		Stabilized supply apparatus for measurement
444		Measurement of quartz crystal unit parameters (multi-part)
445		Identification of apparatus terminals
451		Maximum case dimensions for capacitors and resistors
454		Specifications for pressure-sensitive adhesive tapes for electrical purposes (multi-part)
457		Rigid precision coaxial lines and connectors (multi-part)
472		Solid dielectric tubular-style rotary variable preset capacitors
478		Stabilized power supplies, DC output (multi-part)
489		Methods of measurement for radio equipment used in the mobile services (multi-part)
499		Ceramic dielectric disc-style rotary variable preset capacitors
509		Sealed nickel cadmium button rechargeable single cells
510		Methods of measurement for radio equipment used in satellite earth stations
512		Electromechanical components for electronic equipment; test and measurement (multi-part)
523		Direct current potentiometers
533		Electromagnetic compatibility of electrical and electronic installations in ships
536		Classification of electrical and electronic equipment with regard to protection against electric shock
539		Directly heated negative temperature coefficient thermistors
541		Comparative information on IEC and North American flexible cord types
547		Modular plug-in unit and standard 19 inch rack mounting unit
548		Expression of the properties of sampling oscilloscopes
574		Audiovisual, video and television equipment (multi-part)
581		High fidelity audio equipment and systems (multi-part)
584		Thermocouples (multi-part)
603		Connectors for frequencies below 3 MHz for use with printed boards (multi-part)
605		Equipment reliability testing
	1	General requirements
	3	Preferred test conditions
	4	Procedures for determining point estimates and confidence limits
	5	Compliance test plans for success ratio
	6	Tests for validity of a constant failure rate assumption
	7	Compliance test plans for failure rate mean time between failures
612		Guide to the use of variable capacitors in electronic equipment
616		Terminal and tapping markings for power transformers
617		Graphical symbols for diagrams
	1	General information
	2	Symbol elements
	3	Conductors and connecting devices

Reference	Part	Content
	4	Passive components
	5	Semiconductors and electron tubes
	7	Switchgear, control heat and protective devices
	8	Measuring instruments
	9	Telecommunications: switching and peripheral equipment
	10	Telecommunications: transmission
	12	Binary logic elements
	13	Analogue elements
620		Dimensions of single-hole, bush-mounted, spindle-operated electronic components
622		Sealed nickel cadmium prismatic rechargeable single cells
623		Open nickel-cadmium prismatic rechargeable single cells
642		Piezoelectric ceramic resonators
649		Calculation of maximum external diameter of cables for indoor installations
668		Dimensions of panel areas and cut-outs for panel and rack-mounted industrial-process measurement
669		Switches for household and similar fixed electrical installations (multi-part)
679		Quartz crystal controlled oscillators
686		Stabilized power supplies, AC output
688		Electrical measuring transducers for converting AC electrical quantities into DC electrical quantities
693		Dimensions of optical fibres
695		Fire hazard testing
	1	Guidance
	1–1	General guidance
	1–2	Guidance for electronic components
	2	Test methods
	3	Examples of fire hazard assessment procedures
696		Indirectly heated thermistors with negative temperature coefficient
706		Guide on maintainability of equipment (multi-part)
708		Low frequency cables with polyolefin insulation and moisture barrier polyolefin sheath (multi-part)
716		Expression of the properties of signal generators
717		Method for the determination of the space required by capacitors and resistors with unidirectional terminations
721		Classification of environmental conditions (multi-part)
723		Inductor and transformer cores for telecommunications (multi-part)
738		Directly heated positive step-function temperature coefficient thermistors (multi-section)
747		Discrete semiconductor devices
	1	General
	2	Rectifier diodes
	3	Signal and regulator diodes
	5	Optoelectronic devices
	6	Thyristors
	8	Field effect transistors

Reference	Part	Content
	10	Discrete devices and integrated circuits
	11	Discrete devices
748		Integrated circuits
	1	General
	2	Digital integrated circuits
	3	Analogue integrated circuits
	4	Interface integrated circuits
749		Semiconductor devices: mechanical and climatic test methods
757		Code for designation of colours
760		Flat, quick-connect terminations
776		Expression of the properties of logic and analysers
793		Optical fibres
794		Optical fibre cables (multi-part)
801		Electromagnetic compatibility for industrial-process measurement and control equipment
	1	General introduction
	2	Electrostatic discharge requirements
	3	Radiated electromagnetic requirements
812		Analysis techniques for system reliability
863		Presentation of reliability, maintainability and availability predictions
874		Connectors for optical fibres and cables
875		Fibre optic branching devices (multi-part)
885		Electrical test methods for electric cables
915		Capacitors and resistors for electronic equipment. Preferred dimensions of spindle ends, bushes and for the mounting of single-hole, bush-mounted, spindle-operated electronic components
950		Safety of information technology equipment including electrical business equipment
Guide 2		General terms and their definitions concerning standardization and related activities
Guide 3		Identification of national standards that are equivalent to international standards
Guide 102		Specification structures for the quality assessment of electronic components
CISPR11		Limits and methods of measurement of radio interference characteristics of industrial, scientific and medical radiofrequency equipment
CISPR13		Limits and methods of measurement of radio interference characteristics of sound and television receivers
CISPR14		Limits and methods of measurement of radio interference characteristics of household electrical appliances, portable tools and similar electrical apparatus
CISPR16		CISPR specification for radio interference measuring apparatus and measurement method
CISPR17		Methods of measurement of the suppression characteristics of passive radio interference filters and suppression components

Reference	Part	Content
CISPR19		Guidance on the use of the substitution method for measurements of radiation from microwave ovens for frequencies above 1 GHz
CISPR20		Measurement of the immunity of sound and television broadcast receivers and associated equipment in the frequency range 1.5 MHz to 30 MHz. Guidance on immunity requirements for the reduction of interference caused by radio transmitters in the frequency range 26 MHz to 30 MHz.
CISPR21		Interference to mobile radiocommunications in the presence of impulsive noise; methods of judging degradation and measures to improve performance
CISPR22		Limits and methods of measurement of radio interference characteristics of information technology equipment
CISPR23		Determination of limits for industrial, scientific and medical equipment

Table A1.8 IEC QC standards

Reference	Content
001001	Basic rules of the IEC quality assessment system for electronic components (IECQ)
001002	Rules of procedure of the IECQ
001003	Guidance documents
001004	Specifications list
001005	Qualified products list
160000	Generic specification: electromechanical all-or-nothing relays
160100	Sectional specification: electromechanical all-or-nothing relays
210000	Generic specification: connectors for optical fibres and cables
250000	Generic specification: inductor and transformer cores for telecommunications
250100	Sectional specification: magnetic oxide cores for inductor applications
250200	Sectional specification: magnetic oxide cores for broadband applications
250300	Sectional specification: magnetic oxide cores for transformers and chokes for power applications
300000	Generic specification: fixed capacitors
300200	Sectional specification: tantalum capacitors
300300	Sectional specification: aluminium electrolytic capacitors
300400	Sectional specification: metallized polyethylene terephthalate film dielectric capacitors
300500	Sectional specification: metallized polycarbonate film dielectric capacitors
301200	Sectional specification: metallized polypropylene film dielectric capacitors

Reference	Content
301300	Sectional specification: metallized polypropylene film dielectric AC and pulse capacitors
400000	Generic specification: fixed resistors
400100	Sectional specification: low power non-wirewound resistors
400200	Sectional specification: power resistors
400300	Sectional specification: precision resistors
400400	Sectional specification: resistor networks with individually measurable resistors
400500	Sectional specification: resistor networks in which not all resistors are individually measurable
440000	Generic specification: directly heated positive step-function temperature coefficient thermistors
700000	Generic specification: semiconductor devices
750100	Sectional specification: discrete semiconductor devices (previously numbered QC750000)

Table A1.9 ANSI standards and publications

Reference	Part	Content
American National Standards Institute (prefixed ANSI)		
C18	1	Specifications for dry cells and batteries
C39	2	Specifications for sealed rechargeable nickel-cadmium cylindrical bare cells
C57		Transformers (multi-part)
C63		Specifications for electromagnetic noise and field strength instrumentation
C93	1	Requirements for power line coupling capacitors
C95		Electromagnetic radiation (multi-part)
MC96		Temperature measurement thermocouples
PH7		Audio-visual equipment (multi-part)
S2		Shock and vibration (multi-part)
X3		Information systems (multi-part)
Y1		Abbreviations for use on drawings and in text
Y14		Engineering drawings (multi-part)
Z17		Preferred numbers
Z39		Documentation (multi-part)
American Society for Quality Control (prefixed ASQC)		
Q1		Generic guidelines for auditing of quality systems
A2		Definitions for acceptance sampling involving the per cent or proportion of variant parts
E2		Guide to inspection planning
A3		Quality systems terminology
Q90		Quality management and quality assurance standards – guidelines for selection and use
Q91		Quality system – model for quality assurance in design/development, production and installation

Reference	Part	Content
Q92		Quality systems – model for quality assurance in production and installation
Q93		Quality systems – models for quality assurance in final inspection and test
Q94		Quality management and quality system elements – guidelines

Electronic Industries Association (prefixed EIA)

Reference	Part	Content
162		Test standard for ceramic based printed circuits
172		Fixed composition resistors
186		Passive electronic component parts – test methods 1 to 13
	14	Passive electronic component parts – test methods 14
192		Holder outlines and pin connections for quartz crystal units
195		Electrical and mechanical characteristics for terrestrial micro-wave relay system antennas
196		Fixed film resistors – precision and semi-precision
197		Power filter inductors for electronic equipment
198		Ceramic dielectric capacitors
208		Printed wiring, definition and register
213		Test point locations for printed wiring assemblies
216		Method of test for adhesion of printed wiring
228		Fixed electrolyte tantalum capacitors
232		Interface between data terminal equipment and data circuit-terminating equipment employing serial binary data interchange
236		Color coding of discrete semiconductor devices
251		Test to determine the temperature rise as a function of current in printed conductors
275		Thermistor definitions and test methods
280		Solderless wrapped electrical connections
296		Lead taping of components in axial lead configuration for automatic insertion
303		Variable resistors, commercial non-wirewound, users and service adjust
309		General specifications for thermistors, insulated and non-insulated
310		Racks, panels and associated equipment
315		Rotary switches, low power
	2	Detail specification for rotary selector switch
319		Solderability of printed wiring boards
321		Numbering of like-named terminal functions in semiconductor devices and designation of units in multiple-unit semiconductor devices
325		Flammability tests for electronic components
335		Fixed composition capacitors
336		Color coding of chassis wiring
337		General specification for glass coated thermistor beads in glass probes and glass rods (negative temperature coefficient)
344		Low power, insulated, fixed wirewound resistors
345		Resistors, variable wirewound (lead screw activated)
349		Varistor definitions and test methods

Reference	Part	Content
Std105		Sampling procedures and table for inspection by attributes
Std202		Test methods for electronic and electrical component parts
Hdbk217		Reliability prediction of electronic equipment
Std242		Electronic component parts
Std275		Printed wiring for electronic equipment
Hdbk338		Electronic reliability design handbook
Std414		Sampling procedures and table for inspection by variables for percent defective
Std429		Printed circuit terms and definitions
Std454		Standard general requirements for electronic equipment
Std461		Electromagnetic interference requirements
Std462		Electromagnetic interference procedures
Std470		Maintainability program requirements
Std471		Maintainability verification, demonstration and evaluation
Std756		Reliability prediction
Std781		Reliability test, exponential distribution
Std785		Requirements for reliability program
Std790		Reliability assurance program for electronic parts specification
Std810		Environmental test methods
Std883		Test methods and procedures for microelectronics
D1000		Engineering drawings
Std1495		Multilayer printed wiring boards
Std1772		Certification requirement for hybrid microcircuits
Std2000	1	Soldering technology, high quality and reliability
	2	Part and component mounting for high quality and reliability
	3	Criteria for high quality and reliability soldered technology
	4	General-purpose soldering
C3607		General specification for coaxial radiofrequency connectors, series pulse
C3643		General specification for coaxial radiofrequency connectors, series HN
C3650		General specification for coaxial radiofrequency connectors, series LC
C3655		General specification for plug and receptacle electrical connectors, coaxial series twin
C3767		General specification for plug and receptacle electrical connectors, power bladed
S3950		General specification for environmentally sealed toggle switches
C3965		General specification for fixed tantalum electrolytic capacitors
C5015		General specification for circular threaded connectors, AN type
R5757		General specification for relays, for electronic communications equipment
E6051		Systems electromagnetic compatibility requirements
R6106		General specification for electromagnetic relays
S8805		General specification for sensitive and push, snap action switches and switch assemblies
Q9858		Quality program requirements
R10509		General specification for fixed film, high stability, resistors

Reference	Part	Content
T10727		Tin plating, electrodeposited or hot dipped
C10950		General specification for fixed mica dielectric, button style, capacitors
C11015		General specification for fixed ceramic dielectric, general-purpose, capacitors
C11272		General specification for fixed glass dielectric capacitors
C11693		General specification for feed through, radio interference reduction, AC and DC, hermetically sealed, capacitors
P13949		Copper clad, laminated plastic sheet for printed wiring
F14256		Fluxes
M24365		Maintenance engineering analysis
M26512		Maintainability requirements for weapon systems and subsystems
P28809		Printed wiring assemblies
P38510		General specification for microcircuits
G45204		Gold electroplating
I46058		Insulating compounds, electrical, for conformal coatings of printed circuit assemblies
P50884		General specification for flexible printed wiring boards
P55110		Printed wiring boards
P55640		Multilayer printed wiring

Table A1.11   DIN standard groups and relevant selected standards (groups are shown in bold typeface)

Group	Standard	Part	Content
0010			Sciences and knowledge in general. Terminology
0020			Writings, scripts, signs, symbols
0030			Graphics symbols
	30600		Graphical symbols, registration, designation
	ISO3461	1	Graphical symbols; general principles for the formulation of graphical symbols for use on equipment
		2	Graphical symbols; technical product documentation
0040			Standardization, standards, preparation of technical rules
	820	13	Standardization; adoption of European standards, CEN and CENELEC
		15	ISO and IEC standards
0070			Librarianship, documentation, publications
	1422		Publications in sciences, technology, economy and administration (multi-part)
0102			Ergonomics
	33401		Controls, terms and definitions, suitability
0820			Housings and enclosures
0920			Measurement and control
1160			Electrical engineering in general

Group	Standard	Part	Content
	40041		Reliability of electrical items (multi-part)
1180			DIN VDE specifications group 1: power installations
	VDE1000		General principles for the safety design of technical products
1220			DIN VDE specifications group 5: machine, transducers
	VDE0550		Specifications for small transformers (multi-part)
	VDE0560		Specifications for capacitors (multi-part)
	VDE0565		Radio interference suppression devices (multi-part)
1240			DIN VDE group 7: appliances
	VDE0700		Safety of household and similar electrical appliances (multi-part)
1250			DIN VDE group 8: information technology
1260			Graphical symbols relating to electrical engineering
	40100		Graphical symbols for use on equipment in the electrotechnical field (multi-part)
1270			Graphical symbols used in electrical circuit diagrams
	40700		Graphical symbols (multi-part)
1280			Testing of electrical apparatus and components in general
1290			Environmental testing for electrical engineering
	40046		Environmental tests (multi-part)
1330			Identification and markings for electrical engineering
1360			Cores, sheets, rotors, field magnet systems
1400			Electric components
1420			Testing of electric components
1430			Printed circuits, printed boards
	40801		Printed circuits (multi-part)
	40802		Base materials
	40803		Drawings
	40804		Terms and definitions
	41494		Mechanical structures: 482.6 mm (19 in) racks
	LN9407		Base materials (multi-part)
	VDE3710		Printed circuit board manufacture (multi-part)
1440			Integrated circuits, microelectronics
	41794		Reliability details to be given in data sheets
	41795		Recommendations for data sheets
	41848		Thick and thin film integrated circuits, terms and definitions
	41850		Thick and thin film integrated circuits (multi-part)
	41860		Linear integrated amplifier circuits
	44476		Semiconductor devices and integrated circuits (multi-part)
1442			Measurement methods used for integrated circuits and microelectronic components
	44480		Measuring methods for integrated circuits (multi-part)
1443			Quality assessment of integrated circuits and micro-electronic components
	45901		Harmonized system of quality assessment for

Group	Standard	Part	Content
			electronic components, incorporating the CECC series (multi-part)
1445			Housings for integrated circuits and microelectronic components
	41865		Cases for semiconductor devices
	41870		Cases for semiconductor devices (multi-part)
	41873		Cases for semiconductor devices
1450			Circuit diagram
	40719		Circuits (multi-part)
	40900		Graphical symbols
1540			Transformers
1560			Components of transformers
1600			Cables
1610			Coaxial cables
1630			Insulated wires, winding wires
1640			Multi-conductor lines
1660			Semiconductor technology
1680			Insulating materials
1770			Permanent electrical connections (soldered joints, compression joints, crimp connections)
1780			Non-permanent connections (clamping and screwed connections)
1790			Sleeves
1840			Circuit breakers
1850			Plug and socket devices
1860			Radiofrequency connectors
1870			Connectors for printed circuits
1880			Plug and socket devices for telecommunications
1920			Switches
1970			Resistors
	41099		Determination of the dimensions of capacitors and resistors having two one-sided wire terminations
1980			Potentiometers, variable resistors, varistors
	41450		Potentiometers; preset potentiometers, lead screw actuated or rotary, terms and definitions
1990			Thermistors
1995			Fixed resistors
	44050		Fixed resistors, non-wirewound; terminology, characteristics, methods of test and application
2000			Metallic fixed resistors
	41428		Film resistors
	41431		Vitreous enamelled wirewound resistors
	44061		Metal film lacquered resistors
	44063		Metal oxide film resistors
	44064		Metal glaze film resistors
	VG95295		Fixed resistors, basic specifications (multi-part)
2010			Non-metallic fixed resistors
	41442		Film resistors for telecommunications equipment
	44051		Cracked carbon film resistors
	4054		Carbon composition film resistors

Group	Standard	Part	Content
2030			Fuses
2075			Earthing
2080			Electrical measurement
2090			Electrical measuring apparatus and instruments
2102			Magnetic material
2108			Relays
2110			Capacitors
	41099		Determination of the dimensions of capacitors and resistors having two one-sided wire terminations
	42007		Terms and definitions for capacitors (multi-part)
	42008		Fixed capacitors for use in electronic equipment
2120			Ceramic capacitors, mica capacitors
2140			Paper capacitors, metallized paper capacitors
2150			Plastics capacitors
2160			Electrolytic capacitors
2170			Tantalum electrolytic capacitors
2180			Aluminium electrolytic capacitors
2240			Electroplating, applied electrochemistry
	50960		Electroplated and chemical coatings (multi-part)
2250			Primary galvanic cells and batteries
2260			Secondary galvanic cells and batteries, accumulators
2270			Lead accumulators
2280			Nickel cadmium accumulators
2290			Thermocouples
2310			Electric oscillation, laser technique
2315			Electromagnetic compatibility
	VG95370		Electromagnetic compatibility of and in systems
		1	Fundamentals
		10	Test methods for interference currents
		11	Test methods for interference voltages
		12	Test methods for radiated emissions
		13	Test methods for safety margins against system generated field strengths
		15	Test methods for coupling and screening
		16	Test methods for interference voltages at receiving antenna terminals
		23	Safety margins for radiated susceptibility
		24	Safety margins for conducted susceptibility
	VG95371		Electromagnetic compatibility (multi-part)
	VG95373		Electromagnetic compatibility of equipment
		1	Fundamentals
		2	Equipment identification
		10	Test methods for interference currents
		11	Test methods for interference voltages
		12	Test methods for radiated emissions
		13	Test methods for immunity towards radiated emission
		14	Test methods for immunity towards conducted disturbances
		15	Test methods for coupling and shielding

Group	Standard	Part	Content
	VG95374		Management control procedures (multi-part)
	VG95375		Fundamentals and measures for development of systems (multi-part)
	VG95376		Fundamentals and measures for development and design of equipment (multi-part)
	VG95377		Measuring equipment (multi-part)
2340			Amplifiers
2350			Electronics, photoelectric tubes and cells
2370			Semiconductor devices
2375			Cases for semiconductor devices
2380			Diodes
2390			Thyristors
2400			Transistors
2410			Electron tubes, electron microscope
2440			Telecommunication
2450			Telephone engineering
2460			Radiocommunication apparatus and methods
2470			Television
2515			Vacuum technology
3235			Soldering, brazing
	1707		Soft solders, composition, use
	1912		Concepts and terms for soldered and brazed joints
	8501		Soldering irons
	8505		Soldering and brazing processes (multi-part)
	8511		Fluxes (multi-part)
	8514		Solderability, terms
	8515		Defects
	8516		Soft solders with flux cores
	8526		Testing of soldered joints
	32506		Solderability tests (multi-part)
3310			Gluing, bonding, sealing
	16920		Adhesives, processes, terms
3320			Surface treatment, metal coatings
3355			Spools
5480			Graphic industries, printing
5520			Quality assurance and control
	40080		Sampling procedures and tables for inspection by attributes
	55350		Concepts in quality management, control and assurance (multi-part)
	VG5081		Quality assurance, basic concepts
	VG95082		Statistical methods of quality assurance
	VG95085		Statistical quality control
5970			Metallurgy, metallic materials
6390			Papers, boards
7660			Technical drawing, graphical symbols used on technical drawings
7680			Drawings (rules, regulations, lettering, dimensioning etc.)